MAGNETIC TAPE INSTRUMENTATION

MAGNETIC TAPE INSTRUMENTATION

GOMER L. DAVIES
Consulting Engineer

McGRAW-HILL BOOK COMPANY, INC.

New York   Toronto   London   1961

MAGNETIC TAPE INSTRUMENTATION

15458

PREFACE

This book is an attempt to assemble in one place information on the techniques and equipment used for magnetic tape recording and reproduction of data, as distinguished from voice and music. Such data include any electrical signal and any physical phenomenon which can be converted to or represented by an electrical signal, plus numbers represented by suitably coded pulses. These numbers may be those used in computer operation or those arising from scientific and engineering work. Magnetic tape has become an important element in the storage and processing of a large amount of scientific, engineering, and business information.

The recording of electrical signals in analog form on magnetic tape has presented a completely new tool to the scientist and engineer. It represents an extremely convenient electrical memory requiring no processing between recording and reproduction. The record may be reproduced literally thousands of times for detailed analysis by any desired means and may easily be edited to condense large volumes of information into the most significant and useful form. The time scale of an event or succession of events may be varied over a wide range, making possible the application of analysis instruments and techniques normally not usable. The fact that the tape can easily be erased and reused increases its flexibility.

In the field of recording digital numbers, on the other hand, magnetic tape is not a new *kind* of tool but simply one that is very much faster and occupies much smaller volume than those used previously—punched cards and punched paper tape. The speed and compactness are tremendously useful, nevertheless; it is difficult to imagine what our large high-speed computers would be like without magnetic tape.

The literature in the field of magnetic tape instrumentation is widely scattered in technical periodicals, and much of it is quite difficult to locate. Except in a few restricted areas, notably the recording and reproduction of short pulses, there is little information in the periodical literature regarding the characteristics and fundamental principles of

v

the methods used for data recording on magnetic tape and the characteristics of the equipment involved.

I hope that everyone associated with magnetic tape instrumentation —designer, manufacturer, and user—will find something of value in this book. It is not, however, a treatise on how to design tape instrumentation equipment but rather an attempted exposition of the principles and equipment, their characteristics and limitations. This method of treating the subject has been chosen to make the book useful to present users of equipment and to those who must apply tape recording in their own work without any previous technical acquaintance with it.

Because the basic principles of magnetic recording and reproducing processes have been quite adequately covered in books and periodical technical literature, this phase has been treated rather briefly in Chap. 2. Sufficient material has been included, however, to serve as a suitable background for the remainder of the book without requiring reference to other material. Certain aspects of the magnetic recording process which are of special importance in instrumentation applications are stressed. The remainder of the book is devoted to those techniques which are particularly employed for the recording of analog and digital information in the technical and business fields and to the characteristics of components used in magnetic tape instrumentation systems.

A technical background and at least a speaking acquaintance with electronic terminology on the part of the reader are assumed. No more mathematics is included than is necessary for a clear presentation of the subject. Some mathematical analyses of the effects of flutter, which have not previously been published, are included in the two appendixes.

I am extremely grateful to my wife, Harriet, for continuing encouragement and assistance in the preparation of this book. I also wish to express my sincere appreciation of the assistance rendered by many individuals and organizations who have furnished information to me and granted permission for its publication. Specific references to them are included in the text.

Gomer L. Davies

CONTENTS

CHAPTER 1

BRIEF HISTORY OF MAGNETIC TAPE INSTRUMENTATION APPLICATIONS

All histories of magnetic recording begin with its invention by Valdemar Poulsen at the turn of the century. For roughly 35 years after its invention, interest in applications of this recording technique centered around voice recording and broadcasting. Nearly everyone today is acquainted with magnetic tape recording in home entertainment and dictating machine applications, and most are aware of the use of magnetic tape in broadcasting and phonograph-record manufacture. Since we are concerned here with instrumentation rather than voice and music recording, we shall omit mention of the numerous articles and books dealing with these latter uses; they are adequately covered elsewhere.

Perusal of the bibliography prepared by Wilson [1] * shows that there were published very few articles on the subject until the middle 1930s, at which time it is evident that there was a considerable increase in interest. This resulted from the use of magnetic recording in connection with radio broadcasting, particularly in Germany and England. The first indication of a use for engineering purposes appeared in 1936 [2]. Rather surprisingly, this was an application to aircraft flight testing; a recorder was used to preserve a record of the rudder deflection on an airplane during flight test.

In September, 1940 [3], there was reported another use of magnetic recording in flight testing by Lockheed. This equipment used steel tape, and two 8-channel units could be coupled together to provide a total recording capability of 16 channels. To a considerable degree, this equipment seemed to be used for recording voice comments by pilots and other technical personnel aboard the aircraft. However, the report on it mentions also its use for noise, vibration, and flutter

---

* Numbers in brackets refer to numbered references at the end of each chapter.

recording, including carrier recording from strain-gauge transducers. Noise and vibration recordings were subjected to frequency analysis during reproduction. Darragh, the author of the paper, mentions the possibility of a modulated carrier for recording electrical output from transducers and instruments and discusses methods of analysis of the reproduced data. The equipment was designed and constructed by Herman S. Heller.

Also in 1940 there appeared a German report [4] discussing magnetic recording of data in connection with a phase direction finder.

Just before and during World War II, the Brush Development Company [5] carried out a project for the development of a high-frequency strain analyzer using magnetic recording. In 1945 Hanson [6] and Boyers [7] published descriptions of a tape recorder and a 2-sec tape loop recorder which were used at the U.S. Navy Underwater Sound Laboratory. Later in the same year the U.S. Army Signal Corps [8] reported on a captured German tape recorder used to check the uniformity and characteristics of telephone dial impulses.

What seems to be the first reference on FM carrier recording was published by Shaper [9], also in 1945. He described a tape loop recorder for the recording and reproduction of transients. This equipment used a 10-kc carrier with a steel-tape loop running at 25 fps. The maximum data signal frequency was 1000 cps. A cycle-counting discriminator was employed in reproduction. Compensation for flutter is not mentioned; a fairly wide deviation (apparently in the vicinity of 40 per cent) was used, and a signal-to-noise ratio of 45 db was reported.

Engineering Research Associates [10, 11] reported in 1947 experiments on the magnetic recording of pulses for digital-computer use. This seems to be the first literature reference concerning this presently very important application.

During the years 1948 to 1950 there were increasing applications of magnetic recording in instrumentation work. Killian [12] described in 1948 a complete system for recording data in a gondola containing instruments to measure forces appearing during a parachute opening and descent. This system used FM carrier for all data channels and employed flutter compensation and playback servo speed control to minimize errors. The servo speed control was capable of compensating for speed variations up to ±30 per cent. The paper by Killian illustrates a number of recording mechanisms, some with 6 and some with 12 tracks. This equipment was designed and manufactured by Cook Research Laboratories.

As far as the author can determine, the year 1948 marked the appearance of the first multichannel head with precision alignment of gaps attained by lapping each half of the pole-piece assembly before final assembly of the head. This type of head was designed by Dr. John Bellamy of the Cook Research Laboratories [13]. This design provided 13 tracks on 1-in. tape with a 50-mil track width. Up to 62 channels have been incorporated in one head stack, for 5-in.-wide tape.

During the period 1948 to 1951, Cook Research Laboratories [14] designed a number of recording and reproducing equipments, all the recorders being designed for operation under severe environmental conditions. They were used in aircraft flight test work, parachute testing, missile tests, and other similar work. All of these used FM carrier recording with flutter compensation and servo speed control in playback.

An interesting application of voice recording was described in 1948 [15]. Wire recorders were used for inventory taking, the number and description of items being spoken into the microphone rather than written down. Clerical personnel typed the data or prepared punched cards from the reproduced voice. This was possibly the first application of magnetic recording for business purposes.

Computer applications of magnetic recording in the 1948 to 1950 period included a magnetic tape storage system [16] and a drum system [17]. Other references in the period include discussions of means of recording meter readings and transducer outputs by Zenner [18], application of an endless loop for transient study by Hemardinquer [19], the recording of Geiger-Müller pulses by Miller [20], and a technique for extracting weak signals from noise, using a magnetic drum for time delay and summing, by Suryan [21].

In 1950, Stolaroff [22] and Boothe [23] published papers describing the use of magnetic tape equipment in telemetering. This marks the beginning of the first large-scale instrumentation use of tape equipment in this country. In all the tests of FM/FM subcarrier recording reported by Stolaroff, flutter compensation was used. It is interesting to note that Stolaroff concluded that compensation should be used for recording FM telemetry subcarriers, because it would be impractical to produce in quantity low-flutter transports and, even if this were done, maintenance would require highly skilled technicians and the recorder would be put in the class of delicate, precision instruments. He concluded that it was not practical to achieve accuracies of $\frac{1}{2}$ or 1 per cent without compensation and observed that compensation provided an appreciable factor of safety. The tests reported by

Stolaroff were conducted with Ampex equipment designed for broadcast purposes but modified to run the tape at 15 and 30 in. per sec (ips), rather than 7½ and 15 ips.

Early in 1950 the Wright Air Development Center of the Air Force awarded a contract for the development of airborne recording equipment to permit large-scale vibration studies in aircraft [24]. Included in this system were reproduction equipment with loop playback facilities and an automatic wave analyzer to produce plots of frequency analyses and power spectral densities directly from the tape-recorded data. This system was ultimately expanded into one of the largest vibration recording and analysis installations in the country and is still in operation. It was designed and built by The Davies Laboratories, Inc., now the Industrial Systems Division of Minneapolis-Honeywell Regulator Company.

Late in 1950, Green [25] described a system for recording very-low-frequency phenomena by means of wide-deviation FM carrier. At about the same time the first application of the carrier-erase recording technique was embodied in a recording accelerometer [26].

The year 1950 can be considered the beginning of large-scale application of magnetic tape to instrumentation problems. From this point on there have appeared many standard production equipments designed for instrumentation use, and the literature on the subject expanded rapidly. Chapter 10 and its appended bibliography outline what has occurred.

REFERENCES

1. Wilson, Carmen F.: Magnetic Recording—1888–1952, *IRE Trans. on Audio,* vol. AU–4, no. 3, p. 53, May–June, 1956.
2. Lehmann, H.: The DVL-Rudder Deflection Recorder R11/8m and Its Flight Test, *ZWB Forschungsberichte 644* (in German), PB38249, 1936.
3. Darragh, J. B.: Flight Test Data Mechanically Recorded, *Aero Digest,* vol. 37, no. 9, p. 96, September, 1940.
4. Blaupunkt-Werke: Investigations on a Magnetic Recording Device for 20 kc, PB54174, November, 1940.
5. Brush Development Company: Development of a High Frequency Strain Analyser, NDRC Report D–3–212, PB32604, 1941 (First Report); NDRC Report D–3–256, PB32605, July, 1942 (Second Report); NDRC Report D–3–305, PB32606, September, 1942 (Third Report); OSRD Report 1615, PB24884, June, 1943 (Fourth Report).
6. Hanson, R. O.: The BTL High Fidelity Tape Recorder, Columbia University, Division of War Research, Memo P37/R1320, PB L80603, January, 1945.
7. Hanson, R. O., and J. S. Boyers: Two Second Tape Loop Recorder-Re·

producer Set, Columbia University, Division of War Research, Memo P37/R1334, February, 1945.

8. U.S. Army Signal Corps: German Tape Impulse Recorder, PB2259, 1945.

9. Shaper, H. B.: Frequency-modulated Magnetic Tape Transient Recorder, *Proc. IRE*, vol. 33, no. 11, p. 753, November, 1945.

10. Engineering Research Associates, Inc.: Magnetic Recording of Pulses for the Storage of Digital Information, PB99668, June, 1947.

11. Engineering Research Associates, Inc.: Storage of Numbers on Magnetic Tapes, PB99667, June, 1947.

12. Killian, L. G.: Data Recording on Magnetic Tape, *Electronic Ind. & Electronic Instrumentation*, April, 1948.

13. Private communication.

14. Cook Research Laboratories: Bulletin R–8, 1951.

15. Norris, E.: Wire Recorders for Inventory, *Am. Business*, vol. 18, no. 10, p. 12, October, 1948.

16. West, C. F., and J. E. De Turk: A Digital Computer for Scientific Applications, *Proc. IRE*, vol. 36, no. 12, p. 1452, December, 1948.

17. Booth, A. D.: Magnetic Digital Storage System, *Electronic Eng.*, vol. 21, no. 7, p. 234, July, 1949.

18. Zenner, R. E.: Magnetic Recording of Meter Data, *Audio Eng.*, vol. 34, p. 16, February, 1950.

19. Hemardinquer, P.: Multiple Applications of Magnetic Recording, *Radio Française*, no. 6, p. 8, June, 1950.

20. Miller, W. B.: Use of a Wire Recorder for Recording Geiger-Müller Pulses, *Science*, vol. 3, p. 626, June 9, 1950.

21. Suryan, G.: A New Method of Extracting Weak Nuclear Magnetic Resonance Signals from Noise, *Phys. Rev.*, vol. 80, p. 119, 1950.

22. Stolaroff, M. J.: Performance Results of the Ampex Magnetic Tape Recorder Recording Frequency Modulated and Pulse Width Telemetering Data, *Joint AIEE-NTF Conf. on Telemetering*, 1950.

23. Boothe, K. S.: Uses of Magnetic Tape Recording in Telemetering, *Instruments*, vol. 23, no. 11, p. 1186, November, 1950.

24. Davies, Gomer L.: Magnetic Recorders for Data Recording Under Adverse Environments, *IRE Trans. on Audio*, vol. AU–2, no. 5, p. 133, September–October, 1954.

25. Green, P. E.: Magnetic Tape Recorder for Very Low Frequency Phenomena, *Rev. Sci. Instr.*, vol. 21, p. 893, November, 1950.

26. Engineering Research Associates, Inc.: Instruction Manual for Accelerometer Equipment, Publication PX29547, June, 1951.

CHAPTER 2

FUNDAMENTALS OF RECORDING AND REPRODUCTION

The basic phenomena involved in magnetic recording and reproduction have been treated extensively by a number of authors [1–5]. For this reason, the discussion in this chapter will not go into great detail but will cover the subject only sufficiently to form a satisfactory background for the chapters that follow. Certain characteristics which are of particular importance in data recording are emphasized.

2.1 Basic Magnetic Phenomena

To understand the magnetic recording process, it is helpful first to review briefly what happens to a ferromagnetic material when it is subjected to a changing magnetic field. Figure 2.1 is the normal way of representing the sequence of events [6]. In this figure, flux density in the material, designated by the letter B, is the ordinate, and magnetizing force, designated by H, is the abscissa. The graph is the BH curve.

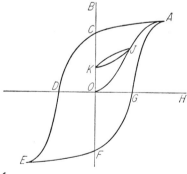

Fig. 2.1. Magnetization curve and hysteresis loop.

6

If the material is assumed to be initially unmagnetized and then subjected to a gradually increasing magnetizing force, the relationship between B and H will follow the S-shaped curve OA. This line is concave upward near the origin, becomes essentially linear over a certain range of values of H, and then becomes concave downward and finally almost horizontal in the vicinity of point A, where B increases only in direct proportion to H. This is the *saturation* region. If the magnetizing force is now decreased to zero, the curve AC is followed, and the curve CDE will be generated by again increasing H in the opposite direction. The E region also represents saturation. If H is now decreased to zero and reapplied in its original direction, the path $EFGA$ will be followed, and the material will be saturated again in the initial direction.

The line OA is the initial magnetization curve, and the loop $ACDEFGA$ is the hysteresis loop of the material. If H is increased from zero to a value less than that required to produce saturation, the material will follow a line such as OJ. Reduction of H from this value to zero and back would carry the material over the minor hysteresis loop $JKKJ$. In tape recording, fresh unmagnetized tape is generally being presented to the magnetizing field by virtue of the motion of the tape, and we usually have to deal with a magnetizing cycle starting from the origin and following first the initial magnetization curve along a path such as OJ or OA. Subsequent traverses of the magnetic material as represented on the BH chart of Fig. 2.1 will depend on the exact nature of the recording field.

It will be noted that changing H from zero to saturation and back to zero will not leave the material demagnetized but will leave it having considerable *residual induction,* as indicated by point C. To reduce this induction to zero requires the application of a magnetizing force in the negative direction to bring the material to point D of Fig. 2.1. The magnetizing force required to do this is called the *coercive force* of the material. These two quantities determine the qualities of the material as a permanent magnet.

In practice, it is generally not possible to leave a magnetic material in a condition represented by point C. This is owing to the fact that there is reluctance in the magnetic path (except in the rather trivial case of a closed ring) and the magnetizing force required to maintain the field in the high-reluctance portion of the path acts as a *demagnetizing force* on the magnetic material and carries it to some point on the curve between C and D. The value of the resultant magnetization is called the *remanence* of the material [10].

2.2 Recording and Recording Heads

A thin ribbon of magnetic material can be magnetized in any of three directions: longitudinally, along the length of the ribbon; transversely, along the width of the ribbon; and perpendicularly, in the direction of the thickness of the ribbon. In so far as the medium is concerned, there is little choice between these directions, but practical considerations relating to head design and attainable resolution make the longitudinal magnetization very much preferable in most applications. The discussion therefore will be confined to the case of longitudinal magnetization.

A typical head structure is depicted in Fig. 2.2. This sort of head is generally referred to as the *ring* type. The core is laminated and made in two halves for convenience in fabrication and winding. There is a front gap over which the recording medium passes, and generally a back gap as indicated. Nonmagnetic spacers of known thickness determine the widths of the gaps. The windings are used to generate the flux necessary for recording from the *recording current.*

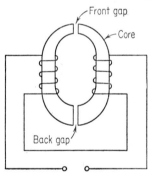

Fig. 2.2. Magnetic recording head structure.

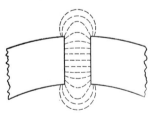

FIG. 2.3. Fringing of flux at air gap.

In a magnetic structure such as the one shown, it is obvious that there will be flux fringing out from the front gap which can penetrate the recording medium, and this, of course, is the mechanism by which the medium is magnetized.

Figure 2.3 is a sketch which indicates in a very rough way the flux distribution at the head gap without the presence of the recording medium. The ferromagnetic characteristics of the medium will naturally modify somewhat the flux distribution indicated. For the purpose of this discussion, however, the exact distribution of flux is not particularly vital. The important point to be noted is that an element of the recording medium, in moving across the gap, passes from a region of no field into a region of varying field and again into a region of no field. In the immediate vicinity of the gap the element experiences a field which increases gradually from zero to a maximum at the center of the gap and then gradually decreases to zero.

Figure 2.4 indicates roughly what would happen, in the form of *BH* curves, to an element of the tape in passing through the field at the gap. The figure represents conditions for four different values of recording current, but each value of current is assumed to be essentially constant during the time that the tape element is passing through the gap field. For a small recording current, a path indicated by *OAC* will be followed. A larger current would produce the path *ODE*, and a still larger one the path *OFG*. In each case the magnetic element is carried up along the initial magnetization curve to a point corresponding to the maximum field intensity at the center of the gap and then returns along the upper branch of a minor hysteresis loop and ends at some point in the second quadrant, which is determined by the maximum magnetizing force encountered and the demagnetizing force occurring after the element leaves the field. It is apparent from the shape of the initial magnetization curve that the final value of induction in the tape will not be proportional to the recording current. Within practical limits, the magnetizing force *H* is proportional to the magnetizing current, but the curvature at the foot of the initial magnetization curve results in a very small magnetization of the tape for small magnetizing forces. In order to achieve reasonable linearity between tape magnetization and magnetizing force, and hence recording current, it is necessary that the peak value of the magnetizing force carry the magnetic element

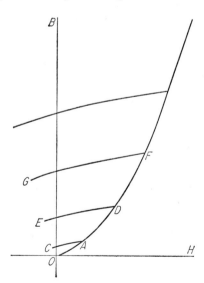

Fig. 2.4. Magnetization of tape without bias.

up to the linear part of the initial magnetization curve. As a result, simply passing a current to be recorded through the head windings will not produce a linear magnetization of the tape. When this is necessary, some method must be used to linearize the tape magnetization.

2.3   Linearization by Use of Bias

Recording can be made linear by *biasing* the tape by means of a fixed magnetic field to a point at the center of the linear portion of the initial magnetization curve [4]. The necessary field could be obtained by a permanent magnet or by a fixed direct current in the head windings in addition to the signal current to be recorded. While this method is successful, the later-developed high-frequency bias technique gives much better results with respect to signal-to-noise ratio and dynamic range of the recording. Consequently, it is used almost universally in preference to d-c bias.

High-frequency biasing is accomplished by passing through the head windings, in addition to the recording current, another alternating current which has a frequency several times the highest frequency that is to be recorded. Bias frequency is high enough that the magnetic element will be subjected to a number of cycles of it in passing through the magnetic field at the recording gap. Since the spatial field distribution at the gap, in the direction of tape motion, is one of gradually increasing intensity to a maximum and then decreasing to zero, the tape element in passing the gap is subjected to an a-c flux which increases from zero to a maximum and falls back to zero as the element passes the gap. This a-c flux carries the magnetic element through a number of complete hysteresis loops which increase in size as the peak field region is approached and then decrease to zero as the element leaves the field.

If there is no recording current, the decreasing hysteresis loops to which the tape element is last subjected collapse about the origin and leave the tape unmagnetized. If there is a recording current, the a-c flux is not symmetrical about zero but rather about a positive or negative flux value which is determined by the recording current, and as the hysteresis loops decrease in size they collapse about a point which is different from zero and corresponds to the recording current. This leaves the tape with a magnetization that is linearly proportional to the recording current up to a point at which saturation effects disturb the linear relationship. A more detailed explanation of the phenomena involved in recording with bias is given in the references [3–5, 8, 11, 12].

It is evident from the above that the final magnetization produced in the tape by the recording process is determined principally by the last flux encountered by the tape, in the region very close to the edge of the gap as the tape element leaves it. This is generally expressed by saying that recording occurs at the trailing edge of the recording head gap. It follows from this that the length of the recording gap, within practical limits, has no appreciable influence on the resolution attainable on the tape. Accordingly, the gaps in recording heads are usually made fairly wide, in the range of one-half to several mils.

Producing a residual magnetization of the tape by passing the signal current plus a high-frequency bias current through the recording head windings is the technique known as *direct recording*. It is the familiar one used in all audio recording for home and professional applications. Occasionally this recording method has been referred to as AM recording, as a distinction from FM carrier recording. This name for the technique is rather unfortunate, as it carries the implication that an amplitude-modulated carrier is used, which is not the case. The signal current in the head does not modulate the bias current but is merely added to it, and the magnetization of the tape corresponds only to the signal current and is not in any way comparable to an amplitude-modulated carrier. Therefore, the term direct recording is very much preferable to AM recording and will be used exclusively in this book.

2.4   Reproduction of the Recorded Signal

The magnetization impressed on the tape by the recording process can be used to reproduce the recording signal by passing the tape over a *playback head*, generally similar in construction to the recording head of Fig. 2.2. The magnetization of the tape produces flux in the core of the playback head, and as this flux changes, a voltage is induced in the head windings. It is important to note here that the output voltage from the playback head is proportional to the *rate of change of flux* and not to the flux itself. Thus the playback head acts as a differentiator, and the signal recovered is actually the derivative of the recorded signal rather than the signal itself.

For a given degree of peak magnetization of the tape, corresponding to a particular value of alternating recording current, the peak flux in the playback head will be constant. The rate of change of flux, however, which determines the magnitude of the playback-head voltage output, will depend upon the rate of change of recording current as well as its magnitude. Therefore, if we record a varying-frequency sine wave with recording current held constant regardless of frequency, the playback voltage will increase linearly with frequency. The slope of the playback voltage curve, on a logarithmic plot such as that of Fig. 2.5, is 6 db per octave or 20 db per decade of frequency change (line AB). Over a portion of the usable frequency range, this line represents the frequency characteristic of the entire record/playback system. At both very low and very high frequencies the system frequency characteristic departs from the straight line of 6-db-per-octave slope. Most of the reasons for these departures are associated with wavelength on the tape rather than frequency per se, and it is thus better to refer to them as wavelength rather than frequency effects.

Departures from the linear frequency response line at low frequencies, or long wavelengths, are not of too much consequence in data recording but are mentioned here to point out one of the difficulties involved in reproducing very low frequencies by direct recording. For a recorded wavelength such that opposite poles of tape magnetization lie close to but on opposite sides of the playback head gap, a maximum amount of flux will be induced in the core of the playback head. As the wavelength is increased, the poles move farther and farther away from the head gap, and when they are separated by a distance greater than the longitudinal dimension of the head core in the direction of tape travel, there is a large air gap between poles and core, and the playback head core can no

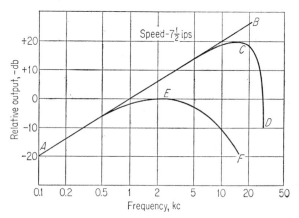

Fig. 2.5. Over-all frequency response.

longer collect all the available flux [2, 3]. When this happens, the playback voltage falls below the 6-db-per-octave line of Fig. 2.5, the slope of the actual playback curve increasing to about 12 db per octave. The frequency at which this long-wavelength effect sets in can be lowered by increasing over-all head dimensions or by the addition of tabs or shoes to the pole pieces of the head to increase its dimension in the direction of tape travel. The "break" point in frequency response occurs when the effective head dimension, in the direction of tape travel, is equal to about one-half wavelength.

2.5 Factors Limiting High-frequency Response

At high frequencies, or short wavelength, a number of factors combine to cause the system response to depart from the ideal straight line. These are:

1. Gap effect
2. Recording demagnetization
3. Self-demagnetization
4. Penetration and spacing losses
5. Head losses

The first four are wavelength effects, while the fifth is dependent on frequency rather than wavelength. In addition to these inherent system characteristics, short-wavelength loss can result from improper head-gap alignment.

Gap Effect. The gap effect is due to the finite length (in the direction of tape travel) of the playback head gap. Since these gaps are generally only a fraction of a mil in length, 0.25 mil being a common value, the gap effect becomes important when the recorded wavelength is 1 mil or less.

The gap effect is exactly comparable to the scanning-slit effect in sound-on-film recording. If we "look" at a sine wave through a slit which is very narrow compared with the wavelength, we see the amplitude of the sine wave essentially at a point. If the sine wave is moved past the slit, the amplitude seen through the slit varies sinusoidally. Now if the slit is widened (or the wavelength shortened) so that the slit becomes one-eighth of a wavelength, it no longer scans the sine wave at a point but rather gives an average value over one-eighth of a cycle. As the slit increases in length in relation to the wavelength, more and more of the cycle is seen through the slit, and the average is extended over more of the cycle. As the slit length becomes a half wavelength, it averages a half cycle to give a value $2/\pi$ times the peak of the sine wave. At this point the response is 4 db below the value read by an infinitely narrow slit.

As the slit increases beyond a half wavelength, the response rapidly falls off, as the averaging begins to include the second half of the wave, of opposite polarity and hence subtracting from the value of the first half cycle. When the slit finally becomes equal to a whole wavelength, the average value seen through it is zero, and the response is likewise zero. All this is fairly simply defined mathematically: If the slit (or gap) length is b and the wavelength λ, then the response is proportional to $\sin (\pi b/\lambda)/(\pi b/\lambda)$ [3, 4, 7].

After the zero response that occurs when the gap is equal to the wavelength, the response rises again for shorter wavelengths, being represented by a series of loops with zeros at wavelengths corresponding to integral submultiples of the gap length. This very-short-wavelength response is of little or no practical value, and essentially all recording work is done with wavelengths greater than the playback head gap length.

The gap effect modifies the linear frequency response so that it takes the form of the curve ACD of Fig. 2.5.

Recording Demagnetization. As the frequency of the recording current is increased, the assumption that the flux due to the signal recording current is constant as the tape passes through the recording field becomes invalid. For very high frequencies, the variation of signal flux in the recording field as the tape passes through this field causes a reduction in the remanent magnetization of the tape, which becomes more and more pronounced as the frequency of the recording current is increased [8]. This phenomenon is known as *recording demagnetization*. It results in a decrease in recovered signal at short wavelengths to a value below that which would be anticipated because of the gap effect alone.

Self-demagnetization. It was mentioned earlier that reluctance in the path of a magnetized medium resulted in a demagnetizing force which reduces the residual induction below the value corresponding to zero magnetizing force (point C of Fig. 2.1). On tape the amount of this demagnetization depends on the separation of the poles of the recorded pattern and increases as these poles move closer and closer together. Hence, as the wavelength is decreased, the self-demagnetization effect further reduces the flux available from the tape and correspondingly reduces the playback voltage. Daniel [2] and Wallace [9] have cited evidence to indicate that self-demagnetization is probably relatively unimportant in comparison with the other factors.

Penetration and Spacing Losses. Experimental evidence indicates that the effective remanent magnetization of the tape is confined to a very thin layer at the surface of the coating at very short wavelengths, while the entire coating thickness becomes magnetized at long wavelengths. This effect results in a smaller volume of magnetized material at short wavelength and a consequent reduction of playback voltage. This phenomenon is generally called *penetration loss* and contributes to the reduction of playback voltage at short wavelengths.

Wallace [9] has shown theoretically and experimentally that any space between the magnetic coating and the playback head produces a wavelength-dependent loss that is defined by the equation

$$\text{Loss, db} = 54.6 \frac{d}{\lambda}$$

where d is the spacing and λ is the wavelength of the recorded signal. Thus, at 1-mil wavelength a separation of 1 mil between tape and head produces a loss of about 55 db—essentially a complete loss of signal. This highlights the need for intimate tape-head contact and shows why even minute foreign particles, by lifting the tape from the head, can cause severe dropouts.

Head Losses [2, 3, 6, 10]. The normal losses encountered in all ferromagnetic materials subjected to a-c magnetizing forces are present in magnetic recording and reproducing heads. As frequency is increased, the recording flux is not exactly proportional to the current, as some of the power delivered to the head windings is dissipated in core and copper losses. This causes an additional loss in high-frequency response when tape speeds and recorded frequencies become high and naturally depends upon the head core material and the usual other factors contributing to such losses.

The curve AEF of Fig. 2.5 represents the combined effects of all short-wavelength losses and is typical of the frequency response of a tape recording system at medium tape speeds.

Head Misalignment. This cause of short-wavelength loss is not inherent in the method of tape recording but rather is due to equipment imperfections or misadjustment. If the gap of the reproducing head is not exactly parallel to the recording head gap, a wavelength-dependent loss will occur. This is defined by the equation [1]

$$\text{Loss, db} = 20 \log \frac{\sin \left[(\pi w \tan A)/\lambda \right]}{(\pi w \tan A)/\lambda}$$

where w = track width
A = angle of misalignment
λ = wavelength

For wide tracks and short wavelengths this *azimuth loss* can be considerable even for very small values of A. In the case of multi-track instrumentation head stacks, the track width is rarely greater than 50 mils, and for a wavelength of $\frac{1}{2}$ mil a 3-db loss occurs for $A = \frac{1}{4}$ degree. Since the gap line of the head stack is usually aligned at 90° to the tape travel direction to a much closer tolerance than this by precision machinery and mounting methods, it is rarely if ever necessary to adjust the stack for minimum azimuth loss. Head-stack manufacturing methods ensure that the gap of each head in the stack is parallel to the line of gaps within very small tolerances.

2.6 Phase Characteristics

Some data-recording applications require control of the over-all phase and frequency characteristics of the system. Since the re-cording-playback characteristic of heads and tape is far from flat, frequency-wise, it is important to recognize also its phase charac-teristics in order to evaluate over-all system characteristics. Be-cause a passive network with a nonflat amplitude-frequency charac-teristic has a nonlinear phase-frequency characteristic, it is natural for engineers to conclude that the head-tape amplitude-frequency characteristic also implies a nonlinear phase-frequency characteristic.

Actually this is not the case. If we assume ideal recording and playback heads with no distributed capacity, a true constant-current drive source for the record head, and an infinite input impedance detector for the playback head voltage, then there is only a fixed 90° phase shift between the current from the recording-current generator and the voltage delivered by the playback head, and this fixed phase shift is independent of frequency. The 90° phase shift follows, of course, from the response of the playback head to the derivative of the flux, rather than the actual flux. This phase shift is associated with the 6-db-per-octave slope of the linear portion of the record-playback frequency characteristic. The departure of the over-all response from this straight line at very low frequencies (long wave-lengths) is not accompanied by phase shift, nor is the departure at short wavelength, in so far as this is produced by gap effect, recording- and self-demagnetization, and penetration and spacing losses. Head losses at very high frequencies will, of course, introduce frequency-dependent phase shifts.

It is important to keep in mind this departure of a tape system from the behavior of normal passive networks. Equalization of the amplitude-frequency characteristic by means of suitable networks in the electronic portions of an over-all system is quite practical, and a flat over-all amplitude-frequency characteristic can thus be obtained. The system, however, will not have the phase-frequency characteristic of a passive network with the same amplitude-frequency characteristic. The equalized tape system will have a nonlinear phase characteristic in regions where the amplitude characteristic is perfectly flat, a distinct departure from the normal behavior of a passive network.

This situation raises a particular difficulty in testing electronic components designed for use with magnetic tape. To the author's knowledge, there is no network, active or passive, which can be used to simulate a head-tape system. Therefore it is impossible to test adequately and completely the electronic components of a tape system without actually recording and reproducing the signal by means of tape.

2.7 Saturation Recording

In certain instances, little importance attaches to a linear relationship between recording current and playback voltage. This is particularly true in wideband FM carrier recording, pulse-width-modulation recording, and digital pulse recording. In these cases no bias is used in the recording process, and sufficient current is passed through the recording head to produce saturation of the tape, to provide the maximum possible playback voltage. This recording method is generally termed *saturation recording*.

2.8 Erasure

It is generally known that a magnetized ferromagnetic material can be demagnetized by subjecting it to a saturating alternating field and then gradually reducing the magnitude of the field to zero. This technique is used for demagnetizing or *erasing* magnetic tape [5]. Erasure can be accomplished by means of an erasing head, generally similar to the normal record or playback heads, or it can be accomplished by means of a separate demagnetizer or *degausser*. Manufacturers of instrumentation tape equipment do not provide erasing heads on their equipment because of the danger of accidental erasure of valuable data. The costs involved in performing a complex test and recording the results on magnetic tape are usually high enough in relation to the cost of tape that the use of new tape for each test is justified. Furthermore, test data are frequently so valuable that the reels of tape carrying them are stored permanently and not reused. It is therefore not necessary to provide an erasing head on the tape equipment to be sure that previously recorded signals are erased before the new recording is made. When it is necessary to erase a roll of tape, the special demagnetizing or erasing machines that are available can be used.

One exception to this general rule in the data-recording field is the loop mechanism often used for time delay or temporary storage. Such equipment frequently incorporates an erase head which may be in continuous operation or turned on by the user when erasure is desired.

Erase heads are usually excited by a high-frequency oscillator, frequencies used generally being in the same region as bias frequencies. The separate erasing devices operate directly from the power line and thus use fields alternating at the 60-cycle power-line rate. With these units, the necessary gradual reduction of the field is achieved by manually moving the reel of tape slowly away from the demagnetizer.

2.9   The Recording Medium

The overwhelming majority of equipment used in data and instrumentation recording employs plastic-base magnetic tape as the recording medium. This is comprised of a thin ribbon of plastic, either cellulose acetate or polyester, upon which is placed a coating containing magnetic oxides. A binder is, of course, necessary to retain the oxides, and lubricants are included to reduce friction between the coating and any fixed object over which the tape must pass, such as the recording and playback heads. The material is fabricated in fairly wide sheets and, after completion of the coating and drying processes, is cut into the desired-width strips on precision slitting machines.

The plastic ribbon on which the magnetic coating is placed is called the *base* of the tape. Two base thicknesses are in common use, 1 mil and 1.5 mils. The coating thickness on the 1.5-mil-base tape is usually in the order of 0.7 mil, making the total thickness 2.2 mils. This is often referred to as *regular*-thickness tape. The coating thickness used on the 1-mil base is slightly under 0.5 mil, so that the total thickness is about 1.5 mils. This is frequently called *thin* tape. Tape made with 0.5-mil polyester base is produced but is generally used only when the thinnest possible tape is necessary because of operating time and size requirements, as it presents more problems with respect to the tape-transport equipment than the thicker tapes.

Tape for instrumentation purposes is normally furnished in lengths of 1250, 2500, or 5000 ft. for the regular thickness and 1800, 3600, or 7200 ft. for the thin material. These lengths correspond to reel diameters of 7, 10½, and 14 in., the two latter sizes being used on most instrumentation equipment.

Because the tape is originally manufactured in wide sheets and subsequently slit, it can be obtained in almost any desired width up to a maximum governed by the capacity of the slitting machines or the coating machines. Usage has produced a certain amount of standardization, most equipment manufacturers using widths which are integral multiples of ¼ in. One notable exception is ⅝-in.-wide tape, which has found considerable use in digital applications. Tape up to 2 in. in width is readily available and commonly used.

Several grades of tape are available, which differ primarily in the coating formulation and the degree of control exercised by the producer in the manufacturing and inspection processes. The better-quality tapes are commonly referred to as *instrumentation* tapes and are subjected to processing and inspection controls to assure the best possible characteristics for critical recording applications, and particularly to guard against *nodules*. These nodules are small lumps in the coating which can cause momentary losses of signal, or *dropouts*.

There is no precise definition of a dropout, but it can be assumed that a temporary reduction of playback level of more than 10 per cent can justifiably be called a dropout. Such level reductions are rather frequent and can be produced by a number of causes, the nodules in tape being one. An actual hole in the tape coating would naturally cause a dropout, but such defects practically never appear in high-quality tapes.

An instrumentation tape should have uniform base and coating thickness, and there should be a close tolerance on the width. Normally this tolerance is +0.000 and −0.004 in. The coating should not rub off on and stick to heads and other portions of the tape-transport mechanism, even at high tape speeds. The tape should be uniform with respect to short-wavelength reproduction, and, of course, dropouts should be minimized. The major mechanical characteristics are governed by the base material. Acetate-base tape is satisfactory for some applications and is usually somewhat less expensive than the polyester-base tape. However, the polyester (Mylar*) base is superior to acetate with respect to moisture absorption and a number

* Trademark of E. I. du Pont de Nemours & Company.

of other characteristics that make it desirable in critical applications.

In recording systems for use in severe environmental circumstances, consideration must be given to the limitations on the temperature extremes to which the tape may be subjected. The operating temperature extremes depend upon the machine characteristics as well as the properties of the base and coating of the tape, and equipment manufacturers' recommendations should not be exceeded.

2.10 Amplitude Accuracy

Signals recorded on tape by either the direct- or saturation-recording techniques cannot be reproduced with high amplitude accuracy. It is generally conceded that an error of about ±10 per cent can be expected. Tape sold for audio purposes is frequently specified by the manufacturer to be uniform in level reproduction within ¼ db or about 2½ per cent within a reel. This specification applies to voice, music, and other similar broadcast or home-recording program material and is subject to measurement with a standard VU meter which averages over a short time period. Consequently, in spite of this specification, it is a safe and correct statement that a ±10 per cent error in the instantaneous amplitude of a reproduced signal is about the best that can be expected with direct or saturation recording.

There are many factors that contribute to this inaccuracy, and it is very difficult to pin them down or isolate them. They depend on transport characteristics as well as tape. Short-wavelength signals are subject to more rapid and pronounced amplitude fluctuations than long-wavelength signals. Head-tape contact is definitely a factor; in some tests performed by the author reproduced signal-level fluctuations were reduced by 20 to 35 per cent when a pressure pad was used to press the tape against the head in playback only. The use of pressure pads in both recording and playback is helpful, but tape nonuniformities and other factors will still contribute to amplitude fluctuation.

While some data on dropouts have been presented from the standpoints of pulse recording for computer applications and telemetry subcarrier recording, the definitions used have been rather extreme and the data do not give much information regarding instantaneous amplitude-level fluctuation. For computer purposes a dropout is usually defined as a reduction of signal level by more than 50 per cent, reflecting the tolerance of the circuitry to amplitude fluctuation. For telemetry subcarrier recording, a dropout has been defined [13] as a reduction of 60 per cent or more in amplitude lasting for 40 μsec or more, using a 70-kc carrier at 60-ips tape speed. Tests for such gross departures from normal output level give little information as to the general accuracy to be expected with direct recording.

At least one study of cycle-to-cycle amplitude fluctuation has been made [14], and Fig. 2.6 gives a bar graph of the amplitude distribution for one particular tape sample. This is one of the best distributions shown in the report, many of the others indicating much wider amplitude scattering. The normalized standard deviation for the distribution of Fig. 2.6 is 0.053, indicating that errors greater than 5 per cent would occur 32 per cent of the time, and errors greater than 10 per cent about 5 per cent of the time. Normalized standard deviations for some samples were observed to be 0.1 or larger.

Figure 2.7, from the same report but redrawn in modified form, gives some idea of the effect of wavelength on amplitude fluctuations. The difference between the peak and minimum observed levels increases rapidly as the wavelength is decreased. The somewhat erratic behavior of the graphs representing levels exceeded 50 and 99 per cent of the time is understandable, in view of the experimental difficulties involved in this work.

2.11 Handling of Tape

It should be remembered that magnetic tape is a flexible plastic-base material, with a coating having different physical properties. This is not the sort of thing that can take rough handling. In addition, the quality of reproduction of a recorded signal is dependent on perfection of the coating and intimate contact between tape and

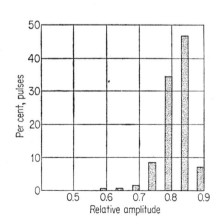

Fig. 2.6. Variation of tape playback level. (*Courtesy of Department of Defense.*)

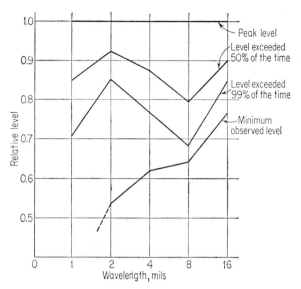

Fig. 2.7. Relative level variation versus wavelength. (*Courtesy of Department of Defense.*)

head. It follows from this that any physical damage to the coating or mechanical distortion of the base may degrade the signal.

Clearly, the tape transports to which are entrusted the handling of tape and the valuable data it carries must treat the tape with great respect. Starting and stopping stresses must not be excessive, and surfaces that contact the tape must be flawlessly smooth. The tape edges particularly must be protected and should not rub against guides or reel flanges, lest serious distortion result.

Tape is sensitive to changes in temperature and humidity and may "creep" in dimensions for a long time after exposure to such changes. It should, therefore, be stored under as nearly constant temperature and humidity conditions as possible, preferably in an air-conditioned space. Ideally, it should never be subjected to a temperature or humidity cycle, but such cycling can hardly be avoided—it may occur during shipment from manufacturer to user, or from recording point to reproducing point, or during recording under adverse conditions. When tape is known or suspected to have been exposed to temperature or humidity variations, it should be inspected at frequent intervals during subsequent storage and rewound under the best possible conditions (see Chap. 4) when any sign of buckling, cinching, or slippage on the reel shows up.

Protection from dust accumulation is very important. Even a

puff of cigarette smoke blown directly on the oxide coating has been known to produce dropouts. Rolls of tape should always be kept in dustproof containers when not in use and handled only in dust-free areas. Recording equipment that must be used in dusty or sandy areas should be loaded in a protected area and kept closed at all times during use. The recorder should be returned to a protected area for unloading. All tape-transport parts in the tape compartment, and particularly the recording and playback heads, should be kept free of dust by careful cleaning at frequent intervals. Reasonable care in this area of dust protection will pay off handsome dividends in cleaner reproduced signals and better data all around.

Excessive starting or stopping strains in the transport, unsuitable reels, improper winding tensions, and poor storage conditions can cause permanent damage to the tape, with the consequent loss of valuable data. Actual separation of base and coating or breakage of the coating is the extreme and visible evidence of such permanent damage, but severe loss of signal can result without visible damage to the tape or its coating. Scalloping, cupping, warping, and blistering may be hardly noticeable and yet cause some portion of the tape to fail to contact the head properly, with corresponding loss of data.

REFERENCES

1. Begun, S. J.: "Magnetic Recording," Rinehart & Company, Inc., New York, 1949.
2. Daniel, E. D., P. E. Axon, and W. T. Frost: A Survey of Factors Limiting the Performance of Magnetic Recording Systems, *J. Audio Eng. Soc.*, vol. 5, no. 1, p. 42, January, 1957.
3. Stewart, W. Earl: "Magnetic Recording Techniques," McGraw-Hill Book Company, Inc., New York, 1958.
4. Westmijze, W. K.: Studies on Magnetic Recording, *Philips Research Repts.*, vol. 8, pp. 161–183, June, 1953.
5. Wetzel, W. W.: Review of the Present Status of Magnetic Recording Theory, *Audio Eng.*, vol. 31, no. 11, p. 14, November, 1947; vol. 31, no. 12, p. 12, December, 1947; vol. 32, no. 1, p. 26, January, 1948.
6. Bozorth, R. N.: "Ferromagnetism," D. Van Nostrand Company, Inc., Princeton, N.J., 1951.
7. Daniel, E. D., and P. E. Axon: The Reproduction of Signals Recorded on Magnetic Tape, *Proc. Inst. Elec. Engrs. (London)*, paper 1499R, vol. 100, part III, p. 157, May, 1953.
8. Muckenhirn, O. W.: Recording Demagnetization in Magnetic Tape Recording, *Proc. IRE*, vol. 39, no. 8, p. 891, August, 1951.
9. Wallace, R. L., Jr.: The Reproduction of Magnetically Recorded Signals, *Bell System Tech. J.*, part II, vol. 30, no. 4, p. 1145, October, 1951.
10. Thompson, C. S.: Application of Experimental Test Procedures and Methods

of Analysis of Results to Research Problems in Magnetic Recording, *AIEE Trans.,* vol. 68 (part 1), p. 407.

11. Toomin, H., and D. Wildefeuer: The Mechanism of Supersonic Frequencies as Applied to Magnetic Recording, *Proc. IRE,* vol. 35, no. 11, p. 664, November, 1944.

12. Holmes, Lynn C.: Techniques for Improved Magnetic Recording, *Elec. Eng.,* vol. 68, no. 10, p. 836, October, 1949.

13. Military Specification MIL–T–21029(SHIPS), Sept. 23, 1957.

14. Magnetic Tape Study, Second Quarterly Progress Report, Signal Corps Contract DA18–119–sc–42.

CHAPTER 3

TECHNIQUES USED IN DATA RECORDING

It has been pointed out that the signal recovered from magnetic tape in playback is not a stable reproduction of the recording signal with respect to amplitude, nor is waveshape particularly well preserved. In recording data signals for preservation and later reproduction and analysis, it is obviously desirable that the over-all system degrade the accuracy of the information as little as possible. Furthermore, the frequency-selective characteristic of ordinary reproduction places a lower limit on the frequency which can be satisfactorily recovered from the tape and makes impossible the reproduction of d-c levels. A very large percentage of data sources comprises d-c or slowly varying signals, so that successful instrumentation recording must encompass such signals.

Carrier techniques provide an obvious solution of the problem of d-c and low-frequency signal response. In most cases, however, the amplitude instability of the signal reproduced from tape militates against the use of amplitude modulation, since the amplitude variations inherent in the recording/reproducing system represent a source of d-c drift and low-frequency noise that destroy system accuracy.

These factors leave only the time-modulation methods for satisfactory data recording by means of carriers, while quantizing and digital encoding of the signal permit it to be recorded on the tape in the form of pulses, the time sequence or lateral pattern of pulses representing the digital number into which the source signal was encoded. The time-modulation methods, plus direct recording in its limited application areas, are generally referred to as *analog* recording, while the digital encoding technique is termed *digital* or sometimes *pulse-code-modulation* recording.

The carrier or analog techniques in most common use are *frequency modulation* and *pulse width modulation,* the latter being also designated as *pulse duration modulation.* Phase modulation as a straight carrier technique is not as desirable as frequency modulation because of its less efficient use of the fixed available bandwidth, although some specialized forms of phase modulation have been applied to the solution of specific problems.

In this chapter we shall discuss the characteristics of the various recording systems. In spite of the lack of amplitude accuracy in direct recording, there are several instrumentation areas in which it is used extensively and therefore it is dealt with first.

3.1 Direct Recording

There are two major applications of direct recording for instrumentation purposes: the recording of multiplexed FM telemetry subcarriers and the recording of acoustic and radio noise for measurement and analysis. Incidental applications include the use of one track of a multitrack data system for voice logging to assist in locating data and to put on the record any voice comments that may be useful. Certain types of timing and recognition signals are also best handled by direct recording.

The amplitude-frequency characteristic of the head-tape combination has been explained in the preceding chapter. Figure 3.1, curve ABC, shows a representative characteristic for 15-ips tape speed. This is the characteristic obtained by maintaining constant current in the recording head as the measuring frequency is varied. Because of recording-head, self- and recording-demagnetization, and penetration losses, the magnetization of the tape will decrease somewhat at the high end of the frequency range, so that this type of recording does not result in maximum possible flux on the tape at all fre-

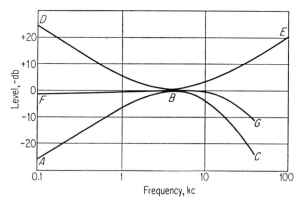

Fig. 3.1. Partial equalization for head-tape characteristics.

quencies [1]. In most cases it is desired that the over-all system amplitude-frequency characteristic be flat over as wide a range as possible. This can be achieved by the use of equalizing networks in the electronic amplifiers used in the system. However, it is necessary that a certain amount of care be exercised in applying this equalization, so that proper system characteristics will be maintained.

Recording current must be controlled carefully to avoid excessive amplitude distortion of the signal. Because of tape-saturation effects, excessive recording current will generate serious odd harmonic distortion [1–3]. The tolerable distortion level depends upon the application, a level of 1 per cent being considered more or less standard for the recording of telemetry FM subcarriers. Playback-head voltages are not large (a fraction of a millivolt at a few hundred cycles per second), and noise at the first grid of the playback amplifier is one of the large factors in over-all system signal-to-noise ratio. Thus it is necessary to operate a direct-recording system at the maximum recording-current level possible, to obtain maximum tape magnetization and thus maximum playback voltage. This maximum record-current level is determined by the tolerable system distortion.

In the equalization of tape systems for audio applications, advantage is taken of the fact that there is considerable foreknowledge of the program material that will be presented to the recorder. Since this program material has maximum energy in the midfrequency region and less energy in the low- and extremely high-frequency regions, certain amounts of low-frequency and high-frequency boost are used in the recording system. If the midfrequencies are to be recorded at maximum recording level, low-frequency boost must be very carefully controlled or serious distortion will result. In the design of equipment for general instrumentation work, there is not necessarily the same foreknowledge of the program material as there is in audio work. Even though equipment is originally purchased for a specific purpose, it may be later used for entirely different purposes, and the design should be such as to permit this.

Because of these factors, low-frequency boost in the recording circuits is not at all advisable, and the recording current must be held constant from the minimum frequency covered by the system up to a frequency at least half of the maximum frequency to be reproduced. Above this point there is some leeway, as distortion frequencies introduced by increased recording current will be cut off by the low-pass system characteristic. These considerations require that equalization in the recording circuits, if used at all, be restricted to high frequencies, and that all low-frequency equalization and most high-frequency equalization be incorporated in the playback amplifier circuits.

If no high-frequency boost is used in the recording circuits, one RC circuit for low-frequency boost and one RC circuit for high-frequency boost incorporated in the playback amplifier will produce an amplifier characteristic shown as DBE in Fig. 3.1 and a system characteristic shown as FBG. This system characteristic FBG neglects response fall-off at low frequencies because of coupling circuits and similar fall-off at high frequencies because of shunt capacitances. Nevertheless, the characteristic is not flat at high frequencies, and some additional equalization is desirable. This can be achieved by additional high-frequency boost in the playback amplifier or by some preemphasis of the high frequencies in the recording circuits. One interesting approach that has been taken involves the use of sufficient high-frequency boost in recording to compensate for recording head losses, the preemphasis thus providing the maximum possible flux on the tape at all wavelengths. Stewart [1] has pointed out that preemphasis cannot compensate for self-demagnetization and penetration losses. Attempts to preemphasize to compensate for recording demagnetization may not be successful, depending on the wavelength. It appears to be slightly simpler to obtain some of the high-frequency boost in the recording circuitry rather than forcing it all into the playback amplifier, and system distortion is not affected.

Figure 3.2 shows the amplitude-frequency response of a representative direct-recording channel with complete equalization applied,

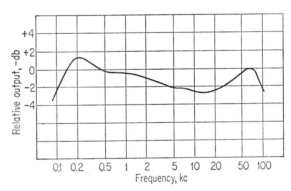

Fɪɢ. 3.2. Amplitude-frequency response, equalized channel (tape speed, 60 ips). (*Courtesy of Industrial Systems Division, Minneapolis-Honeywell Regulator Company.*)

for 60-ips tape speed. Because of the large amount of equalization necessary and the inevitable tolerances which must be permitted on circuit components and playback head gap length, certain tolerances must be permitted in the amplitude-frequency characteristic to achieve reasonable system costs. Small variations in head characteristics will move the high-frequency portion BC (Fig. 3.1) of the head-tape characteristic by corresponding amounts in a horizontal direction in the figure. Because of the high slope of this curve near the upper frequency limit of the system, small horizontal displacements produce rather large variations in output level at a particular frequency. If the electronic circuits were all identical, system frequency response with different heads would vary somewhat, particularly at the high-frequency end. Tolerances on the capacitors and resistors used for equalization, as well as on other circuit components, produce additional variations, so that systems are usually specified to be flat within a certain number of decibels over a particular frequency range. So long as the system response characteristic is between the limits spelled out by the specification, it is considered acceptable, and it is to be expected that peaks and valleys within these limits will show up on the response characteristic of some channels.

It was mentioned in the preceding chapter that there is only a fixed 90° phase shift associated with the recording and reproduction process. It follows from this that the phase-frequency characteristic of an equalized system will be determined primarily by the phase shifts of the equalizing networks. There must be added to this the phase shifts produced by other components of the electronic system and by the recording and playback heads. The over-all phase-frequency characteristic of a channel cannot be measured directly because a large and rather variable time delay must be introduced between the recording and playback process. It thus becomes rather difficult to determine the characteristic, and no information on commercial systems is available. The computed phase and amplitude characteristics of an idealized system are shown in Fig. 3.3; this neglects phase shifts due to heads, coupling capacitors, and stray shunt capacitances in the electronic circuits.

It is possible to obtain a very close approximation to the phase characteristic by physically associating the recording and playback heads, so that a normal voltage is induced in the playback head, and then measuring the over-all phase shift with all electronic components in the circuit. The normal bias oscillator used during recording must be disconnected. This type of measurement gives a

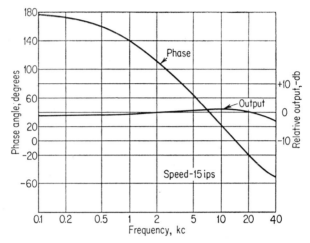

Fɪɢ. 3.3.   Theoretical phase and amplitude characteristics.

correct result except for the small effect produced by the tape on the head impedance, and even this might be simulated satisfactorily by fixing small pieces of tape over the head gaps.

Fortunately, it is usually not necessary to know the phase characteristic over wide ranges of frequency. This system parameter is important principally when multiplexed FM carriers are to be recorded, and to evaluate the tape system for this purpose information is necessary only over the band occupied by each modulated carrier. In practice this band is restricted to 15 or 30 per cent of the carrier frequency, and it is usually satisfactory to measure the phase shift over this band in the electronic circuits alone, neglecting the heads.

In a direct-recording system for critical applications, such as telemetry subcarriers, recording adjustments must be made quite carefully to maintain optimum system performance. Too much bias in the recording head will cause a fall-off in high-frequency response [1, 2]. Too little bias will permit system distortion to rise above the acceptable limits. Too much recording current will produce excessive distortion, while too little recording current will cause system noise levels to rise [2]. Normal practice calls for setting recording current to a predetermined value for the particular recording head used and then adjusting bias for specified distortion at some relatively low frequency, preferably the minimum frequency of interest in the application. In the initial design and adjustment of the equipment, the manufacturer must juggle bias current and recording current so that distortion specifications are met at low frequencies and frequency response is held within specifications at the high-frequency end of the range. This procedure serves to determine the recording- and bias-current levels, which are furnished to the customer for his use in maintaining system adjustments. The proper levels are often dependent upon the tape used. It is particularly important in recording telemetry FM subcarriers to avoid excess distortion, as this can cause serious crosstalk between channels multiplexed on the same tape track.

The frequency range of direct-recording channels in instrumentation equipment usually extends from either 100 or 300 cps to about 120 kc at 60-ips tape speed and proportionately lower top frequencies at lower tape speeds. The low-frequency end is usually independent of tape speed. Flatness of frequency response over the frequency range is variously specified as within 3 db; ±2 db; +0, −4 db; and so on.

3.2 FM Carrier Recording

Frequency-modulated carriers are extensively used in tape recording to achieve d-c response and moderately high-accuracy reproduction of data signals. In a well-designed system the amplitude accuracy of data reproduction will depend almost solely on the electronic circuits used and will be essentially free of any errors due to tape or tape-transport characteristics, although the time scale of the reproduction may be disturbed slightly by tape-speed errors.

Two ways of using FM carrier on tape are common. In the so-called wideband system, only one carrier is used on one track on the tape, and the percentage deviation of the carrier is large, ranging from 20 to 40 per cent or more. The carrier is recorded at rather short wavelength, so that the tape-head system cannot pass carrier distortion components, and saturation recording without bias is almost always used. With relatively narrow-percentage carrier deviations, such as those used in FM/FM telemetry, it is possible to record a number of carriers, each on a different frequency, on a single tape track. This is usually termed multiplexed FM carrier recording. Because harmonics of lower-frequency carriers could interfere with higher-frequency carriers, the carrier signals must be essentially undistorted before recording, and direct-recording techniques using bias must be employed to avoid introduction of distortion in the recording process. Bandpass filters are used in reproduction to separate the various carriers.

FM Signal Characteristics. This section covers briefly some characteristics of a frequency-modulated carrier signal which are pertinent to a full understanding of the problems of recording and reproducing such signals with magnetic tape. Thorough discussions of frequency modulation have been published in many books and in the periodical literature. Two of these are referenced at the end of the chapter [4, 5].

An a-c electrical voltage can be expressed rather generally by the equation

$$e = A \cos \Phi \tag{3-1}$$

where e = instantaneous value of voltage

A = peak amplitude of voltage

and the argument Φ of the cosine function is a generalized angle. For a constant frequency voltage, Φ can be considered to be given by

$$\Phi = \int \omega \, dt = \omega t + \phi \tag{3-2}$$

where $\omega = 2\pi f$ equals the angular frequency and ϕ equals the constant of integration. Thus, for a constant frequency voltage, Eq. (3-1) can be written

$$e = A \cos (\omega t + \phi) \tag{3-3}$$

A voltage represented by (3-3), with A and ω constant, conveys no intelligence. By making A or ω variable with time, we can modulate the voltage and by the manner of modulation convey such intelligence as we wish. If A is varied with time, we have an amplitude-modulated signal, while if ω is varied with time we have a frequency-modulated signal. It is possible for both quantities to vary, and in such a case we have a combination of amplitude and frequency modulation.

As soon as we depart from the constant frequency defined by Eq. (3-3) it is helpful to bring in the concept of *instantaneous frequency,* and this is best accomplished by defining the instantaneous frequency as the derivative of the argument Φ of (3-1); in other words, $\omega = d\Phi/dt$. It should be kept in mind that this concept of instantaneous frequency is only an approximate one, although very convenient; its lack of precision will become more apparent later when we consider the bandwidth of a frequency-modulated signal.

If the amplitude A is sinusoidally modulated about a mean value A_0, we have

$$A = A_0(1 + m \cos \omega_1 t)$$

and, writing ω_0 for the constant carrier frequency and letting $\phi = 0$,

$$e = A_0(1 + m \cos \omega_1 t) \cos \omega_0 t \tag{3-4}$$

By a little trigonometric manipulation this becomes

$$e = A_0 \cos \omega_0 t + \frac{mA_0}{2} \cos (\omega_0 + \omega_1)t + \frac{mA_0}{2} \cos (\omega_0 - \omega_1)t \qquad (3\text{-}5)$$

This represents three different frequencies, the *carrier* of frequency f_0 $(= \omega_0/2\pi)$, an *upper sideband* at frequency $f_0 + f_1$, and a *lower sideband* at frequency $f_0 - f_1$. The amplitudes of the two sidebands are equal and are given by the quantity $mA_0/2$, m being called the modulation factor $(m \leq 1)$. The carrier is fixed in amplitude, independent of the modulation, and the total bandwidth occupied by the signal is $2f_1$, or twice the modulation frequency.

Suppose now that the amplitude is kept constant at the value A_0 and that the instantaneous frequency is varied sinusoidally about a center or carrier frequency, so that

$$f = f_0 + m \, \Delta f \cos \omega_1 t \qquad (3\text{-}6)$$

Here m, the modulation factor, is equal to or less than 1 and is determined by the modulating voltage. The quantity Δf is the *frequency deviation* and represents the extreme departure of the instantaneous frequency from the carrier. If we multiply (3-6) by 2π, to convert the f's to ω's, and substitute in (3-2), we obtain

$$\Phi = \int (\omega_0 + m\Delta\omega \cos \omega_1 t) \, dt$$

$$= \omega_0 t + \frac{m\Delta\omega}{\omega_1} \sin \omega_1 t + \phi$$

and putting this in (3-1) gives us

$$e = A_0 \left(\cos \omega_0 t + \frac{m\Delta\omega}{\omega_1} \sin \omega_1 t + \phi \right)$$

$$= A_0 \left[\cos (\omega_0 t + \phi) \cos \left(\frac{m\Delta\omega}{\omega_1} \sin \omega_1 t \right) \right.$$

$$\left. - \sin (\omega_0 t + \phi) \sin \left(\frac{m\Delta\omega}{\omega_1} \sin \omega_1 t \right) \right] \qquad (3\text{-}7)$$

Now let $\Delta\theta = m\Delta\omega/\omega_1 = m\Delta f/f_1$. Textbooks covering Bessel functions [6, 7] show that

$$\cos (\Delta\theta \sin \omega_1 t) = J_0(\Delta\theta) + 2J_2(\Delta\theta) \cos 2\omega_1 t \cdots$$
$$+ 2J_{2n}(\Delta\theta) \cos (2n\omega_1 t) \cdots$$

and

$$\sin (\Delta\theta \sin \omega_1 t) = 2J_1(\Delta\theta) \sin \omega_1 t + 2J_3(\Delta\theta) \sin 3\omega_1 t \cdots$$
$$+ 2J_{2n+1}(\Delta\theta) \sin (2n + 1)\omega_1 t \cdots \qquad (3\text{-}8)$$

where $J_n(\Delta\theta)$ is the Bessel function (of the first kind, to be exact) with argument $\Delta\theta$ and order n, n being an integer in this case. Substituting (3-8) in (3-7), converting terms of the form of cos x cos y or sin x sin y into the form cos $(x + y) \pm$ cos $(x - y)$, and letting $\phi = 0$ produce the result

$$
\begin{aligned}
e = A_0[J_0(\Delta\theta) \cos \omega_0 t &+ J_1(\Delta\theta) \cos (\omega_0 + \omega_1)t - J_1(\Delta\theta) \cos (\omega_0 - \omega_1)t \\
&+ J_2(\Delta\theta) \cos (\omega_0 + 2\omega_1)t + J_2(\Delta\theta) \cos (\omega_0 - 2\omega_1)t \\
&+ J_3(\Delta\theta) \cos (\omega_0 + 3\omega_1)t - J_3(\Delta\theta) \cos (\omega_0 - 3\omega_1)t + \cdots]
\end{aligned} \qquad (3\text{-}9)
$$

Here again there are terms of different frequencies, but the result is quite different from the relatively simple amplitude-modulation case. We still have a carrier; however, its amplitude is not fixed but is dependent on the *modulation index* $\Delta\theta$ $(= m\Delta f/f_1)$. Instead of a single pair of sidebands for a single modulation frequency, there appears an infinite series of sidebands, separated from the carrier frequency by the modulation frequency and integral multiples thereof. The frequency band occupied by the signal is not clear-cut, as it is in amplitude modulation, and to determine what it is we can inquire into the nature of the Bessel functions, the J's of (3-9). Tables of these functions are given in a number of references [8].

A little study of the magnitudes of the Bessel functions shows that the sideband spectrum of the signal is *not* contained within the range $f_0 - \Delta f$ to $f_0 + \Delta f$. Sidebands removed from the carrier by more than Δf are by no means insignificant. For example, if $\Delta\theta = 5$, the fifth sideband is at Δf $(\Delta f = \Delta\theta f_1 = 5f_1)$, and its magnitude is 26 per cent of the unmodulated carrier $[J_5(5) = 0.26]$. The sixth sideband, at $\Delta f + f_1$, has an amplitude of 13 per cent, and the eighth sideband at $\Delta f + 3f_1$ is still 1.8 per cent of the unmodulated carrier. To handle the eight pairs of sidebands with amplitudes greater than 1 per cent of the unmodulated carrier, a total bandwith of $3.2\Delta f = 16f_1$ would be necessary. Thus, the spectrum of an FM signal is considerably broader than that of an AM signal, is wider than $2\Delta f$, and cannot be defined precisely in general terms. As $\Delta\theta$ becomes large $(f_1 << \Delta f)$, the sideband spectrum approaches more closely the total frequency deviation range of $2\Delta f$. For very small $\Delta\theta$ $(f_1 >> \Delta f)$, the spectrum width approaches that of an AM signal, or $2f_1$. Bandwidth, noise, and distortion have been discussed by a number of authors [9–18].

In most transmission systems, it is assumed that a flat amplitude-frequency characteristic over the requisite bandwidth is all that is necessary. This is true so long as the system has a normal phase-frequency characteristic corresponding to its flat amplitude-frequency characteristic. In other words, the phase characteristic is linear over the required bandwidth. There are systems, though, and magnetic tape is one of these, in which the normal relationship between amplitude-frequency and phase-frequency characteristics does not hold. In these cases, we must consider carefully the effect of the system on the modulated carrier signal.

A vector picture of a modulated wave is sometimes helpful. To create such a picture clearly, let us look back to the basic concept of a vector. When we represent a sinusoidal function by means of a fixed vector, we are really presenting a stroboscopic picture of the "real" vector. The function is visualized as the projection, on a preselected axis, of a continuously rotating vector of fixed magnitude. If this vector is viewed stroboscopically, once per revolution, it will appear to be fixed in a position, relative to the preselected axis, which is dependent on the phase of the stroboscopic illumination with respect to the instant at which the vector is coincident with the axis.

If we bear this picture in mind, we can consider vector representations of two or more signals of different frequencies. We assume the stroboscopic illumination to be synchronized with one of the signal frequencies, so that the vector representing this reference frequency is stationary. A higher frequency will be represented by a vector rotating faster than that of the reference frequency, so that its vector will rotate counterclockwise in the stroboscopic picture, at a rate in revolutions per second equal to the difference in frequency between its rotation rate and that of the reference frequency. Similarly, a signal of frequency lower than the reference will be represented by a vector rotating clockwise in the stroboscopic picture, again at a rate determined by the frequency difference between the signal and the reference.

To make use of this concept with respect to an amplitude-modulated signal, Eqs. (3-4) and (3-5) give a starting point, (3-5) saying that we have three different frequencies, which must be represented by three vectors. If the carrier-frequency vector is the reference, it will be stationary, while the upper-sideband vector rotates counterclockwise and the lower-sideband vector rotates clockwise. At the instant when $\cos \omega_1 t = 0$ [Eq. (3-4)] the resultant vector must have the magnitude A_0, which is the carrier amplitude of (3-5). The vector picture at this instant must, then, be that of Fig. 3.4a. The vertical carrier vector has the amplitude A_0, while each of the sideband vectors has an amplitude $mA_0/2$; the rotational directions of the sideband vectors are indicated by the curved arrows, the vector pointing to the left being the upper-sideband vector and that to the right the lower-sideband vector.

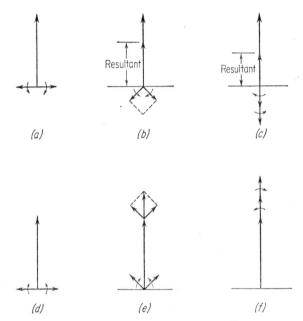

Fig. 3.4.   Amplitude-modulation vector diagrams.

Note that the positions of these three vectors are directly determined by Eqs. (3-4) and (3-5).   We assumed to start with that $\cos \omega_1 t = 0$. When the carrier vector is in the position shown in Fig. 3.4a, then $\cos \omega_0 t = 0$ for a horizontal reference line as the projection axis.   Both sideband vectors must lie at right angles to the carrier vector so that they have no component in its direction, because of (3-4) with $\cos \omega_1 t = 0$, and so both sideband vectors must be horizontal.   Now, with $\cos \omega_0 t = 0$ and $\cos \omega_1 t = 0$, $\cos (\omega_0 + \omega_1)t = -\sin \omega_1 t$ and $\cos (\omega_0 - \omega_1)t = \sin \omega_1 t$.   Therefore, the upper sideband vector lies to the left of the origin and the lower sideband vector to the right of the origin, both along the horizontal axis as indicated in the figure.

At a time later by one-eighth of a period of the modulation frequency, the sideband vectors will have rotated 45°, and the situation will be as indicated by b of the figure.   The resultant of the two sideband vectors is opposite in direction to the carrier vector, and so the over-all resultant of the three vectors is one which is less than the carrier vector.

Part c of Fig. 3.4 represents a time later than b by another one-eighth of a period.   Here the sideband vectors are aligned with but opposite in direction to the carrier vector, and so the resultant of the three has its minimum possible value.   One-eighth of a modulation period after c the vector picture will be similar to b, and one-quarter period after c the vectors will be back to the relationship shown in a, except that the sideband vectors will have exchanged positions, as indicated in d. The resultant is again the carrier vector as in a.

The next one-eighth period of the modulation frequency ends with the diagram shown in e, while the following one-eighth period brings us to the maximum possible resultant, as in f. This corresponds to the peak of the modulation cycle, as c corresponds to the minimum. After passing through a configuration similar to e, the vectors will return, at the end of the modulation period, to the configuration shown in a, thus completing the cycle.

The important point to be noted about this sequence of events is that the resultant vector in all the diagrams lies along the line of the original carrier vector; the resultant changes in magnitude but never shifts in phase.

Now let us consider the first three terms of Eq. (3-9). Under the same initial conditions, $\cos \omega_0 t = 0$, $\cos \omega_1 t = 0$, the carrier term $J_0(\Delta\theta) \cos \omega_0 t$ appears as a vertical vector, as in the amplitude-modulation case. The second term becomes $-J_1(\Delta\theta) \sin \omega_1 t$, and the third term also assumes the same value, $-J_1(\Delta\theta) \sin \omega_1 t$. The initial vector diagram thus appears as Fig. 3.5a, starting with $\sin \omega_1 t = 1$, $\omega_1 t = \pi/2$. The resultant, as indicated, does not coincide in phase with the carrier vector. Equation (3-6) for the instantaneous frequency shows that at this instant it is f_0, as $\cos \omega_1 t = 0$. Thus, in the a diagram of Fig. 3.5, the resultant vector is momentarily stationary, and the "instantaneous" frequency is f_0, the carrier frequency.

Later by an eighth of a period of the modulation frequency, the vector picture becomes that shown in b in Fig. 3.5. The resultant has shifted in phase toward the carrier. In c, the sideband vectors cancel each other, and the carrier vector alone is the resultant. This situation corresponds to $\sin \omega_1 t = 0$, $\cos \omega_1 t = -1$ ($\omega_1 t$ is now equal to π), $\cos \omega_0 t = 0$. The instantaneous frequency, by (3-6), is $f_0 - m\Delta f$ so that, at this instant of $\cos \omega_1 t = -1$, the frequency is a minimum. It is clear from the sequence of the figures that the resultant vector is moving clockwise, indicating a frequency lower than the carrier frequency. At the instant the resultant passes through the vertical position, it has its maximum clockwise velocity, corresponding to minimum frequency.

The d diagram shows conditions one-eighth period after c, and e represents still another one-eighth period later. In e it is clear that the resultant has swung as far to the right as it can, and hence it must be momentarily stationary, ready to start a counterclockwise

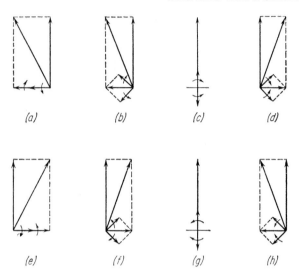

FIG. 3.5.   Frequency-modulation vector diagrams.

swing.   This corresponds to an instantaneous frequency of f_0 again, as in a.   In diagram f we have returned to a condition similar to d, and in g the picture is similar to c.   Here in g the resultant is moving counterclockwise at a maximum rate corresponding to the maximum frequency $f_0 + m\Delta f$.   The cycle is completed by two more diagrams, one shown as h and the other being identical with a.

Differences between the amplitude- and frequency-modulated cases are immediately apparent.   The amplitude-modulation resultant vector remains in a fixed position, indicating no phase or frequency change, but varies in amplitude.   The frequency-modulation resultant swings back and forth in phase, indicating frequency changes, with little change in amplitude.   It is also clear that the quantity $\Delta\theta$ introduced previously in place of $m\Delta\omega/\omega_1$ represents the maximum phase deviation of the frequency-modulated signal.   For full modulation of the signal, $m = 1$, and

$$\Delta\theta = \frac{\Delta f}{f_1} \tag{3-10}$$

While the amplitude of the resultant vector in Fig. 3.5 does not change radically, nevertheless it is not exactly constant.   Thus the simplified picture of one carrier and two sideband vectors is not sufficient to represent precisely the frequency-modulated wave except in the range of $\Delta\theta$ over which the tangent is equal to the angle—a range of roughly 0 to 10°.   If $\Delta\theta$ exceeds this range, additional sidebands are necessary to complete the picture and produce a resultant of constant amplitude whose terminus traces out a circular arc.

For phase swings of 10 to 60°, the addition of a second pair of sidebands, separated from the carrier by twice the modulation frequency and hence rotating twice as fast as the first-order sidebands, improves the amplitude constancy of the resultant. This is shown in Fig. 3.6. The second-order sidebands will add to the carrier in its center position and be directed downward at the times of extreme phase excursion, thus causing the terminal point of the resultant vector to follow an essentially circular arc. As the total phase deviation is increased, additional sidebands are necessary to maintain a constant-amplitude resultant. The *number* of sidebands necessary obviously depends on the maximum phase deviation or modulation index. The separation of these sidebands from the carrier frequency is a function of the modulating frequency. The bandwidth occupied by the signal is the product of the *total* number of necessary sidebands and modulation frequency. It is thus a complex function of the frequency deviation and modulation frequency and is not determined by either one alone.

This bandwidth problem points up the lack of precision in the "instantaneous frequency" concept which was mentioned earlier and is particularly clear for $\Delta\theta = 1$ and the conditions of Fig. 3.6. For this value of $\Delta\theta$, $f_1 = \Delta f$, and so the first pair of sidebands are at frequencies equal to the extreme maximum and minimum values of the instantaneous frequency defined by Eq. (3-6). Figure 3.6 shows vividly, however, the necessity for two additional sidebands separated from the carrier by $2f_1$, or $2\Delta f$. Consequently, even though the instantaneous frequency is never greater than $f_0 + \Delta f$ or less than

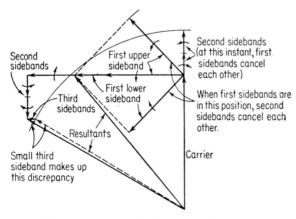

FIG. 3.6. Frequency-modulation vector diagram, $\Delta\theta = 1$.

$f_0 - \Delta f$, there are important frequency components of the signal at $f_0 + 2\Delta f$ and $f_0 - 2\Delta f$.

The apparent dilemma here is not due to any "trick" or error in the mathematics but comes solely from our concept of frequency. We can measure frequency by counting cycles over a known time interval, but the frequency must be constant during the measuring interval for the measurement to have a meaning. Also, we can measure the period of one cycle and call the reciprocal of this the frequency, but this necessarily involves the assumption that the period measured includes exactly one cycle of a pure sine wave, of constant frequency during the cycle. Yet it is easy to show, with perfectly practical numbers that are well within the range of values in everyday use, that the "frequency" at the end of a carrier cycle can be appreciably different from what it was at the beginning of the cycle. Here we have a requirement for a definition of frequency that is valid from instant to instant within the period of one cycle of the signal. With no way available to measure this frequency, it is naturally rather difficult to define.

To show how wild the instantaneous-frequency concept can become, suppose that we consider an example. It is perfectly possible to modulate a 25-kc carrier with a 5-kc modulation frequency and a frequency deviation of 5 kc; quite a bit of equipment is in operation using these numbers. Under the instantaneous-frequency concept, the modulated signal frequency has to change from 20 to 30 kc ($f_0 - \Delta f$ to $f_0 + \Delta f$) in one-half cycle of the modulation frequency, or a time of 100 μsec. The period of a 20-kc wave is 50 μsec, so that the cycle that starts out as a 20-kc signal ends up roughly as a 25-kc signal, and the frequency must get to 30 kc in approximately 1½ more cycles. It is really much easier to visualize this signal as a carrier and sidebands, at 15, 20, 25, 30, and 35 kc, plus smaller ones at still lower and higher frequencies.

On the other hand, when the modulation frequency is low and $\Delta \theta$ becomes large, a great number of sidebands become necessary to define the signal, and the spectrum becomes almost continuous over the deviation range. In this case the concept of instantaneous frequency is reasonably accurate, as the actual signal frequency changes only very slightly during the time of one cycle, and a period measurement is a valid means of determining the frequency. Under these conditions the instantaneous-frequency concept is quite valuable and generally gives a simpler mental picture than the sideband concept. The engineer who works a great deal with FM systems usually ends up making use of both concepts—the one of a sinusoidally varying frequency for low modulation frequencies (the so-called *quasi-static* case) and the other of carrier and sidebands when the modulation frequency is high and the carrier frequency moves around so fast that a cycle is no longer a cycle.

The quantity $\Delta f/f_{1,\text{max}}$, where $f_{1,\text{max}}$ is the maximum modulation frequency used, is called the *deviation ratio*. It is a rather important parameter, as it determines to a large degree the susceptibility of the system to noise and spurious signals other than noise. The deviation ratio for FM broadcasting is $5\,(\Delta f = 75\text{ kc}, f_{1,\text{max}} = 15\text{ kc})$, and the same value is normally used in FM/FM telemetry subcarriers. In wideband FM recording, deviation ratios in the range of 1 to 2 are common.

The *percentage deviation*, $100\,\Delta f/f_0$, is another parameter of major importance in telemetry and tape recording. For the telemetry subcarriers, deviations of $7\frac{1}{2}$ and 15 per cent are standard, while wideband recording systems use deviations ranging from 20 to 75 per cent.

Transmission-system Requirements. In the *transmission system* here is included all circuitry or media between the source of the frequency-modulated carrier and the demodulator (or discriminator) input terminals, excepting only the radio or wire link and associated components involved in telemetry. For telemetered and recorded signals, we thus include the recording amplifier, the head-tape system, the playback amplifier, bandpass filters, and limiter-amplifiers preceding the demodulator. For wideband FM recording, the transmission system includes the recording circuitry following the FM oscillator, the head-tape system, and the limiter-amplifiers between the playback head and the demodulator.

The ideal transmission system has a flat amplitude-frequency characteristic and a zero or linear phase-frequency characteristic over the bandwidth required by the signal. Strictly, these are the same requirements as those for an amplitude-modulated signal, but the importance of the phase characteristics is much greater in the FM than in the AM situation. If a bandpass filter with a nonlinear phase response but a flat amplitude response is used for an AM signal, the phase nonlinearity causes a small loss of amplitude in the AM sidebands and introduces a small amount of frequency modulation. The loss of amplitude in the sidebands affects slightly the amplitude-modulation-frequency response of the over-all system, but this is usually lost because many other parts of the system have much more effect than that of the phase nonlinearity. Also, the error can be rather easily corrected if necessary. The AM demodulator is normally not sensitive to phase or frequency modulation, and so the spurious frequency modulation introduced into the AM signal is not harmful.

With an FM signal, the nonlinear phase response causes distortion of the modulation signal, the relationship between phase nonlinearity and distortion being quite complex. In addition to this, if there is any spurious amplitude modulation on the FM signal, the nonlinear phase response will partially convert this to FM, whereupon it will be carried on through the system to the demodulator and appear as a noise or spurious signal in the system output. As in the AM case, the phase nonlinearity causes a small reduction in the sideband amplitudes and hence affects slightly the over-all amplitude versus modulation-frequency response of the system, but again, as in AM, this is small and is usually overshadowed by the effects of other system components.

Thus, if we have a flat system with respect to amplitude over the requisite bandwidth, we can tolerate phase nonlinearities in an AM system but they will cause trouble in an FM system. Conversely, if we have a linear phase response, we can tolerate some lack of flatness in amplitude with an FM system, but such lack of amplitude flatness produces immediate detrimental effects in an AM system. It is particularly undesirable for FM to have a nonflat amplitude portion of the system followed by a nonlinear phase portion.

These qualitative considerations can be readily understood by a little study of the vector diagrams of Figs. 3.4 and 3.5. The effects of different phase shifts of the two sideband vectors are fairly easy to see. A nonflat amplitude response causes one sideband to be larger than the other. Such unequal sidebands can be broken down into a pair of equal AM sidebands and a pair of equal FM sidebands. Thus the amplitude modulation produced on an FM signal by a nonflat amplitude characteristic can be predicted from either the quasistatic or the sideband viewpoint.

Multiplexed FM Subcarrier Recording. Direct recording is used for multiplexed telemetry subcarriers, because of the requirement for low distortion to avoid crosstalk between carriers. The phase response of such a recording-reproducing system has been shown to be somewhat nonlinear. In a properly designed system, the nonlinearity over the band of any one carrier is not large enough to be particularly important. For example, the nonlinearity over the 70-kc band with 15 per cent deviation can be held to about $1°7$ with almost perfectly flat amplitude response. This carrier represents the worst condition. If some amplitude nonflatness is tolerated, the phase nonlinearity can be reduced somewhat. Thus, in specifying a tape recording system for telemetry subcarriers, it may not be the best practice to set up extremely flat amplitude-frequency requirements; some leeway in this respect, in exchange for more linear phase response, may well result in a better system.

In the complete transmission system for the telemetry subcarrier, the bandpass filter needed to separate each subcarrier from the others simultaneously present on the same channel may be the poorest link. Some early requirements imposed on these filters called for very flat amplitude response over the passband and extremely sharp skirt selectivity. At the same time, phase linearity was neglected entirely. In order to meet the amplitude-response requirements, filter designers had to incorporate circuits that produce some rather sharp phase changes within the passband; production tolerances on filter parts result in wide variations in the phase nonlinearities, and severe dissymmetries about the center frequency are frequently encountered. As a result, many of the bandpass filters used in these systems introduce far more dynamic signal error than any other link in the chain. As a consequence of the sharp filter skirts, center frequencies must be maintained quite accurately, and any disturbance of the center frequency by system vagaries such as tape-transport flutter causes the signal to "spill over" the flat-top with consequent poor performance. This tends to put a high premium on precise tape speed control and low flutter, at a corresponding premium in the price of the tape system. A bandpass filter properly specified for the system requirements permits a more economical over-all solution of the telemetry subcarrier recording problem.

Wideband FM Carrier Recording. This is probably the most generally useful analog recording technique. It can provide moderately high amplitude accuracy (at worst 1 to 2 per cent), d-c response, good d-c linearity, low dynamic distortion, and the maximum bandwidth achievable with high accuracy at a given tape speed. In addition, tape speed changes over a very wide range (at least 200 to 1) are feasible, permitting corresponding time and frequency scale changes to facilitate data analysis and reduction. Excellent electronic equipment design is the key to maximum performance levels with this recording method.

As previously mentioned, percentage deviations range from 20 to 40 per cent or more, and the deviation ratio is in the 1 to 2 region. Carrier frequency in recording is proportional to tape speed, and there are two commonly accepted ratios of carrier frequency to tape speed: 5:6 and 9:10. These ratios are expressed in terms of carrier frequency in kilocycles and tape speed in inches per second. Maximum intelligence or modulation frequency in kilocycles is usually one-sixth the tape speed in inches per second, although this has been doubled in some cases with a reduction in S/N ratio. Table 3.1 shows the carriers and maximum modulation frequencies for the more common tape speeds.

The 5:6 ratio has been most used with 20 per cent deviation and electronic flutter compensation; the latter, as will be shown later, makes the percentage deviation relatively unimportant. The 9:10 ratio has been most used with 40 per cent deviation and without flutter compensation, the lack of compensation putting a premium on maximum possible deviation. The 5:6 ratio and 20 per cent deviation utilizes a minimum wavelength of about 0.86 mil, while the 9:10–40 per cent combination uses a minimum wavelength around 0.7 mil. The smaller ratio and deviation are hence a little more conservative with respect to dropouts, as the playback-head output level does not fall so far at the upper-frequency limit of the signal. Discriminators for reproduction of the 9:10 ratio–40 per cent deviation system should have a wider range of limiting and a lower noise-quieting threshold than those used in the 5:6–20 per cent systems.

Figure 3.7 shows a typical amplitude-frequency response curve for saturation recording at 30-ips tape speed. With this type of recording the relative high-frequency response is generally a little better, and the playback-head voltage level higher, than with direct recording. The carrier frequencies and band limits (quasi-static, very low modulation frequency) are indicated for both of the common systems. For the 20 per cent deviation system, the level variation over the band

TABLE 3.1. CARRIER AND MODULATION FREQUENCIES

Tape speed, ips	Carrier frequency, kc		Maximum modulation frequency, kc
	5:6 ratio, 20 per cent deviation	9:10 ratio, 40 per cent deviation	
60	50	54	10
30	25	27	5
15	12.5	13.5	2.5
12	10	. . .	2
7½	6.25	6.75	1.25
6	5	. . .	1
3¾	3.12	3.38	0.625
3	2.5	. . .	0.5
1⅞	1.56	1.69	0.31
1½	1.25	. . .	0.25
15⁄16	0.78	0.84	0.15
½	0.42	. . .	0.084

is about 3.25 db, with the minimum level 1.5 db below the carrier level. For the 40 per cent systems, the variation over the band is 7.5 db, and the minimum level is 4 db below the carrier and 3 db lower than that for the 20 per cent system. For the maximum modulation frequency of 5 kc, the sideband spectrum limits of the 40 per cent system are indicated by x's, and those of the 20 per cent system by circles.

Level variations could be considerably reduced and playback voltage increased if the carriers were centered at the peak of the response curve. Modulation signal bandwidth would be materially decreased by this much reduction of the carrier frequency, however. Amplitude equalization in the electronic circuits cannot be used because phase nonlinearities will be introduced in the signal band and cause dynamic distortion. Consequently, we must accept the level variation introduced by the head-tape combination and allow for it in the design of playback electronic components.

Resonance of the head inductance with cable or other circuit capacitances must be avoided at frequencies near the FM signal band, again because of phase nonlinearities.

Over-all performance of an FM tape system is governed mostly by the quality of the recording oscillator. This component introduces d-c nonlinearities of $\frac{1}{2}$ to 1 per cent and dynamic distortion ranging from 1 to 2 per cent, and should not introduce drift errors greater than $\frac{1}{2}$ per cent of full-scale signal. Gain stability should be nearly perfect. Once the FM carrier signal is generated at this quality level, the rest of the recording and reproducing system should

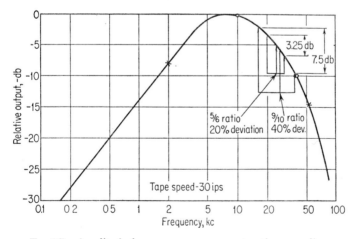

Fig. 3.7. Amplitude-frequency response—saturation recording.

have little effect. Flutter in the tape-transport mechanism introduces a direct noise component, but this can be readily eliminated by compensation techniques, as discussed later. Crosstalk in multichannel heads can introduce noise, but intertrack shielding can easily hold this below oscillator errors.

In playback, a well-designed discriminator with a 40-db noise-quieting threshold of a few microvolts will hold dropouts to a very low occurrence rate. Phase nonlinearities must be held to a value that produces negligible distortion and avoids spurious noise which might be introduced by conversion of the amplitude modulation of the reproduced signal to frequency modulation. This is particularly important with the 9:10 carrier-speed ratio and 40 per cent deviation, because of the larger amplitude fluctuations introduced. Limiting wipes out the AM introduced by tape-head characteristics. Finally, a cycle-counting demodulator and output d-c stages can be built to introduce no more than a few tenths per cent error due to all causes, including zero drift, gain stability, nonlinearity, and distortion. Thus, error contributions by any parts of the system other than the recording oscillator can be made very small.

Since a well-designed system hangs on the performance of the recording oscillator, it would seem logical to concentrate development effort on this component. A great deal of work has been done in this direction, and oscillators with almost perfect linearity and distortion, together with low drift, have been built; actually, a reasonable percentage of the oscillators sold commercially are probably much better than the published specifications. Variations of components cause sufficient spread of the critical performance criteria, however, to make it uneconomical to hold tighter tolerances in production units.

The author is inclined to believe that the development of vacuum-tube frequency-modulated oscillators has been carried to the point of diminishing returns in at least some designs. Improvement of the wideband FM channel seems to depend on other approaches, to be discussed in Chap. 8.

3.3 Pulse Duration Modulation Recording (PDM)

This is another form of time modulation which is very suitable for data recording on magnetic tape. It is sometimes called *pulse width modulation* (PWM). The information is contained in the duration or width of a pulse, which varies from a minimum to a maximum value to cover the full input range of the data signal.

Commutated PDM. The most widespread use of PDM is in commutated, or time-division-multiplexed, systems, wherein a commutator or switch is used to sample sequentially a large number of data channels. For each sequential channel sample, a pulse is generated, the width or duration of the pulse being dependent on the value of the data signal on that channel. The pulse recurrence rate is determined by the switch or commutator rate. Once during each revolution the switch contacts a grounded terminal and another terminal connected to a full-scale calibrating voltage; these frequent calibration voltages permit compensation for drift in zero and gain.

In the standard system for telemetry [19], the basic pulse recurrence rate is 900 per second, which can be generated in four ways: by a 30-contact switch rotating 30 times per second, a 45-contact switch rotating 20 times per second, a 60-contact switch rotating 15 times per second, or a 90-contact switch rotating 10 times per second. The number of data channels is at least two fewer than the number of switch contacts because of the calibration points, and frequently additional contacts are used for synchronizing purposes in the decommutation process. The four switch arrangements can thus handle a maximum of 28, 43, 58, and 88 data channels, respectively, with 30, 20, 15, and 10 samples per channel per second. The frequency response per data channel is dependent on how the data are read out and on the current quotation as to the number of samples required per cycle of data frequency. Conservatively, the channel frequency responses can be said to be 3, 2, 1½, and 1 cps for the 30, 20, 15, and 10 per second sampling rates. Thus the system is particularly adapted to the handling of quasi-static data from a large number of channels.

The PDM signal, whether direct from the basic equipment or from the output of a telemetry receiver, is a pulse of 1 to 5 volts amplitude, with a duration ranging from 90 ± 30 to 700 ± 50 μsec, at the standard 900-pps (pulse per second) repetition rate. In some special applications for tape recording only, a system slowed down by an 8:1 factor has been used, the recording taking place at 3¾ ips with playback at 30 ips to recreate the 900-pps standard repetition rate for the decommutation gear. However, most systems operate at the regular 900-pps rate.

This signal might be recorded by simply magnetizing the tape in accordance with it. The differentiating action of the playback head would then produce an output consisting of a positive pulse at the beginning and a negative pulse at the end of each signal pulse. At reasonable tape speeds these pulses would be somewhat rounded, and the determination of the exact time between pulses would be difficult.

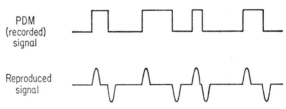

Fɪɢ. 3.8. Possible PDM recording-reproducing method.

Figure 3.8 illustrates the recorded and reproduced pulses. An improvement in timing accuracy might be achieved by differentiating the playback pulses and detecting the zero crossings of the differentiated pulses. This process would tend to increase noise, however, and it is simpler and more effective to differentiate the signal prior to recording. The signal sequence in this case is shown in Fig. 3.9.

By this method, the recorded pulses can be made as sharp as desired for best reproduction, and each reproduced pulse has a fast zero crossing whose timing can be determined with reasonable accuracy. Recording in this manner can be accomplished with an ordinary direct-recording amplifier, a differentiating circuit being added, the bias oscillator disabled, and the recording current increased to assure tape saturation on the recording pulse peaks. All three changes are necessary for optimum results, and all can be accomplished by one switch. This arrangement is incorporated in several of the available direct-recording amplifiers, so that they are useful for both FM/FM and PDM telemetry signals.

The PDM decommutation and readout equipment likes to see at its input the original PDM pulse signal. The signal from the playback head would be unrecognizable to it. Therefore the playback electronic system for PDM must regenerate the original waveform from the playback-head voltage. This can be achieved by triggering

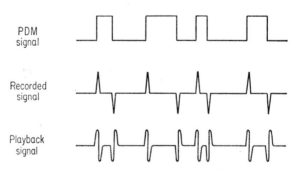

Fɪɢ. 3.9. Better PDM recording technique.

a flip-flop from the playback pulses. Some methods for doing this can be thrown into incorrect operation by loss of a trigger pulse. The seriousness of this sort of error is reduced by including a timing circuit to reset the flip-flop after a predetermined time (less than the pulse repetition period). This results in one lost data point if the trailing edge of the signal pulse is lost by a dropout. Signal level variations, which must be expected from tape, may affect the flip-flop triggering and thus spoil a certain amount of data.

A very ingenious method of wiping out a large part of the signal-level fluctuations was devised by John L. MacArthur [20]. Passing the playback signal through a heavily limiting high-gain amplifier will produce the pulse shape shown in Fig. 3.10. The relatively slow leading and trailing edges can be easily distinguished from the sharp central crossover, and the latter is very little affected by playback signal level because of the limiting. Such an arrangement thus becomes relatively immune to tape dropouts. However, between pulses, the limiting amplifier develops full gain, and thermal or other noise at its input can produce spurious pulses which can trigger the output flip-flop.

MacArthur found that the amplifier could be quieted by injecting a low-level high-frequency (about 1 Mc) voltage at or near the input; this signal serves to keep the gain under control between pulses, when there is no signal input, and effectively prevents triggering on noise. Additionally, the injected 1-Mc signal appears to trigger the main crossover of Fig. 3.10 so that it occurs stably within less than 1 μsec of the proper time. This is probably the most accurate method yet devised for the reproduction of PDM signals from tape and is remarkably free from system output spikes due to level fluctuations in the tape signal.

The PDM signal is relatively little affected by the tape system, except for the possible errors in pulse-spacing detection mentioned immediately above. This is an electronic system problem. Tape characteristics are not important, but the level fluctuations inherent in a tape system may introduce errors or signal loss if the electronic gear is not properly designed. Flutter in the tape transport has relatively little effect on system accuracy unless there are pronounced flutter components at or near the switch rotation rate or the pulse

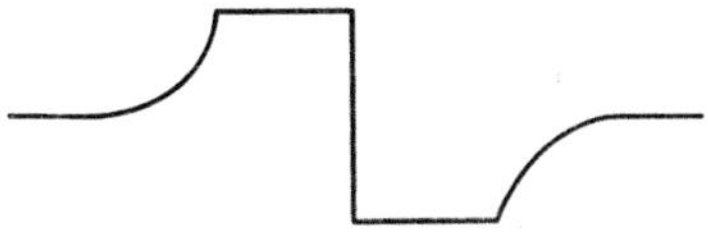

Fig. 3.10. PDM play-back pulse after heavy limiting.

recurrence rate. These effects will be treated more fully in Chaps. 5 and 6.

PDM as a Continuous Carrier System. Pulse duration modulation is usable as a normal carrier method without commutation. In this form it has one outstanding advantage and one serious drawback. The advantage is its freedom from tape-speed variations over a wide range (provided that there are no flutter components near the pulse repetition rate); the disadvantage is the limited bandwidth capability as compared with wideband FM carrier.

PDM carrier can be best understood by considering a square wave as the basic signal when the modulation input is zero (Fig. 3.11). Modulating voltage causes the negative-going (or positive-going) crossover to move back and forth in time with respect to the other crossover. If the amplitude excursions are held to fixed and equal positive and negative values, the average value will represent the modulation, and the data signal can be recovered by simple low-pass filtering. So long as a reasonable number of cycles are averaged by the filtering process, the pulse recurrence rate (carrier frequency) is not important. To put this in another way, the data value is determined by the duty cycle and is independent of the pulse recurrence frequency.

The bandwidth limitation results from the frequency spectrum of this signal. The basic square wave, with zero modulation input, is comprised of a fundamental of the same frequency as the square wave and a number of odd harmonic components, in accordance with the standard Fourier-series representation. When the square wave is exactly symmetrical, no even harmonics are present. Modulation produces departures from symmetry, and while this produces some changes in the amplitudes of the fundamental and odd-harmonic components, the major changes occur in the even harmonics. Thus we can say, with reasonable accuracy, that the modulation intelligence is contained mostly in the even harmonics of the repetition rate, and a reasonable number (say five) of these harmonics must be preserved to reproduce accurately the crossover time. The maximum bandwidth required to handle this signal is thus about $10f_0$, where f_0 is the carrier or pulse repetition frequency. With wideband FM, the

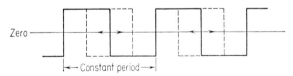

Zero

|← Constant period →|

Fig. 3.11.   PDM carrier.

maximum frequency is roughly $1.5f_0$. The maximum frequency required is the limiting factor in tape systems, as we have seen. If we assume the same ratio between carrier and maximum modulation (intelligence) frequency for the PDM and FM carriers, it is apparent that the FM system has almost seven times the intelligence frequency bandwidth of the PDM system at a given tape speed.

However, the fact that the data signal can be recovered from the PDM carrier by simple filtering is appealing, and the ability of the PDM system to undergo wide variations in tape speed without any change in the electronic system (except perhaps for the filter) lends itself to certain applications. Probably the most important of these are continuously variable-tape-speed situations, where the FM system would require a reference frequency and servo control of the playback discriminators to maintain d-c zero. The PDM system is capable of operating quite satisfactorily under such conditions, the only requirement being that the pulse recurrence rate must not become so low as to pass through the low-pass output filter. Within this limitation, a data signal can be recorded at any speed and reproduced at the same or any other speed, without any change in the data signal except the shifts of frequency and time scales which follow naturally from the speed change between recording and playback.

3.4 Digital Pulse Recording

In this type of recording, the signal must be in, or converted to, a digital form, i.e., a group of pulses of different weights to represent a numerical value. The weights of the pulses of a group may be determined by the relative time of occurrence of the pulses on a single line or channel. This is a *serial* digital signal. Alternatively, a number of lines or channels equal to the maximum possible number of pulses in a group can be provided, the pulses representing a number then appearing simultaneously on these lines. The weight of each pulse is determined by the line on which it occurs. This is a *parallel* digital number. A combination of these two methods is also possible, giving a *serial-parallel* representation of the number.

Because of the unreliability of level reproduction with tape, no effort is made in digital recording to do other than recognize the presence or absence of a pulse; amplitude is not pertinent. Thus the method is binary in nature, and the number represented by a pulse group is determined by the coding. Saturation recording is almost invariably used.

A number of methods have been devised for handling digital signals on tape; they all use one of two basic methods of recording a pulse. These methods are called *return-to-zero* (RZ) and *non-return-to-zero* (NRZ).

In the RZ method, the recording-head current is normally zero. When a pulse is to be recorded, a current sufficient to saturate the tape is passed through the head for a short period of time. The rise and fall times of the current pulse are made as short as is feasible. The time during which the current must remain at the saturation value is determined mostly by the head and tape characteristics. Too short a pulse will produce a small playback voltage. A pulse longer than necessary simply wastes time and tape. If it is desirable to retain maximum playback voltage, a reasonable rule of thumb requires that the current pulse last long enough to permit $\frac{1}{2}$ to $1\frac{1}{2}$ mils of tape to pass the recording-head gap. Thus at 60-ips tape speed, the pulse duration should be in the range of 8 to 24 μsec.

Figure 3.12 indicates the recording current for the serial binary number 1101. The playback-head voltage is the derivative of the tape flux and thus for each recorded pulse consists of a pulse of one polarity followed by a pulse of the opposite polarity, as shown also in Fig. 3.12. If the recording pulse were longer than necessary, the two playback pulses would be separated, with a period of zero voltage between them.

The playback voltage can be approximately doubled by biasing the record head with a direct current so that the tape is saturated in one direction in the absence of signal, the recording-pulse current being sufficient to cause opposite polarity saturation during the pulse. This is sometimes called *return-to-bias* recording. Some increase in noise between pulses results because of the magnetization of the tape.

In the NRZ method, indicated in Fig. 3.13, the recording-head current is always sufficient to saturate the tape. Each time a pulse is to be recorded, the direction of current flow in the head is reversed. As an alternative, a center-tapped head can be used and current passed through one half or the other of the winding, the switching of the current corresponding to the recording of a pulse. The differentiation

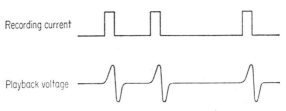

Recording current

Playback voltage

FIG. 3.12.   RZ pulse recording.

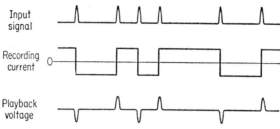

FIG. 3.13. NRZ pulse recording.

in playback produces a set of pulses which duplicates the pattern of input pulses except that alternate ones are of opposite polarities.

These two basic methods of recording a pulse have been used in a number of ways to record digital signals. RZ recording can use a pulse of one polarity to indicate a 1 and a pulse of the opposite polarity to indicate a 0. This is a *self-clocking* system in that a pulse is always present regardless of the binary digit being recorded. RZ or return-to-bias systems can employ a pulse to represent a 1, while 0 is indicated by the absence of a pulse. In this case a separate *clock* or *sprocket* record is desirable to indicate each time that a pulse might be present.

In its simplest form, the NRZ method can also be used in two ways, which are indicated in Fig. 3.14. In the first of these, the recording current (and hence the tape magnetization) is reversed each time a 1 is to be recorded, while no current change occurs for a 0. A recording current of this form is easily derived from an input signal in which a pulse represents a 1 and lack of a pulse represents a 0. In the second, one polarity of magnetic saturation represents a 0 and the opposite polarity represents 1. Then a recording-current change

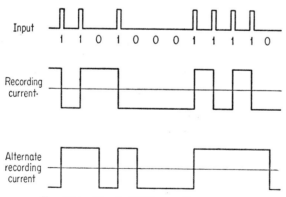

FIG. 3.14. Simple NRZ recording methods.

occurs only when there is a change from 0 to 1, or vice versa, in the input pulse train. Neither method is self-clocking, and it is desirable to add a clock signal to indicate the times when magnetization changes might occur.

In parallel recording, any of the techniques which are not self-clocking in themselves can be made so in the group. It is merely necessary to code the parallel-recorded character so that there is always at least one pulse present. This can be done, for example, by the use of an odd parity check bit; if the sum of the bits in the character is odd, the parity bit is 0, while if the sum of the bits is even, the parity bit is 1. A 0, represented by no pulses, is considered even and a parity bit is added, so that there is one pulse present in the character. Many coding systems have been devised having always at least one pulse present, regardless of a parity check pulse, and these are equally applicable. So long as there is a pulse in at least one of the tracks, the combined output of all tracks may be used as a clock pulse.

We desire to store as much information as possible on a given piece of tape, to achieve both minimum storage space and maximum rate of transfer of data to and from the tape. Consequently, the *packing density*, or number of pulses or bits per inch of track length, is a very important parameter. The usable packing density in an actual system is affected by many things, not the least of which is tape skew, to be discussed in Chaps. 5 and 8. We shall concern ourselves here only with those factors that affect packing density in a single track.

As we increase packing density, or decrease pulse spacing, with either RZ or NRZ recording, the peak playback signal decreases for closely packed pulses and its character becomes dependent on the particular sequence of the 1's and 0's in the input signal. There is no longer a clear-cut pulse, or absence of one, in the playback-head output. Since RZ recording requires two flux reversals per pulse and NRZ only one, it would seem, offhand, that the latter method permits twice the packing density—a statement made not infrequently. Unfortunately, the situation is not this simple. Hoagland [21, 22] and Eldridge [23] have shown that a single essentially instantaneous current reversal in the recording head gives rise to a playback pulse of appreciable duration, equivalent to a length of tape several times the playback-head gap width. The pulse on the tape is not so long, but it causes appreciable voltage in the playback head while it is in the vicinity of the gap. Now Hoagland, in the first reference, points out that an RZ pulse of very short length produces a playback voltage proportional to the derivative of the pulse produced by a simple flux reversal. This mathematical relation appears to be the basis for the statement by Eldridge that the length of an RZ pulse, on playback, is only slightly greater than that of an NRZ pulse. However, the mathematical case is a limiting one, and in the limit of an infinitesimally short RZ pulse the playback voltage would be zero, which has little practical value. We may then reasonably assume that an RZ pulse giving a usable value of playback-head voltage will be longer than an NRZ pulse.

On the other hand, since pulses may occur at any spacing from the minimum determined by the chosen packing density to a very large value, in the recording systems so far mentioned we may well have essentially isolated pulses along with others spaced at the minimum intervals. In NRZ recording, the isolated pulse will produce maximum playback signal voltage, while a succession of the closest-spaced pulses will give a minimum voltage. Figure 3.15 shows a typical graph of output voltage versus pulse packing. If the packing density were 1300 pulses per inch (ppi), for example, the output for a succession of pulses would be 6 mv, while that for an isolated pulse would be 14 mv. Allowing for 50 per cent dropouts, we would have to deal with a range of pulse amplitudes from 3 to 14 mv, which might not be conducive to maximum reliability. In the case of RZ recording, we can control the amplitude of the output for the isolated pulse by selecting the duration of the input pulse, and until the spacing between pulses approximates the duration of the input pulse the output voltage will remain constant. Thus, in RZ recording, to a degree, we can sacrifice absolute output voltage to gain a smaller change in output voltage as a result of variable pulse spacing. It is necessary to use quite short RZ pulses, with a serious

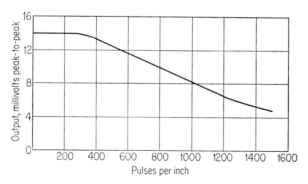

Fig. 3.15. Pulse packing curve. (*Courtesy of Clevite Electronic Components Division of Clevite Corp.*)

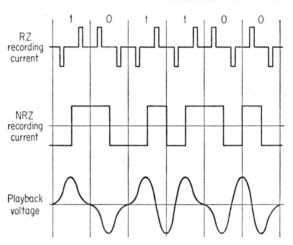

Fig. 3.16.   Phase-modulation digital recording.

reduction in output as compared with the maximum of Fig. 3.15, to accomplish this, however.

The type of RZ recording used also affects the picture.   If a pulse represents 1 and absence of a pulse represents 0, then we have to deal only with the relative output voltages for an isolated pulse as compared with that for closely packed pulses.   On the other hand, if a positive pulse represents a 1 and a negative pulse indicates a 0, a succession of 1's or 0's will give a smaller voltage than an isolated pulse, while a 1 followed by a 0, or vice versa, will give an appreciably larger voltage than an isolated pulse.   This considerably increases the range between maximum and minimum output pulse voltages and correspondingly increases the difficulty in reliable pulse detection.   Considering all these factors, it is apparent that any flat statement regarding packing density of NRZ vs. RZ is rather questionable. However, it is safe to say that, with the recording methods so far mentioned and under most conditions, higher packing densities are usually achievable with the NRZ technique.

The variations in playback-head voltage that result from extreme differences in pulse spacing have given rise to several methods of recording which limit the voltage variation and in addition give more positive criteria about the recorded pulse during reproduction.   The more widely used of these are the *phase-shift* or *phase-modulation* and the *frequency-doubling* techniques.   They are discussed in considerable detail by Richards [24].   The recording currents and approximate playback signal for the phase-modulation method are shown in Fig. 3.16, and those for the frequency-doubling method in

Fig. 3.17. Recording currents are shown for both RZ and NRZ techniques, while the output is indicated for the NRZ method at moderate packing density. In each case a specific *cell* is allocated to each bit, at least one flux reversal occurs per cell, and the ratio of maximum to minimum pulse spacing is never more than 2. With the phase-modulation system the voltage at the center of the cell determines whether the recorded bit was 1 or 0, while with the frequency-doubling scheme the voltages at the cell boundaries are the determining criteria. Gabor [25] states that the two methods are equivalent but that some circuit simplifications are possible with frequency doubling. Both methods are self-clocking, and clock and data pulses can be obtained from a single track.

Packing densities in computer applications vary from 200 to 500 or 600 ppi, while for original data recording they range upward into the 1000- to 2000-ppi region. This reflects the several-orders-of-magnitude difference in reliability required by the two cases. It is a minor catastrophe if one number comes out wrong in a computer, while a similar mistake, provided that it can be detected, is almost immaterial in an acquisition system recording thousands of data points per second.

The accuracy of digital recording is essentially unaffected by the tape system. Occasionally a pulse is lost by virtue of a dropout, and sometimes a noise pulse is registered as a signal pulse. The latter event can be practically eliminated by conservative system design, so that dropouts represent the only important source of error. A dropout is not the least interested in the weight of the pulse that

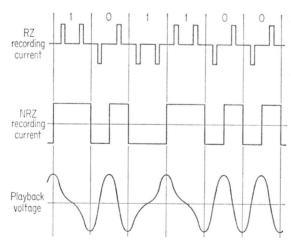

Fig. 3.17. Frequency-doubling digital recording.

it eliminates, and so it affects high-weight pulses just as much as low-weight ones. The error produced by a dropout is therefore equally likely to be very large as very small. Large errors, producing "wild" data points, are easily detected, so that actual data errors due to dropouts are quite rare.

Neglecting this possible dropout error, there is nothing else in the digital recording system that degrades the data presented in digital form at the input. Hence the accuracy of a digital system depends on the accuracy of the transducers (if they are digital output devices) or on the accuracy of the analog-digital converter used for conversion of the analog signal to digital form. Since a digital number represents one discrete value of the data signal and can change only by discrete steps, a digital system is inherently a sampling system. For economic reasons it is usually a commutated or time-multiplexed system also. Because commutation must occur before digitization, the system accuracy and stability will also depend on the multiplexing system as well as the analog-digital converter.

A serial digital number requires a certain amount of time for its presentation, the interval being the product of pulse spacing and the number of bits in the number. Serial digital data can be recorded on one tape track, although an additional clock track is often desirable. The product of maximum packing density and tape speed determines the top feasible pulse recurrence rate; this figure, divided by the number of bits per data value, governs the maximum number of data points that can be handled per second by the serial method.

By the use of multiple tape tracks, a quantity represented by a reasonable number of bits can be recorded in the time it takes to put one pulse on the tape. In this parallel recording method the track location determines the bit weight, and an entire number plus a clock track pulse is recorded on one line across the tape at the same instant. The number of data values that can be recorded per second equals the packing density times the tape speed.

The serial recording method is more economical as it uses at most two recording and two playback amplifiers and only two-track heads. The parallel recording method requires as many recording and playback amplifiers as there are bits in the data "word," plus one (generally) for the clock track. Multitrack heads are also necessary. Thus equipment cost and complexity buy speed in the system.

Serial-parallel methods represent a compromise in both cost and speed. By reducing the number of electronic circuits, they may increase reliability. The use of fewer tracks also reduces problems associated with tape skew (see Chap. 5).

When the data are in the binary-coded-decimal form (or one of its many variations), four bits are needed for each decimal digit. These, plus a clock track and an additional one for parity checking, make a total of six tracks. Still another track is handy for "word" or other identification pulses, and seven tracks are readily accommodated on ½-in. tape. This therefore makes a very popular combination, although it does not by any means represent the maximum track density that is practical.

3.5 Miscellaneous Methods

In the preceding sections we have discussed the most-used methods for recording data signals. There are a number of others that merit mention, however, as they may have specific advantages for particular applications. It may be assumed that each has some disadvantages as a general-purpose method, in comparison with the more widely applied techniques already discussed.

Compound Modulation. A number of transducers do not directly generate an electrical signal but require some form of power supply or excitation signal from which the output signal is generated. The excitation signal must be a-c in some cases and may be a-c in many others. For such transducers, a method of recording, termed *compound modulation* (CM) by Sink [26] and Newhouse [27], is applicable. The method has been used by others in a number of cases, but there is no published information which describes them. With transducers which produce an electrical output, a modulator may be used to convert this output to a modulated carrier signal.

Figure 3.18 shows the basic block diagram for a system using a transducer with a-c excitation. Differential transformers, synchros, strain gauges, and potentiometers are among the numerous possible transducers. The physical input to the transducer causes the a-c output to vary, zero input usually but not necessarily corresponding

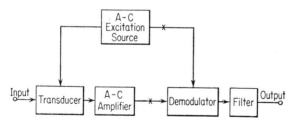

Fig. 3.18. A-C transducer excitation. (*Courtesy of Consolidated Electrodynamics Corp. and Instrument Society of America.*)

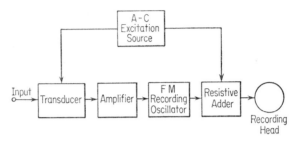

FIG. 3.19. Compound-modulation recording system. (*Courtesy of Consolidated Electrodynamics Corp. and Instrument Society of America.*)

to zero output. After amplification, if necessary, the transducer output is combined in the demodulator with the excitation signal to produce a d-c plus low-frequency a-c electrical output which corresponds to the transducer physical input.

When it is desired to apply tape recording to such a system, the designer has two choices. The final electrical output may be recorded by the FM carrier method, or the a-c system may be broken at the points marked X and the signals there present recorded by appropriate methods. If the first choice is made, d-c drifts and other inaccuracies of both systems will be compounded, while the second choice can be shown to permit tape recording with only very slight increase in the errors already inherent in the system of Fig. 3.18.

We may note, in the figure, that the transducer output signal amplitude must be accurately preserved, as it represents the physical input signal. Also, the relative phase between transducer output and excitation, at the demodulator, must not vary by more than $\pm 5°$ for 1 per cent demodulation accuracy. However, neither the amplitude nor the waveshape of the excitation signal need be preserved; it is necessary only that the demodulator receive a constant-amplitude symmetrical-wave excitation signal of the proper frequency and phase.

These requirements may be met by recording the transducer output by FM carrier, and the excitation by direct or saturation recording. Since the FM carrier frequency required to handle the transducer output signal is several times the excitation frequency, both signals may, but need not, be recorded on the same tape track. When they are so recorded, the FM carrier acts as bias for the lower-frequency excitation signal. For single-track recording, this leads to the block diagram of Fig. 3.19. Note that the amplifier and the FM recording oscillator are required to handle only the excitation frequency and the sidebands introduced by the transducer input signal.

No d-c response is necessary, and d-c drift, including center frequency drift of the FM oscillator, does not enter as an error.

Figure 3.20 shows the reproducing equipment necessary for single-track reproduction. The playback-head signal is amplified and then separated into the FM carrier and excitation signal components by filters A and B, both of which are bandpass. The FM carrier is demodulated and the resultant output passed through bandpass filter C to the final synchronous demodulator. The excitation signal is amplified and limited, to remove tape-system amplitude fluctuations, and applied to the demodulator through a time-delay network. This last network is necessary, to make up for the delay in filter A, if filters B and C have equal passbands. It is possible to eliminate the time-delay network if the bandwidth of filter C is made wider than that of filter B by an amount such that the sum of the delays of filters A and C is equal to that of B. Such an adjustment of filter delays is a bit difficult to hold in production units, however, and an adjustable time delay as indicated is helpful in achieving best system accuracy.

The FM discriminator need not—in fact, should not—have d-c response. Thus, there is no need for d-c response anywhere in the system except at the final output of the demodulator. FM oscillator and discriminator center frequency drifts do not affect the output, although drifts in slope (or gain characteristic) will introduce equivalent errors. Changes in average tape speed have no effect except on the time base, provided that the signals remain within the playback filter passbands. Flutter has only a second-order effect, except for components within the passbands of filters B and C. Compensation can be added to cancel these, if necessary.

Thus, when a-c transducer excitation is dictated by the nature of the transducer or by other considerations, the compound-modulation technique furnishes a recording and reproducing method that preserves

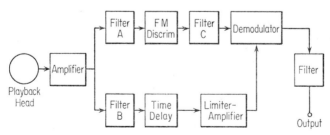

Fig. 3.20. Compound-modulation reproducing system. (*Courtesy of Consolidated Electrodynamics Corp. and Instrument Society of America.*)

very well the accuracy capabilities of the a-c excitation system. This is gained at the cost of decreased information capacity on the tape. If we assume 5:1 carrier-to-maximum-intelligence-frequency ratios, then the FM carrier in compound modulation must be 25 times the maximum data frequency; it must be five times the excitation frequency and this in turn five times the data frequency. Hence, the tape speed must be five times as great as would be required for a wideband FM system having the same data-signal bandwidth. In addition, some extra electronic equipment is required for the compound-modulation system. When there is a choice between a-c and d-c transducer excitation, the d-c excitation with standard wideband FM recording is preferable in terms of equipment economy and tape information capacity, while the over-all accuracy is comparable to or better than that of the compound-modulation system.

When a-c excitation is required and a number of channels are to be recorded, some equipment economy can be realized by recording the reference excitation signal on only one track, with the FM carrier transducer output signals on other tracks. With reasonable control of the time-delay characteristics of the discriminator output filters, only one time-delay network and limiting amplifier are needed for the excitation signal channel. Phase errors due to tape skew will now enter the picture, but these can be controlled by proper location of the reference signal track with respect to the others. In one such system, with 400-cps transducer excitation, two reference tracks were sufficient on 1½-in.-wide tape at 6 ips. This held phase errors at the demodulators to less than 5°, including the time-delay tolerances on production filters.

For a large number of fairly low-frequency channels, a low excitation frequency (under 100 cps) can be used, and the necessary FM carriers frequency-multiplexed on a number of tape tracks at moderate tape speed. The reference, or excitation frequency, need be recorded on only one track, even for wide tape. This arrangement is even more wasteful of tape information capacity, as all multiplexed carriers except the lowest are operated at less than their maximum modulation frequency capabilities. It does, however, offer the possibility of increasing the channel capacity of a given number of tape tracks at the expense of recording time. In this respect, the technique represents a compromise between multiplexed FM, ordinary compound modulation, and PDM.

These various forms of compound modulation have seen limited use. The method is most advantageous when a-c excitation of the transducers is dictated by considerations other than those involved in tape recording. When this is not the case, multiplexed or wideband FM may be preferable.

Erasure of Prerecorded Signal. The fact that a d-c magnetic field will cause partial or complete erasure of a prerecorded signal on tape is the basis for several recording systems. A sine-wave carrier signal is first recorded on the tape, usually at a saturation or near-saturation level without bias. In the data-recording process, the prerecorded tape is passed through a magnetic field whose strength is varied in accordance with the data signal. The maximum field intensity, corresponding to one extreme of the data signal range, will cause nearly complete erasure of the tape, while the minimum magnetic field, corresponding to the other extreme of the data signal range, will reduce only slightly the prerecorded carrier. Thus, on playback, the level of the residual carrier will give an indication of the data signal amplitude.

In one application of this method [28], a seismic-type accelerometer element moves a permanent magnet toward or away from the prerecorded tape. The distance between magnet and tape is a function of the acceleration, and the residual carrier indicates the acceleration magnitude when the tape is played back. Two tracks provide for the recording of two orthogonal accelerations, while a third track records the motion of a magnet attached to a torsional pendulum, thus giving a timing signal.

Another application [29] makes use of a conventional multitrack recording head and direct currents derived directly from transducers such as thermocouples or strain gauges. The field produced at the recording-head gap partially erases a prerecorded carrier. Figure 3.21 shows the erase characteristic. The portion between 0.25- and 0.95-ma head current is quite linear and usable for data recording. A separate bias winding on the head permits setting the initial operating points at either *A* or *B*, depending on the range of the

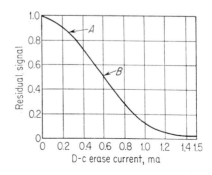

FIG. 3.21. Erase recording characteristics. (*Courtesy of BJ Electronics Division of Borg-Warner Corporation.*)

signal current. A full-scale value of 0.7 or ±0.35 ma is required from the signal source. Since the signal winding resistance is 40 ohms, this corresponds to a full-scale voltage of 28 or ±14 mv. The equivalent transducer generator voltage must be higher than this to include the drop in the internal resistance of the transducer.

The system accuracy is stated to be 5 per cent. This is somewhat better than would normally be expected from an AM recording technique, but it must be remembered that the prerecorded carrier saturates the tape. This tends to remove one source of level variation in direct recording, the fluctuation in tape flux resulting from imperfect contact between tape and recording head.

The outstanding advantage of the carrier-erase technique is the complete elimination of recording electronic components and their power supply. For moderate recording times, rather extreme miniaturization can then be achieved. As an example, a seven-channel recorder, with d-c to 250-cps data frequency response and 2-min recording time, is contained in a cylinder 4 in. in diameter and 5¼ in. long. This package includes a timing oscillator recording on an eighth tape track and the necessary operating batteries, so that no external power is required.

Video Recording. The major commercial application of video-frequency magnetic tape equipment is, rather obviously, in the field of television program recording. Tape has tremendous advantages over photographic film in that processing is eliminated and the tape can be erased and reused.

In data recording, there are a number of applications for equipment having maximum frequency response of a few megacycles, and the systems developed primarily for television use are applicable.

Two methods have been successfully applied to video recording. One of these is conventional, using very high tape speeds and special heads [30–32]. Extremely narrow gaps must be used in the playback heads, and core materials must have low losses into the megacycle region. Head design has been carried to the point that a high-frequency response of 8 to 10 kc per in. per sec is feasible. In spite of head improvements, tape speeds must still be so high that large reels are required for a reasonable recording time, and mechanical tape-handling problems arise. Multitrack recording is also used, and sometimes the total frequency range is split into two or more narrower bands which can be recorded at lower tape speed and recombined on playback [33].

A second method uses a rotating head sweeping transversely across the tape, longitudinal tape motion being just fast enough to space properly the transverse tracks [34–37]. Four heads are included in the rotating assembly so that the tape need be curved only around a 90° arc. This is accomplished by vacuum holding arrangements. Tape width is 2 in., and forward (longitudinal) velocity is 15 ips, providing over 1 hour recording time with standard 14-in. reels and 1.5-mil-base regular-thickness tape. A sound track is recorded on one edge of the tape by conventional methods, and a control track is placed at the opposite edge to maintain the proper relation between the forward tape motion and the rotating head.

The conventional method with high-speed tape runs into some difficulty with low-frequency reproduction, since the wavelength becomes so long that the reproducing head is small in comparison. As a consequence, the sound track or other similar low-frequency information is usually handled by means of FM carrier on a track separate from the video signals. The dual-channel FM and direct-recording technique discussed in a later paragraph has also been employed. The recording is continuous, without breaks or transients due to head switching.

The rotating-head system requires special tape (particles oriented transversely rather than longitudinally), and the switching transients associated with the start and stop of each crosswise sweep may be disturbing in some data-recording applications. However, it offers wide frequency range in combination with long recording times, without unwieldy reels and unusual lengths of tape. A discussion of potential instrumentation applications has been given by Koller [38].

It may be of interest to note that the rotating-head technique has been used previously at very low speeds to achieve long recording times on relatively short lengths of tape. A number of equipments of this type have been designed and marketed for long-term (24-hr) voice recording.

Boundary-displacement Recording. This method was described by Daniels [39]. If a tape track is magnetized to saturation longitudinally in one direction on one side of center and in the opposite direction on the other side of center, a normal playback head will pick up no net flux, as that received from one side of the track will cancel the flux from the other half. Displacement of the boundary between the opposite magnetizations will disturb this flux balance and produce a flux in the playback head proportional to the displacement of the boundary from center. A voltage will be induced in the playback-head windings proportional to the rate of change of the flux.

This type of recording can be produced from mechanical motion or by means of an electrical current. To produce it mechanically, the

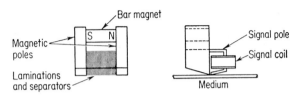

(a) Using signal current to record

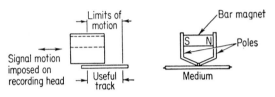

(b) Using mechanical motion to record

Fɪɢ. 3.22. Boundary-displacement recording heads. (*Courtesy of Electronics.*)

tape is prerecorded by saturating the entire track width in one direction. A conventional head carrying sufficient direct current to saturate the tape, or a similar structure with a permanent magnet, is then used to make the recording. Zero level results when this head overlaps half of the prerecorded track, and lateral movement of the head about this zero position varies the amount of the track in which the prerecorded magnetization is reversed. A varying area alongside the prerecorded track is magnetized during the recording process; its width is governed by the amount by which the recording head does not overlap the initial track.

A special recording head is used for producing the desired flux pattern from a signal current, and no prerecording is necessary. The head structure is indicated in Fig. 3.22. The permanent magnet (or a winding carrying direct current) produces a fixed magnetic field which has a gradient across the track width because most of the reluctance of the magnetic path is presented by the laminations. The magnetic shunt, together with the lamination stack, distorts the field so that it traverses the recording gap. The flux in the gap (and that fringing into the tape) is in one direction in one half the track width and the opposite direction in the other half. Its magnitude is sufficient to saturate the tape except in the small boundary region at the center.

Now, a current in the signal coil will produce a unidirectional flux across the whole width of the gap, or track. This adds to the fixed flux on one side and subtracts on the other, so that the boundary is shifted to the right or left of center, depending on the direction of current in the signal coil. When the flux due to the signal current is equal to the maximum value of the permanent flux, the boundary is shifted to the edge of the track. The gap flux and remanent induction in the recording medium are indicated in Fig. 3.23.

This recording method requires no bias, and its linearity is not dependent on the characteristics of the medium but rather on the geometrical accuracy of the boundary. Lateral motion of the tape, during recording, playback, or both, will introduce d-c drift and low-frequency noise. When playback is accomplished by means of a conventional head, the frequency-response characteristic will be generally similar to that of conventional recording. If a flux-responsive head is used in reproduction, the system frequency characteristic will again approximate that which is obtained by conventional longitudinal recording coupled with reproduction by flux-responsive methods.

Boundary-displacement recording and normal recording are related in essentially the same way as are variable-area recording and variable-density recording on sound film.

Dual Channel FM and Direct Recording. The recording of certain types of signals, such as moderately long-duration pulses, without serious distortion, cannot be accomplished by any of the standard methods at moderate tape speeds. FM carrier bandwidth is not sufficient to reproduce fast rise and fall times. Direct recording without equalization introduces serious distortions because of nonflat

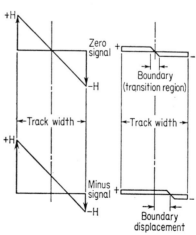

Fig. 3.23. Gap flux and tape induction in boundary-displacement recording. (*Courtesy of Electronics.*)

amplitude-frequency response, while equalization of the amplitude-frequency characteristic introduces other distortions due to the resultant nonlinear phase-frequency characteristic.

By a combination of a wideband FM channel and a direct-recording channel on two tape tracks, it is possible to achieve a response flat from direct current to the upper limit of the direct-recorded channel, with a phase characteristic approximating that of a normal passive network having the same frequency response. The FM channel handles the d-c and low-frequency portions of the input signal spectrum, while the direct-recording channel passes the high-frequency portions. By properly combining the two outputs, a single output is available with bandwidth from direct current to approximately 1.0-kc-per-ips tape speed.

In such a system, relative channel gains and phase shifts must, of course, be adequately controlled. The phase shifts are quite stable (aside from a small amount of phase jitter between the two tracks) and, once properly adjusted, can be expected to remain correct for a considerable time. The relative gains are not so stable, particularly in the recording system, so that it is usually desirable to record first a calibrating square wave at a reasonably low frequency. Such a calibration signal permits adjustment of absolute channel gain and also provides the criteria for relative gain adjustment. Proper relative levels result in the best square-wave output.

Flux-reading Methods. To improve low-frequency response and permit signal reproduction at tape velocities approaching zero, methods have been devised for reading the flux from the tape rather than its derivative. A survey of such methods was published by Kornei [40].

Broadly, flux-reading methods which have seen major use can be divided into four classes:

1. Standard heads associated with mechanical motion, either of the head itself or of an auxiliary magnetic member

2. Special heads in which the core reluctance can be varied periodically, by mechanical or magnetic means

3. Hall-effect heads

4. Electron-beam heads, wherein the beam is deflected by the magnetic field from the tape

Numerous other possibilities exist, as pointed out by Kornei, but the four mentioned are the ones which have been studied or applied most extensively. Of the four, only the first three are applicable to multitrack use on tape of moderate width; the electron-beam head uses a small cathode-ray tube with the beam direction, and therefore the maximum tube dimension, transverse to the tape. At best, such heads would have to be spaced longitudinally along the tape to permit multitrack operation, thus introducing intertrack timing errors.

A flux-reading system differs from the conventional system only in the playback or "reading" head (with perhaps some modifications in the playback electronic system), and the details of the heads will be discussed in Chap. 9. We are concerned here with their characteristics as recording systems.

The first two methods listed are basically carrier systems, the carrier being generated during the reproducing process, rather than prior to recording. In this situation, the carrier frequency is limited by mechanical or electrical loss considerations, rather than the frequency characteristic of the head-tape combination. The maximum reproduced intelligence frequency is thus not dependent on tape speed but on other head-design parameters.

Playback signal level is independent of tape velocity. Thus, if the recorded signal frequency is too high for the carrier used in the reproducing system, the playback speed can be reduced to bring the maximum signal frequency down to a suitable value. This freedom of playback signal level from change due to tape speed is particularly useful when wide speed variations must be handled in reproduction and when an extremely large ratio of recording to playback speed is necessary to fit data reduction system characteristics. Typical examples include the matching of wideband analog signals to a slow-speed direct-writing recorder and the direct transfer of closely packed digital data to a printer, paper tape punch, or card-punching machine.

For analog recording, the flux-reading techniques are subject to amplitude inaccuracy to essentially the same degree as direct recording. All factors causing amplitude uncertainty in the recording process and in the tape itself are still operative, and phenomena affecting level accuracy in the playback process would appear to be essentially the same for conventional and flux-reading systems. Thus, the flux-reading systems cannot be considered as precision instrumentation recording systems but they have great advantages in the low-speed playback area and when very low frequencies must be recorded with moderate accuracy and the simplest possible recording equipment.

Magnetography. Variously called *ferrography, ferromagnetography,* and *magnetography,* this is radically different from the other methods that we have discussed in that it produces a visual rather than an electrical output. It is thus a form of graphic reproduction. A number of authors have discussed the subject [41–46].

The technique is similar to Xerography. Powdered iron or black magnetic oxide is deposited on the magnetized tape and then transferred by contact to a suitable carrier, such as wax-coated paper. A magnetization pattern of any type is thus rendered visible and stored permanently, while the tape can be demagnetized and reused. Alphabetic, numeric, and other patterns can be formed.

Gehman [46] describes an application to oscillography, using a variation of the boundary-displacement recording method. To obtain a black line on a white background and to improve resolution, Gehman used a premagnetized tape. The premagnetization is achieved by passing the tape over a wire carrying a pulsed current to produce a large number of small dipoles over the entire coating surface. The signal is recorded by means of a boundary-displacement recording head, modified so that the saturating flux produced remains entirely in the tape coating. In this manner the prerecorded pattern is erased everywhere but in the boundary region, and in such a way that there is little or no flux emerging from the newly saturated regions. When the black magnetic oxide is applied to the tape, it adheres only in the boundary region to form a fine line representing the waveform of the recording current. The pattern is transferred by pressing the tape against a suitable transfer material, such as wax- or plastic-coated paper. The latter can then be heated to embed the record permanently.

Since no moving galvanometer elements are involved in the recording process, very high-frequency response is attainable. Further work remains to be done to determine all the possibilities and limitations of the process.

3.6   Relative Information Capacity

It is both interesting and informative to look into the relative information capacity of the most important recording methods. In many cases the tape-carrying capacity of a recording unit is quite important as it reflects in the size of the unit, and in such situations the information capacity of the tape may be a pertinent factor in system design.

In order to compare such diverse systems as wideband FM and digital, we must agree on a common ground in certain respects. One of these is the ratio of carrier or sampling frequency to the maximum data frequency that can be handled. This is a complex subject in itself, and, rather than become involved too deeply in it here, we shall simply assume a ratio of 5. At least this is a practical one for the analog systems, and the actual ratio is not too important so long as it is the same for all systems. For direct recording, of course, we need no ratio, as no carrier is involved.

A reasonable criterion for information capacity is bandwidth per square inch of tape. This takes into account the closer track spacing that is possible in digital recording as compared with analog, because of the less stringent crosstalk requirements. Since all systems except direct recording can handle d-c data, the bandwidth can be reasonably expressed in terms of the maximum data frequency that can be handled. No particular error is involved in this treatment of the direct-recording case, as the lower frequencies that cannot be handled represent a negligible portion of the total spectrum.

Information capacity can be expressed as the number of data frequency cycles that can be recorded per inch of track, multiplied by the number of tracks that can be recorded per inch of tape width. Direct recording with conventional techniques can handle about 2000 cycles per track-inch; with high-resolution heads this can be pushed to 8 or 10 kc per track-inch, although this involves some sacrifice in signal-to-noise ratio. Wideband FM provides 180 cycles per track-inch, on the basis of the 9:10 ratio of carrier frequency to tape speed and the 5:1 ratio of carrier to top signal frequency. Pulse duration modulation can accommodate roughly 27 cycles per track-inch.

Digital recording must be considered on the basis of an accuracy comparable to that of the analog systems. Straight binary coding is the most economical in information capacity, and a seven-bit code provides accuracy roughly comparable to wideband FM or PDM. Now each cycle of the data frequency must have five samples (by our 5:1 convention), and each sample requires seven pulses (or pulse possibilities) to define it. Therefore, 35 pulses are required per cycle, and if 1000 ppi are accepted as the maximum packing density, the digital recording method permits 28 cycles per track-inch.

Now direct recording and wideband FM are rather intolerant of crosstalk, so that tracks must be reasonably separated. PDM and digital recording are not so finicky, and tracks can be packed more closely together. For direct and wideband FM recording, 16 tracks per inch of tape width are feasible, while for PDM and digital 32 tracks can be recorded on 1-in.-wide tape.

We then obtain the following theoretical maximum information densities, in cycles per square inch of tape, with comparable accuracy for all methods except direct recording:

Direct recording	32,000–160,000
Wideband FM	2,880
PDM	864
Digital	896

This may be a rather surprising result, in view of the many statements that the information capacity of magnetic tape for digital data is extremely high. This is true in comparison with punched cards and punched paper tape, but in comparison with the capacity of the magnetic tape with other recording methods, the digital technique shows up as rather poor. Figure 3.24 depicts graphically these results.

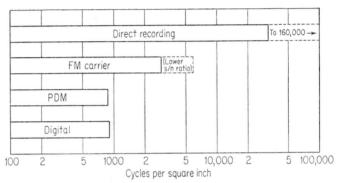

Fig. 3.24. Relative information capacity of magnetic tape.

There is one factor which is not included in these figures. In digital recording, bandwidth (or information capacity) can be traded for accuracy (or at least for resolution). By reducing the information capacity we can achieve arbitrarily high resolution, and the accuracy can be pushed as far as the transducers, multiplexers, and analog-digital converters will allow. This is not true of the analog methods, where accuracy would be affected by the tape system if electronic-system accuracy were pushed far enough, and there is a limit to what can reasonably be achieved. In common with the analog techniques, the accuracy of the digital systems is finally limited by the electronic components such as multiplexers and analog-digital converters, except in those situations in which the original data are in digital form.

REFERENCES

1. Stewart, W. Earl: "Magnetic Recording Techniques," McGraw-Hill Book Company, Inc., New York, 1958.

2. Wetzel, W. W.: Review of the Present Status of Magnetic Recording Theory, *Audio Eng.,* vol. 31, no. 11, p. 14, November, 1947; vol. 31, no. 12, p. 12, December, 1947; vol. 32, no. 1, p. 26, January, 1948.

3. Holmes, Lynn C.: Techniques for Improved Magnetic Recording, *Elec. Eng.,* vol. 68, no. 10, p. 836, October, 1949.

4. Hund, August: "Frequency Modulation," McGraw-Hill Book Company, Inc., New York, 1942.

5. Goldman, Stanford: "Frequency Analysis, Modulation, and Noise," McGraw-Hill Book Company, Inc., New York, 1948.

6. McLachlan, N. W.: "Bessel Functions for Engineers," Clarendon Press, Oxford, 1955.

7. Warren, A. G.: "Mathematics Applied to Electrical Engineering," Chapman & Hall, Ltd., London, 1939.

8. Jahnke and Emde: "Tables of Functions," Dover Publications, New York, 1945.

9. Arnstein, P. B.: Note on Frequency Distribution of an FM/FM Signal, *IRE Trans. on Telemetry and Remote Control,* vol. TRC–3, no. 2, p. 13, May, 1957.

10. Baghdady, Elie J.: Theory of Low Distortion Reproduction of FM Signals in Linear Systems, *IRE Trans. on Circuit Theory,* vol. CT–5, no. 3, p. 202, September, 1958.

11. Clavier, A. G.: Application of Fourier Transforms to Variable-frequency Circuit Analysis, *Proc. IRE,* vol. 37, no. 11, p. 1287, November, 1949.

12. Corrington, M. S.: Variation of Bandwidth with Modulation Index in Frequency Modulation, *Proc. IRE,* vol. 35, no. 10, p. 1013, October, 1947.

13. Crosby, M. G.: Frequency Modulation Noise Characteristics, *Proc. IRE,* vol. 25, no. 4, p. 472, April, 1937.

14. Gladwin, A. S.: The Distortion of Frequency-modulated Waves by Transmission Networks, *Proc. IRE,* vol. 35, no. 12, p. 1436, December, 1947.

15. Gold, Bernard: The Solution of Steady-state Problems in FM, *Proc. IRE,* vol. 37, no. 11, p. 1264, November, 1949.

16. Hupert, J. J.: Normalized Phase and Gain Derivatives as an Aid in Evaluation of FM Distortion, *Proc. IRE,* vol. 42, no. 2, p. 438, February, 1954.

17. Runyan, R. A.: Noise and Cross-talk in Multiplexed FM Systems, *IRE Natl. Conv. Record,* part 1, p. 194, 1956.

18. Uglow K. M.: Noise and Bandwidth in FM/FM Radio Telemetering, *IRE Trans. on Telemetry and Remote Control,* vol. TRC–3, no. 2, p. 19, May, 1957.

19. Telemetry Standards for Guided Missiles, IRIG Document 103–56, reprinted in *IRE Trans. on Telemetry and Remote Control,* vol. TRC–3, no. 3, p. 13, December, 1957.

20. Unpublished reports.

21. Hoagland, A. S.: Magnetic Data Recording Theory: Head Design, *Communication and Electronics,* no. 27, p. 506, November, 1956.

22. Hoagland, A. S.: High Resolution Magnetic Recording Structures, *IBM J. Research and Develop.,* vol. 2, no. 2, p. 90, April, 1958.

23. Eldridge, D. F.: Magnetic Recording and Reproduction of Pulses, *IRE Natl. Conv. Record,* vol. 7, part 9, p. 141, 1959.

24. Richards, R. K.: "Digital Computer Components and Circuits," D. Van Nostrand Company, Inc., Princeton, N.J., 1957.

25. Gabor, A.: High-density Recording on Magnetic Tape, *Electronics,* vol. 32, no. 42, p. 72, Oct. 16, 1959.

26. Sink, R. L.: Recording of Precision Data on Magnetic Tape, Instrument Society of America, paper 54-35-3, presented at ISA Instrument Congress and Exposition, September, 1954.

27. Newhouse, George B.: Compound Modulation—Method of Recording Data on Magnetic Tape, *IRE Natl. Conv. Record,* part 10, 1955.

28. Instruction Manual for Accelerometer Equipment, Engineering Research Associates, Inc., Publication PX29547, June, 1951.

29. Application Notes, BJ Miniature Magnetic Tape Recorders, BJ Electronics, Borg-Warner Corporation, Santa Ana, Calif., Feb. 20, 1959.

30. Olson, H. F., et al.: A System for Recording and Reproducing Television Signals, *RCA Rev.,* vol. 15, p. 3, March, 1954.

31. Television Tape Recorder, *Electronic and Radio Engr.,* vol. 35, p. 193, May, 1958.

32. Olson, H. F., et al.: Magnetic Tape System for Recording and Reproducing Standard FCC Color-television Signals, *RCA Rev.,* vol. 17, p. 330, September, 1956.

33. Maxwell, D. E., and W. P. Bartley: Synchronization of Multiplexed Systems for Recording Video Signals on Magnetic Tape, *IRE Natl. Conv. Record,* part 7, 1955.

34. Snyder, R. H.: Magnetic Tape Recording System for Video Signals, *IRE Trans. on Broadcast Transmission Systems,* vol. PGBTS-7, p. 35, February, 1957.

35. Ginsburg, C. P., C. E. Anderson, and R. M. Dolby: Video Tape Recorder Design, *J. Soc. Motion Picture Television Engrs.,* vol. 66, part 1, p. 177, April, 1957.

36. Ginsburg, C. P.: Achievement of Practical Tape Speed for Recording Video Signals, *IRE Trans. on Broadcast Transmission Systems,* vol. PGBTS-8, p. 25, June, 1957.

37. Snyder, R. H.: Video Tape Recorder Uses Revolving Heads, *Electronics,* vol. 30, p. 138, Aug. 1, 1957.

38. Koller, E. L.: Instrumentation Applications of the Ampex Videotape Recorder, *IRE Wescon Conv. Record,* part 5, 1957.

39. Daniels, H. L.: Boundary-displacement Magnetic Recording, *Electronics,* vol. 25, no. 4, p. 116, April, 1952.

40. Kornei, O.: Survey of Flux-responsive Magnetic Reproducing Heads, *J. Audio Eng. Soc.,* vol. 2, no. 3, p. 145, July, 1954.

41. Atkinson, R. B.: Ferrography, *J. Franklin Inst.,* p. 373, November, 1951.

42. Berry, T. M., and J. P. Hanna: Ferromagnetography—High Speed Printing with Shaped Magnetic Fields, *Gen. Elec. Rev.,* p. 20, July, 1952.

43. Hanna, J. P.: Ferromagnetography, *Proc. Fifth Annual Technical Meeting,* Technical Association of the Graphic Arts, Washington, D.C., p. 22, Apr. 27–29, 1953.

44. Reinert, W.: The Magnetic Tape Oscillograph, *Elektrotech. Z.,* vol. 9, p. 493, Dec. 21, 1957.

45. Begun, S. J.: Theory of Magnetography, *IRE Natl. Conv. Record,* vol. 6, part 5, p. 190, 1958.

46. Gehman, J. B.: Applications of Magnetography to Graphic Recording, *IRE Natl. Conv. Record,* vol. 6, part 5, p. 198, 1958.

CHAPTER 4

TAPE-TRANSPORT MECHANISMS

A basic component of all magnetic tape recording and reproducing systems is the mechanism employed to move the tape past the recording and playback heads. Such mechanisms have been variously named, but the term *tape transport* seems to be approaching the status of general acceptance and standardization. Machines for intermittent operation with fast start-stop capabilities are often called *tape handlers*.

According to the manner of operating, tape transports can be divided into two general classes:

1. Continuous-running
2. Intermittent-motion (fast start-stop)

Each of these general types can be further classified according to application and power source as

1. Laboratory or computer types, which operate from standard power lines in a reasonably controlled environment
2. Airborne, mobile, and special types, operating from d-c or high-frequency a-c power sources, often under severe environmental conditions

There are many cases in which it is desirable to form a length of tape into a continuous loop and run it repetitively; thus, loop drive arrangements are necessary, which are sometimes provided by means of accessories to a standard reel-type transport and sometimes as entirely separate machines without provisions for reels.

The complete list of operating modes for a tape transport consists of the following:

1. Forward, under control of capstan
2. Reverse, under control of capstan
3. Forward search, under control of special high-speed capstan
4. Reverse search, under control of high-speed capstan

5. Fast forward, no capstan control
6. Rewind, no capstan control
7. Stop

All these operational functions are not included in every transport. Reverse operation under normal capstan control is, for example, very rarely encountered in continuous-running machines and very frequently incorporated in intermittent fast start-stop equipment. The forward and reverse search functions, controlled by a high-speed capstan, are usually provided by an accessory to a continuous-running machine; in intermittent fast start-stop equipment this function is usually accomplished under normal capstan control at regular speed.

For many years, low flutter has been emphasized as the most (and sometimes only) desirable characteristic of a continuous-running tape transport. This, combined with inadequate attention to the possibilities of flutter compensation techniques, has forced the concentration of so much engineering design effort on the elimination of flutter that other very important areas of transport performance have been seriously neglected. As a result, an alarmingly high percentage of the machines in use handle the tape so roughly that it is positively dangerous, with respect to the preservation of valuable data, to stop and start the transport when data-carrying tape is within reach of the operating strains. This includes at least all the tape from the outer layer of the supply reel to the outer layer of the takeup reel and in some cases may even include some portions of the tape on the reels. In addition, the reel characteristics and winding-tension patterns may be conducive to tape damage during storage. The preoccupation with flutter has been so great that special studies, instigated by considerable losses due to damaged tape, have been required to bring to light these other important factors [1].

To attempt to put the subject in a little better perspective, there are listed below, in approximate order of importance, what appear to be the desirable characteristics of an ideal tape transport, in the light of present knowledge:

1. Starting, stopping, and operating stresses and reel accelerations well within the range that will not degrade a recorded data signal

2. Maximum protection of oxide coating—ideally no contact with anything except heads, and this only during record, playback, or search

3. Lateral guidance without edge damage—ideally no mechanical contact with tape edges

4. Properly designed precision reels, perfect "lay" of tape when wound, and proper winding-tension pattern for storage

5. Maximum ease of operation, but with control interlocks so that it is *impossible* to stress tape in a way that will degrade a recorded data signal even though this may force some waiting between executions of control operations

6. Uniform temperature throughout tape compartment

7. Flutter consistent with required over-all data accuracy and reasonable maintenance—ideally servo speed control and flutter compensation by movable playback head under all reproducing conditions

8. Dustproof tape compartment, slightly pressurized

9. Single-stack heads, rather than interleaved dual stacks

All the items prior to flutter have to do with the protection of recorded information. Certainly this is worthy of the most serious consideration in view of the high cost and irreplaceability of such data. To paraphrase an ancient saying, "It profiteth a man little to gain minimum flutter, and forever lose his data by rough tape handling." Clearly, however, gentle tape handling is not inconsistent with low flutter; in fact, a transport designed to fulfill the above requirements might well exhibit exceptionally low flutter.

Certain characteristics of present-day transports may have to be modified to permit attainment of the goals outlined. Starting and stopping times may have to be increased, and fast forward and rewind times lengthened. Control facility would be decreased by the interlocks mentioned in item 5; it would probably not be possible to "shuttle" the tape back and forth by alternate use of the fast forward and rewind modes or to perform other mode switching operations now possible. These sacrifices, if they are really that, would clearly be justified by the gain in safety of data.

The last item of the list, single-stack heads, may not seem pertinent to transport performance. Nevertheless, their use reduces from four to two the number of stationary surfaces on which the oxide must rub, simultaneously removing two sources of excitation for random flutter and reducing the length of tape subject to such excitation. Finally, single-stack heads eliminate the serious intertrack timing error inherent in the dual-stack system and make practical the application of the best flutter-compensation method—a movable playback head.

4.1 Continuous-running Tape Transports

Continuous-running transports are used for essentially all analog recording and in certain cases for digital recording in systems for original data acquisition. The primary features that should be incorporated in such machines have just been mentioned. Secondary requirements include simple, trouble-free control arrangements, easy loading, and reasonable accessibility for maintenance. Operation at a large number of speeds is frequently necessary. The ability to accommodate all standard reels of various sizes is important, provided that it involves no compromises in proper reel design and winding patterns. Relatively simple adaptation to various tape widths is a useful characteristic in a general-purpose transport; replaceability of heads without disturbance of their precision alignment is desirable.

Many early transports used in instrumentation applications were adaptations of high-quality professional audio machines. As experience was gained and applications increased, it became apparent that some characteristics that are important in audio machines are of little or no value in instrumentation equipment, while other characteristics not necessary in audio work are highly desirable in data recording and reproducing applications. This naturally led to the design of special equipment for these applications with basic designs quite different from those used in the audio field.

Laboratory Types. These machines are designed for the environmental conditions encountered in the laboratory or similar reasonably sheltered environments and for operation from standard a-c power lines. They are, however, usually sufficiently rugged to be usable in suitably designed carrying cases as portable equipment and to be mounted in trailers or trucks for certain types of mobile installations. Also, for some laboratory and factory uses they may be mounted in racks or cabinets with wheels so that they can be readily moved from place to place. They are almost always general-purpose units and incorporate many of the operating modes outlined earlier.

Because early instrumentation transports were adapted from audio equipment, they followed generally the "straight-through" tape path used in audio machines and indicated schematically in Fig. 4.1. In this figure, A is the supply reel and B is the takeup reel. The items encountered by the tape in its path from the supply to the takeup reel are, in order, the tensioning arm C, inertia idler D, tape guide E, heads F, tape guide G, capstan H, and pinch roller I. Three motors are used for driving, one for each reel and one for the capstan. The two reel motors are torque motors designed to operate at speeds

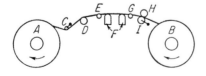

Fig. 4.1. Early-type tape transport.

very much less than their maximum capabilities and to develop a torque which can be controlled by the voltage applied to the motor. The capstan motor is almost always a hysteresis synchronous motor so that its speed is governed by the frequency of the power supply. In normal operation, voltages supplied to the reel motors are adjusted so that the motor torques approximately balance when half the tape is on each reel, the supply-reel motor tending to turn its reel backward against the direction of tape motion indicated in the figure. The pinch roller I is operated by a solenoid and presses the tape tightly against the capstan. In this manner, the speed of the capstan controls the velocity of the tape, the reel motors merely maintaining tension.

Guides E and G are fixed nonrotating elements which constrain the tape laterally against one or both edges and serve to maintain the lateral position of the tape as it passes over the heads. The tensioning arm C and inertia idler D are used to smooth out rapid variations in tension of the tape as it comes from the supply reel. Such tension variations can result from torque pulsations in the motor and mechanical imperfections in the supply reel and its mounting.

Depending upon the applicational requirements and head-stack arrangement, from one to four head stacks may be mounted on the transport. For recording only or playback only, one or two head stacks would be used, two being necessary when track interleaving is employed. For recording and playback applications or when monitoring from the tape is necessary during recording, two in-line stacks or four interleaved head stacks would be necessary.

In this sort of system the tension applied to the tape by the reel motors varies in accordance with the amount of tape on the reels. When the tape is first started, so that the supply reel is full and the takeup reel practically empty, the takeup reel produces maximum tension and the supply reel gives relatively less. This is because the torques supplied by the motors do not vary appreciably over the range of speeds at which the motors operate, and the effective radius arm for the takeup reel is small and that for the supply reel is large. Under these circumstances the capstan must act to hold back the tape against the excessive pull of the takeup reel, and the tension in the tape as it passes over the heads is at a minimum value. When half the tape is on each reel, the pull of the takeup reel is approximately balanced by the holdback tension developed by the supply reel and the capstan furnishes sufficient forward driving power to overcome frictions.

When the takeup reel is almost full and the supply reel nearly empty, the holdback tension is at a maximum and the forward pull of the takeup reel is at its minimum value. In this situation the capstan must furnish sufficient forward driving force to make up for the differences in the reel pulls as well as the frictions present, and the tape tension in the section passing over the heads is a maximum.

These variations in tape tension while a reel of tape is being run through the machines are undesirable and tend to cause variations in the flutter and other irregularities of tape motion. Because of the tension variations, any slippage at the capstan will result in a speed change as the tape transfers from the supply to the takeup reel. To avoid this, rather heavy pressure is necessary between the pinch roller I and capstan H. This pressure in turn increases the load on the capstan motor and may result in small speed variations as the load varies because of inhomogeneities in the rubber covering of the pinch roller.

While tensioning arm C and inertia idler D are helpful, they do not entirely remove tension variations produced by the supply reel. Such tension variations can produce changes in tape speed at the heads even though the speed at the capstan is constant. As tension increases, the section of tape between capstan and flywheel stretches slightly, and during the time that it is stretching the speed across the heads must be slightly less than the speed at the capstan. While the tension is decreasing, speed at the heads will be slightly greater than at the capstan.

When this type of transport is designed for four head stacks, it is unavoidable that a fairly long section of tape will exist between the capstan and the inertia idler D. This relatively long unsupported section of tape is subject to small erratic motional nonuniformities due to variations in the friction between tape and heads and to roughness in the tape coating. In some cases, longitudinal resonant vibrations occur in the tape which produce a flutter component at a fairly sharply defined high frequency. This is a "violin-string" sort of vibration except that it is longitudinal rather than transverse. It is induced by friction between the tape and the heads analogous to the friction between a violin string and bow.

Because of the pressures for low flutter in instrumentation recording and the shortcomings of the system illustrated in Fig. 4.1, the so-called *closed-loop* drive was developed and is employed in many tape-transport designs. The critical portions of this drive are illustrated schematically in Fig. 4.2. Tape is clamped to the capstan by a pressure roller as it enters the closed loop. It then passes over

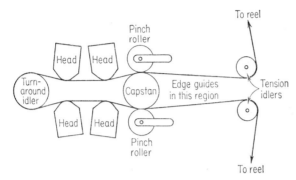

Fig. 4.2. Closed-loop drive.

one or two head stacks, depending on the stack arrangements, over a turn-around idler, past an additional one or two head stacks, and finally is again clamped to the capstan by a second pressure roller as it leaves the loop. In so far as there is no slippage at either point of contact with the capstan, any initial tension established in the loop will be maintained. Actually, many machines using this closed-loop drive operate with fairly high tension in the tape sections external to the loop, to overcome slight slippage at the capstan which might alter loop tension. In one design, a special capstan and pinch-roller arrangement maintains tension in the loop independently of external tensions, thus permitting operation with very low tensions between the reels and the capstan drive points.

The closed-loop design reduces materially the unsupported length of tape between capstan and heads, which increases proportionately the frequency of any violin-string vibration in the tape. It has been mentioned that the use of single-stack heads rather than dual interleaved stacks permits still further reduction of the size of the loop, with attendant advantages.

The closed-loop arrangement also minimizes the effects of tension variations external to the loop, although it does not eliminate them. To reduce still further these tension variations that cause effective speed changes, the reel motions are controlled by a servomechanism to maintain essentially constant tension in the tape external to the loop.

Two different sensing methods for control of the reels have been employed. One of these is direct sensing of the tension in the tape between the reel and the capstan by means of a movable arm carrying a roller over which the tape passes. The other employs an arm resting on the tape on the reel to sense the amount of tape present. This is readily related to the torque that must be delivered by the reel motor to maintain constant tension.

Two types of reel control have been used also. One of these is mechanical and consists simply of a brake, actuated by the tension-sensing means, which controls the effective torque delivered to the reel by the motor. The other method makes use of electrical means to control the torque delivered by the reel motor and dispenses with mechanical brakes for torque control. Various control techniques have been used in the electrical servo systems, including saturable reactors, thyratron circuits, field current control of d-c motors, and others. Band or disk brakes are mounted on the reel shafts to stop the reels when the tape is to be stopped or when power is removed.

Capstan drive systems usually incorporate considerable inertia for flutter reduction and are therefore operated continuously when power is supplied to the tape transport to permit fast starting of the tape. Sudden actuation of the capstan pressure rollers when the tape is standing still may produce excessive strains in the tape, which can be extremely detrimental if data are already recorded on the tape. To alleviate starting strains, some transports bring the tape up to speed by means of the reel-drive motors before the pressure rollers are depressed against the capstan. In these systems, a tachometer measures the tape speed and actuates the pressure-roller arms when the tape is traveling at the same speed as the surface of the capstan. There is little or no published information on the stresses imposed on the tape in fast starting and stopping. It is quite possible that, when such information does come to light, it will be necessary to revise specifications with respect to starting and stopping times, to avoid destruction of valuable data by excessive strain in the tape.

Three different capstan-drive arrangements have been frequently used. In one, the capstan is a precision-ground extension of the capstan-motor shaft, a flywheel being mounted on a shaft extension at the opposite end of the motor to minimize speed fluctuations. A second arrangement incorporates a rubber-rimmed wheel on the capstan shaft, the motor shaft being pressed against the rubber rim to drive the capstan. A variation of this uses a rubber idler held by strong tension against both the motor shaft and a metal wheel or disk on the capstan shaft. The third arrangement uses a flat-belt drive between a pulley on the motor shaft and a flywheel on the capstan shaft.

Speed changes are accomplished by pole switching in the motor, by a sleeve over the capstan to change its diameter, and by changing the pulley size in the case of belt-driven capstans. Pole switching in the capstan motor is most convenient and is feasible for two, three, or four speeds. The speed ratios must conform to those attainable in the motor design. It appears generally desirable to run the capstan motor at a speed of 900 rpm or more, as with lower motor speeds it is difficult to provide a sufficiently large flywheel in the system to smooth out the torque pulsations in the motor.

When multiple-speed operation is necessary, it can be obtained by the use of several capstan motors or by a single capstan motor and multiple belt and pulley combinations with a jackshaft to provide the large reductions necessary at low tape speeds. Several capstan motors can be cascaded with magnetic clutches to decouple those not in use, to provide a completely electrically operated system with front-panel speed selection. The single-motor and multiple-belt arrangement usually uses a two-speed motor to provide two speeds in a 2:1 ratio by means of pole switching in the motor, together with a suitable number of belts running on different-size pulleys to achieve the desired speed reduction between the motor and capstan shaft. The active drive belt is selected by an idler which applies tension to the belt, the other belts in the system remaining slack. The belt-selection idlers may be either manually or solenoid operated, the latter again making the system all-electric and capable of speed selection by a front-panel switch.

Another speed-changing arrangement is combined with a servo speed control. An a-c generator on the capstan shaft generates a speed-sensing signal which is passed through a series of frequency dividers. The resultant low-frequency signal is compared with a locally generated standard frequency or with the power-line frequency. Any difference generates an error signal, which acts on the capstan motor to change the capstan speed to reduce the error to zero and provide a phase lock between the standard and the capstan generator signal. Speeds can be changed simply by changing the division ratio between the generator signal frequency and the standard frequency.

Airborne, Mobile, and Special Types. In equipment designed for operation from standard a-c power lines, capstan drive at a reasonably precise rate is readily accomplished by means of hysteresis synchronous motors. The capstan rate is then determined by the frequency supplied to the drive motor. In airborne, missile, some mobile, and other special applications, the available power supply is either d-c, 60- or 400-cps a-c with relatively poor frequency control, or a combination of these. Also in many of these applications the environmental conditions with respect to ambient temperature, shock and vibration, humidity, and other factors are extremely severe as compared with those encountered in the laboratory or industrial plant. For such applications special transports are necessary.

Environmental conditions prescribe design considerations essentially similar to those applying to other electronic and mechanical equipment for use in similar applications. Extremely low ambient temperatures produce changes in the mechanical characteristics of the tape, and to maintain proper operation it is desirable that the tape compartment be enclosed and heated so that the tape temperature does not fall below −10 or −20°C. Heaters must be properly disposed to avoid extreme temperature gradients in the tape compartment. The tape compartment must also be well sealed to prevent entrance of sand or dust.

Special attention must be given to elimination of any undue effects from shock, vibration, and acceleration, particularly with respect to tape motion. Certain mechanical parts, such as pressure-roller arms, must be balanced to prevent loss of pressure against the capstan, and necessarily unsupported structures such as reel flanges require careful design to avoid vibrational resonances. There seems to be no way to avoid tape speed changes due to rotational motion of the recorder with a component parallel to the capstan or motor axis. When this is encountered during recording, the only solution is servo speed control plus flutter compensation in playback.

Constant-speed capstan drive is a particularly difficult problem in view of the available power supply and the fact that size and weight are usually critical. Small-size d-c and 400-cps a-c motors are inherently high-speed devices. Since very small capstans are undesirable from the standpoint of strength and extreme tolerances, a large speed reduction is necessary when such motors are used. Gear reducers are small in size and are attractive for this reason, but the degree of precision required in tooth grinding and assembly, for low flutter, is considerably beyond that normally available in precision gear production. Even with otherwise perfect gears, extremely slight variations of tooth shape can produce nonuniform output speed, while eccentricities, of course, are fatal. Output speed variations are generally encountered at rates corresponding to the various shaft rotational rates and the products of these rates by the number of teeth in the associated gears. In the case of governor-controlled d-c motors, very high-frequency speed fluctuations can be introduced by improperly operating governors. When in good operating condition, however, such motors will nearly always run with short-term speed variations under 0.1 per cent. In spite of the drawbacks with respect to nonuniform capstan speed, a high-speed governor-controlled d-c motor plus a well-engineered gear reducer represents the most compact available capstan-drive arrangement and for this reason has frequently been used in very small systems. When the application is one that can tolerate moderate flutter, such drives are acceptable.

When low flutter is desired, uniform-speed capstan drive can be achieved at the expense of additional size and weight. An electronic power converter is used in one system to generate 60-cps power for a capstan motor. This permits a flat-belt and pulley-drive arrangement similar to those used in conventional laboratory-type transports. Another system uses a 400-cps motor with a gear reducer to achieve part of the necessary speed reduction. This is followed by a belt-drive system with a mechanical low-pass filter to eliminate high-frequency speed variations introduced by the gear box. A rate servo controls average speed.

Since the 400-cps power available in aircraft or missiles is rarely controlled in frequency to better than ±5 per cent, it is not eminently satisfactory as a power source for 400-cps synchronous motors unless a playback speed control servo with a wide pull-in range is available. However, a power transistor inverter operating at 400 cps and synchronized from a 1200-cps quartz-crystal oscillator has been used in some instances to furnish power to a 400-cps synchronous capstan-drive motor. This naturally gives very precise average speed control but, unless a large multipole motor is utilized, considerable speed reduction between motor and capstan is still necessary and must be accomplished without introduction of too much flutter.

Since transports of the type under discussion are almost always associated with systems for recording only, no motor is used on the supply reel. Instead, a friction brake to produce suitable holdback tension is common practice. For recorders with small reels or those operating exclusively at fairly low speeds, such a drag brake is the only one necessary on the supply reel, and if the takeup reel is driven through a gear reducer, no solenoid stopping brakes are necessary. However, with large reels and moderate to high speeds, a drag brake alone on the supply reel will not prevent tape "throwing" when the transport is stopped, and an additional stopping brake must be incorporated.

The conventional coplanar arrangement of reels used exclusively in transports for laboratory use can result in appreciable waste space. For this reason, a number of transports have been designed with the reels mounted coaxially. In some of these, reels are mounted directly adjacent to each other, and in others the reels are mounted on opposite sides of the complete assembly with all the mechanism between the reels. In either case, the form factor of the device is radically changed and a more compact over-all structure achieved, although the volume occupied by the reels is not reduced. The coaxial reel structure requires special design of the tape path to handle properly the twisting that the tape must undergo in passing from one reel to the other. It offers the possibility of magazine loading, and some equipment has been designed taking advantage of this.

Since there is only one full reel of tape present at any time in the transport, designs exploiting this can achieve reduced volume. Single-flange reels with the flanges overlapping on opposite sides of the tape permit a spacing between the reel shafts less than the total reel diameter. The minimum spacing is dictated by the clearance required with half the tape on each reel. This configuration reduces the total volume occupied by the reels and, when properly combined with a compact and coordinated design for the rest of the mechanism, results in a minimum-volume transport for a given tape capacity.

4.2   Intermittent-motion (Fast Start-Stop) Tape Transports

These machines, often called *digital tape handlers,* or just tape handlers as previously mentioned, were initially designed to meet requirements for large-scale storage of data for digital computers. With few exceptions, the same characteristics make the unit applicable to other digital-recording applications including, in some cases, the recording of original data. As the terminology "digital tape handler" implies, they are used exclusively in connection with digitized information.

The salient characteristics of these intermittent-motion machines, as contrasted with continuous-running transports, are the ability to start and stop the tape very quickly, generally within a few milliseconds, and the ability to transport the tape in either direction in response to a command signal. The fast forward and rewind features of the continuous-running transports are frequently incorporated. Searching is generally done at the normal operating speed rather than at a special high speed.

Laboratory and Computer Types.   Equipment designed for use with a large-scale business or scientific computer naturally has available to it commercial power for operation, and its environment will be that of the computer—normal office environment, frequently air-conditioned. The design therefore can take advantage of these operating conditions.

The requirements for intermittent motion and fast start-stop stem directly from the computer application. The information capacity of a reel of tape with a reasonable number of tracks is greater by orders of magnitude than the normal internal memory of the computer; this is the major reason for the use of magnetic tape storage. The limited capacity of the internal computer memory requires that only a small fraction of the total information which may be stored on a reel of tape be transferred to or from the computer at one time. This makes it necessary, in recording information from the computer on the tape, to start the tape, run it for a brief period of time, and then stop it until the computer is ready to record more data. The same requirements apply in transferring the information from the tape to the computer. To minimize the time required for transfer of data, the tape must be run at fairly high speeds; to minimize the loss of storage capacity which results from the necessarily blank sections occurring during starting and stopping, it becomes necessary to execute the starting and stopping functions in the shortest possible time. Most transports designed for this kind of operation have start and stop times in the range of 1.5 to 10 msec. Tape speeds range from 60 to 150 ips in computer applications, but much lower speeds, down to a fraction of an inch per second, may be useful in other situations.

It is rather immediately obvious that it is impractical to start the tape reels as rapidly as would be necessary to accommodate change of tape speed from zero to 60 ips or more in a few milliseconds. Even if it were mechanically and economically feasible to provide sufficient drive power to accomplish this, operation would not be satisfactory because the outer layers of tape on the reel could not accelerate as quickly as the inner layers, the result being that the tape would be either excessively tightened or loosened on the reel, with probable damage.

It is therefore essential in these intermittent-motion transports that the portion of tape that is accelerated rapidly—that is, the portion in the vicinity of the capstans and the heads—be isolated mechanically from the reels by some sort of slack-takeup mechanism. This permits storage of a sufficient length of tape between the fast start-stop portion and the reels to allow a reasonable length of time for the reels to be brought up to operating speed. A means of sensing the amount of tape in these temporary storage loops furnishes a signal to servo systems which control the motion of the reels. By this arrangement, only a small section of the total amount of tape is subjected to the extreme acceleration that must occur during the start and stop operations.

The ability to move the tape in either the forward or reverse direction is obtained by the use of two counterrotating capstans. Actuation of a pressure roller against one of these capstans produces forward motion; actuation of the other pressure roller produces reverse motion. This facility for transport in either direction is required in recording to locate an unused portion of the tape or a previously used portion which is to be changed; in reproduction it is required to locate desired information.

Clamping of the tape against the capstan by means of a pressure roller is replaced by vacuum holding of the tape against the capstan in some machines [2, 3]. Ports in the capstan are connected through the capstan shaft to a vacuum manifold so that vacuum is applied to those ports that are in the area of contact between the tape and capstan. As the tape leaves the capstan, the ports immediately under that section are vented to the atmosphere through the manifold and thus release the tape. In such machines, a fixed member contacting the back of the tape is also equipped with vacuum ports and serves as a brake to stop the tape upon connection to the vacuum system. Control of tape motion in this type of machine is achieved by appropriate operation of vacuum valves. Nothing except the heads need touch the oxide side of the tape.

When pressure rollers are used to clamp the tape to the capstan, the entire roller-moving mechanism must be designed with as low an inertia as possible to achieve fast operation. Although time lag in operation of the pressure roller does not contribute to loss of useful tape area, it does represent lost time, which is important in computer operation. Solenoids used to actuate pressure rollers are frequently overvoltaged initially by means of a capacitor and resistor combination in the power supply circuit, the power supply voltage being higher than the normal solenoid operating voltage. While the solenoid is not energized, the capacitor charges to the full supply voltage; when the circuit to the solenoid is closed, the capacitor discharges through the solenoid, giving a large initial surge of current; the resistor in series with the power supply keeps the holding current and power within the solenoid rating.

Stopping of the tape in such pressure-roller-controlled machines is usually also accomplished by a roller pressing the tape against a fixed member. In some cases, the capstan, pressure roller, and fixed member are so disposed that the same roller serves to press the tape against the capstan or against the braking member. With this arrangement, the roller not in use for driving the tape must be in a neutral position when the other idler presses the tape against its capstan.

The problem of providing a slack or temporary storage loop between each reel and the central moving portion of the tape has been solved in several ways. Probably the simplest is a movable takeup arm. When the loop length required is greater than can be handled by the arm alone, several rollers are mounted on the arm and the tape is looped back and forth several times between these rollers and a set of fixed rollers. As soon as the tape is driven in either direction, the slack-takeup arm must move and thus acts as the sensing device to control the reel-drive servomechanisms. Although this arrangement is reasonably simple and inexpensive, some or all of the inertia of the moving arm is added to the inertia of the tape section that is being accelerated, thus increasing the total driven mass and adding to the stress in the tape. Therefore, the method is better adapted to medium tape speeds and starting times than it is to the combination of very high tape speeds with very short start and stop times.

Another way of establishing the necessary slack loop employs a vacuum column, the tape being pulled into a loop chamber by a vacuum system incorporated in the machine. The location of the end of the loop can be sensed by ports and pressure-sensing devices or by photoelectric means. In either case the sensing device again controls the reel servomechanism. With this arrangement there is no inertia load added to the tape, so that only the mass of a section of tape itself need be accelerated or decelerated. A constant tension is exerted on the tape by the pull of the vacuum system, but this need not be large.

Still another method of providing a slack loop has small storage bins at either side of the fast-moving section of tape, the desired amount of slack tape being permitted to accumulate in these bins. In operation the tape is pulled from one bin and discharged into the other. The amount of tape in each bin is sensed by a weighing device, and this controls the reel-drive servomechanism. In this case only a very short length of tape is accelerated or decelerated during starts and stops, no additional mass is coupled to the tape, and no tension is exerted on the tape by the storage loop.

Each reel must be driven during operation so that the proper length of tape is always maintained in the slack loop or storage system. Each reel is driven independently in accordance with the amount of tape in the loop associated with it. The maximum acceleration that can be applied to the reel is, as implied above, determined by that acceleration which can be applied without producing tape damage due to motion of all or part of the tape stack with respect to the reel hub. The required acceleration is a function of the maximum operating tape speed for the machine and the amount of tape that is stored in the slack-takeup mechanism. For example, storage of 5 ft in the slack loop in a 60-ips machine would give a total time of almost 1 sec for the reel to reach a takeup or payout speed slightly greater than 60 ips. Thus, the design of the reel servomechanisms is intimately associated with the slack-takeup-system design and is also a function of the operating speed. It is not directly affected by the starting and stopping times.

When moving arms are used for slack takeup, sensing of the arm position is achieved by some form of mechanical motion to electrical signal transducer such as a photocell, potentiometer, switches, or other similar means. Sensing devices for the vacuum and bin storage systems have been mentioned as air-pressure and photoelectric devices for the former and weight sensing for the latter. Control of the reel-motor speed can be accomplished by means of thyratrons or by magnetic, vacuum-tube, or transistor amplifiers. Alternatively, the reel motors can be run continuously and electromechanical clutches used to transfer power to the reels as needed. With this arrangement, either a reversing-type clutch or counterrotating reel motors driving through two clutches are necessary.

Airborne, Mobile, and Special Types. Intermittent-motion machines for airborne, missile, and similar applications have seen relatively little use compared with the computer and laboratory-type installations. Most requirements have been for recording systems only, and it is necessary therefore that the tape run in one direction only. Intermittent motion is required primarily when the original data tape is to be used for immediate transfer of the information to a computer or other processing equipment without extensive editing. In effect, the information is edited before recording. This type of operation results in recording at infrequent intervals instead of continuous recording and makes it possible to assemble the information into a suitable format prior to recording.

Such applications generally do not require high tape speed, and start and stop times may sometimes be fairly large. However, if the times at which it is desired to record occur strictly at random, start-stop times may have to be restricted to fit the occasional circumstances when two blocks of data are to be recorded in immediate succession.

Even though actual magnitudes of start-stop times are often unimportant, it is frequently necessary that the blocks of recorded data have a certain length on the tape and that the lengths of blank tape between data blocks be controlled and accurately duplicated. Such requirements call for stability and reproduceability of operation of the tape transport so that a control pulse of specific duration will cause a predetermined length of tape to be transported, with a definite fraction of this length being moved at normal recording speeds. It is then possible to record a block of data at a specific time related to the tape-motion control pulse, so that it will be recorded while the tape is moving at its normal constant velocity.

The usual design considerations dictated by environmental conditions apply to these machines in the same way as they do to continuous-running machines. There is little or no difference between the two sets of design considerations, except perhaps that the intermittent-motion machine, being a digital recording device, requires less attention to flutter than the continuous-running machine. On the other hand, if pulses are to be closely packed in each track, and relative track-to-track timing is important, excessive skew must be prevented, and shock, vibration, and acceleration must not increase the skew beyond tolerable limits.

4.3   Loop Mechanisms

The repetitive reproduction of a signal is frequently of great value for analysis purposes. For this and other reasons it is often desirable, in a tape data system, to have facilities for recording on and reproduction of endless tape loops. The mechanical handling facilities for such a loop can be provided by accessories to a conventional reel-type transport or by means of an entirely separate mechanism for loop operation only.

When a tape transport is designed so that it mounts in a rack with its panel flush with other rack panels, it is generally quite simple to arrange an adapter of some sort so that loops can be handled. The adapter may consist of a bin mounted below the transport or of panels with a number of rollers on them so that a loop may be stretched back and forth over the rollers. For short loops, a simple dumbbell-shaped weight hung in the bottom of the loop will suffice. The bin arrangement is not satisfactory for speeds greater than about 15 ips when loop lengths of the order of 50 to 100 ft must be used. Static charges accumulate on the tape and cause the folds in the bin to stick together and be pulled up into the operating mechanism, which generally results in destruction of the loop. Accessory panels and rollers can easily be used up to 60-ips tape speeds, but available space and the number of practical convolutions limit the maximum loop length to roughly 35 or 40 ft.

Many transport designs use a "dished" or depressed panel structure. In this case only the surface area of the transport itself is available for loop operation by means of accessories, and it is rarely possible to handle loops longer than about 5 ft. When longer loops must be handled, a special loop mechanism is necessary. Such a mechanism incorporates the same capstan-drive and head-mounting arrangements as a reel transport and includes, in addition, a number of rollers over which the tape may be passed in successive convolutions. At least one of the rollers in the system must be movable so that it can be adjusted to fit the exact loop length. Rough control of the loop length is obtained by selection of the number of rollers over which the convolutions are passed.

A loop mechanism should have flutter performance comparable to that of a reel-type transport, although it is extremely difficult to avoid an appreciable "jolt" each time the loop splice passes the capstan and heads. Also, particularly at high speeds, the lengths of tape between rollers may be excited into low-frequency transverse vibration which inevitably introduces a flutter component. It is therefore highly desirable to use electronic compensation in connection with loop devices used with FM carrier recording.

Loop mechanisms represent the one type of instrumentation tape transport on which erase heads are frequently used. Once a loop is mounted on the machine, data can be transferred to it, reproduced as often as necessary for analysis, and then erased preparatory to recording new data. When a loop is used for delay purposes, it is usual to record at one point, reproduce at another point, and then erase the tape just before it again reaches the recording head.

4.4   Tape Speeds

The availability of two-speed hysteresis synchronous motors with speeds in a 2:1 or 4:1 ratio, plus a certain amount of "hangover" from audio and entertainment recording practices, has resulted in the design of many instrumentation transports with speeds in a series of continuing 2:1 ratios. Thus a six-speed machine with speeds of 60, 30, 15, 7½, 3¾, and 1⅞ ips is quite common.

When multispeed operation is really important to a user for expansion or compression of time and frequency scales, this selection of a binary series of speeds by manufacturers is somewhat unfortunate. Since it is far easier to apply a multiplication factor of 10 or 100 than those such as 8, 64, or 128, it would be much more convenient to have speeds of instrumentation equipment standardized in a 1:2:5:10: · · · series rather than the 1:2:4:8: · · · series. In so far as the author knows, there is no technical advantage to the binary series from the user's standpoint, and it is unfortunate that the user, to whom 10:1 and 100:1 speed ratios are important, must pay extra for them.

In the relative-number sequence 1:2:5:10:20: · · · there are three successive numbers, 5, 10, and 20, in 2:1 ratios. By matching these three successive numbers to the commonly used tape speeds of 15, 30, and 60 ips or 30, 60, and 120 ips, two slightly different series of tape speeds are obtained. These are given in Table 4.1. Such speed ratios facilitate considerably the scale multiplication and division computations that must be made when speed changes are used for changing time and frequency scales.

TABLE 4.1. TAPE SPEEDS IN 1:2:5:10 RATIOS

Base: 15/30/60 ips	Base: 30/60/120 ips
150 ips	120 ips
60	60
30	30
15	12
6	6
3	3
1.5	1.2
0.6	0.6
0.3	0.3

These speed ratios can be obtained without undue difficulty in the belt and pulley speed reducers and speed changers most frequently used. They are equally easy to obtain when speed control servos utilizing frequency divider chains are employed.

4.5 Reels and Winding Tension

For audio entertainment equipment, using ¼-in. tape, standard reels have long been established. One design, using a die-cast hub and metal flanges attached by screws, is readily adaptable to tape wider than ¼ in. by adding additional hubs between the flanges. One drawback exists, in that the hub thickness allows considerable clearance between the tape and the flanges for ¼-in. tape, so that when additional hubs are added clearances become excessive. This can be dodged by machining the extra hubs to ¼-in. thickness so that

the total clearance for any tape width is always the same as that for
$\frac{1}{4}$-in. tape. Such reels were used on much equipment for a long time,
while on the other hand some manufacturers recognized the necessity
for precision reels at the outset and used them exclusively.

Ultimately the inferior performance of reels conforming to the audio
standards forced the design and adoption of precision reels for instrumentation purposes, with very much tighter tolerances than
those specified in the audio standards. Such close tolerances are desirable to assure reasonably good concentricity of the reel and tape
pack with respect to the supporting and driving shaft. Otherwise,
the large unbalance forces resulting from high-speed rotation of an
off-center reel of wide tape during fast forward or rewind could cause
damage to the tape and the transport. Additionally, reel eccentricities are a potential source of flutter, and bent flanges may scrape the
edges of the tape, causing physical damage as well as increasing
flutter.

Thus it has finally been accepted that reels used on instrumentation equipment should have close tolerances on the concentricity of
the outer and inner hub surfaces, small clearances between inner hub
dimension and mounting-shaft dimension, minimum hub runout, and
flat flanges that are not susceptible to acquiring a permanent set as a
result of normal handling. Additionally, the moment of inertia of
the reel about its axis should be as small as is consistent with the
other requirements.

Because so much equipment was designed to operate with the de-
cidedly inferior adaptations of audio standard reels, it has appeared
necessary to compromise slightly in the design of precision reels to
maintain interchangeability with the nonprecision ones. The compromises are principally in flange thickness and tape-to-flange clearances to keep the total thickness of the precision reel within the same
dimension as the maximum thickness of the other reel. An instrumentation transport should be designed for best operation with precision instrumentation reels, and adapters, if necessary, used for the
composite audio reels.

Because precision reels are necessarily considerably more expensive
than assemblies of audio reel parts, there appears to be some justifica-
tion for using the cheap reel for storage purposes. In addition, tape
is often purchased on audio hubs, either with or without flanges, for
the same economic reason. Thus, users have generally demanded that
instrumentation equipment be capable of mounting the cheaper reel
and hub assemblies, if only for the purpose of transferring tape from
them to precision reels for actual operating use. In the light of

present knowledge regarding tape damage due to unsatisfactory reels, there is some question as to the genuine economy of these practices.

The report previously referenced [4] has shown that it is extremely important to have a properly designed reel and a suitable winding-tension pattern for reasonably safe storage of tape. The study has shown that it is entirely possible, under common conditions, to have a wound reel of tape partly in tension, partly in compression, and with a zero tension zone between. Figure 4.3 shows a few of the many computed tension patterns included in the referenced report; these are for a reel wound with constant tension in the tape. The parameter R is the ratio of the outer radius of the fully wound roll to the hub radius, while the abscissa r is the radius of any point in the roll, expressed as its ratio to the hub radius. Hence a value of 1 for r represents a point on the hub. R is slightly greater than 2 for the standard $10\frac{1}{2}$-in. reel, and about 3 for the 14-in. reel. The parameter b is the ratio of hub compressibility to longitudinal tape compliance. An incompressible hub corresponds to $b = 0$, while the value $b = 5$ is a medium value for a plastic hub. The value of b ranges from 1.5 to 10 for various types of plastic hubs and is stated to be about 0.5 for metal hubs.

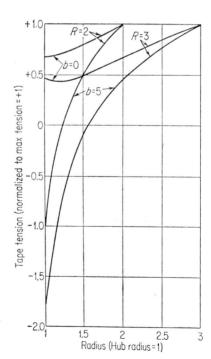

Fig. 4.3. Tension patterns in wound reel of tape. (*Courtesy of Department of Defense.*)

The curves for $b = 0$ show positive tension at all points in the wound roll, while those for $b = 5$ show zero tension at one radius and compression in the region close to the hub. Now, looseness of the winding, resulting in insufficient friction between adjacent layers, may permit slipping or *cinching*. The compression near the hub tends to cause *buckling, spoking* (deformation into a more or less regular polygonal shape), and folding. Thus, tension patterns such as shown for $b = 5$ are highly conducive to tape damage.

With poor tension patterns, temperature and humidity cycling, shock, and vibration can cause severe degradation in the reproduction quality of signals recorded on the tape. These hazards can hardly be avoided in shipment, and humidity cycling is very difficult to avoid unless the tape is used and stored under closely controlled environmental conditions. It follows that suitable reels and appropriate winding-tension patterns are very important to the preservation of recorded data. Desirable factors include reel hubs with low compressibility (with one exception to be mentioned) and a small ratio (not much greater than 2) in the radius of the wound roll to the radius of the hub. These conditions are fairly well met by a $10\frac{1}{2}$-in. reel with a strong metal hub but are less well fulfilled by 14-in. reels.

Given the proper reel characteristics, then maximum safety is attained by winding in such a way that a suitable tension pattern is developed in the reel. Under some conditions, this can be approximated by winding with constant tension, and under other conditions a constant-torque winding produces better results. Program control of the tension during the winding will result in the best final tension patterns.

Acetate-base tape poses more problems than polyester-base tape because of its greater dimensional changes under temperature and humidity variations. Because of these changes, acetate-base tape should usually not be stored on a metal hub but preferably on a plastic hub with a humidity coefficient of expansion as close as possible to that of the tape. Winding should probably be done under constant-torque conditions.

For polyester-base tape, reasonable safety is assured by holding the ratio of outer diameter to hub diameter to a value of 3 or less, using a strong metal hub, and winding with constant tension.

All this discussion of reels and winding assumes uniform leading of the tape onto the reel so that the tape is wound with no unevenness in the edge pattern of the winding. In view of this and the preceding considerations, it would seem worthwhile to add a "wind for storage" operating mode to tape transports, with facilities to control the winding tension in a suitable program.

REFERENCES

1. Signal Corps Contract DA18–119–sc–42.
2. Lawrance, R. B., R. E. Wilkins, and R. A. Pendleton: Apparatus for Magnetic Storage on Three-inch Wide Tapes, *Proc. Eastern Joint Computer Conf.*, p. 84, 1956.
3. Lawrance, Richard B.: An Advanced Magnetic Tape System for Data Processing, *Proc. Eastern Joint Computer Conf.*, 1959.
4. Progress Report 2, Signal Corps Contract DA18–119–sc–42.

CHAPTER 5

TAPE-MOTION IRREGULARITIES

Ideally a tape transport should move the tape across the heads at a precisely known absolutely uniform velocity. Since ideal goals are rarely achieved in man-made machines, it is to be expected that no tape transport will attain such ideal motion. Departures from the desired average velocity may be corrected by servo speed control during reproduction of the recorded signal, as discussed later in Chap. 7. Short-term variations in velocity cannot be eliminated in this manner and must be taken into consideration in the performance characteristics of the system. Short-term velocity variations are of two kinds: those which are uniform across the width of the tape, so that the velocity at a given instant is exactly the same at all points on a straight line across the tape perpendicular to the direction of tape travel, and those which are not uniform across the tape. In some cases and for some purposes these two types of motion irregularity are indistinguishable, while in other cases the distinction is clear and important.

5.1 Definition and Description of Flutter

Velocity variations that are uniform across the tape are properly called *flutter*, although numerical flutter specifications, because of measurement methods, generally include a certain amount of non-uniform velocity variations as well. The term "flutter" comes from the original definitions of motion irregularities in sound-recording equipment, in which case two terms were used: *wow*, to define speed variations at a rate of a few cycles per second, and *flutter*, to describe those of higher frequency. The terms were derived from the different effects upon the ear, depending on the frequency or rate of the speed variation. The audio distinction between wow and flutter

98

does not apply in instrumentation equipment, and the tendency has been to use the one term, flutter, only.

Flutter arises from numerous sources in the tape-transport mechanism, many of which have been mentioned in the preceding chapter. Obviously, any eccentricities in the capstan and any imperfections in its drive system will produce nonuniform velocity of the capstan surface with corresponding variations in tape velocity. Tension variations in the tape tend to cause the velocity to vary, and friction between the tape and heads or other nonrotating members can cause high-frequency velocity variations because of roughness of the tape and nonuniform friction. In some cases, as has been mentioned, longitudinal vibrations in the tape and vibrations of the heads themselves are excited by particular combinations of design parameters of the tape transport and produce specific high-frequency flutter components. The designer of a tape transport makes every effort to eliminate or reduce to an absolute minimum the flutter caused by various mechanism imperfections.

It is reasonable to anticipate that a certain amount of random flutter will be generated. The tape coating is granular in nature, and when this surface rubs on fixed surfaces, such as the heads, the tape will be subjected to a large number of very small impulse forces. These would be produced by the particle nature of the tape coating, variations in individual particle coefficients of friction, and minute imperfections in the surface contacting the tape. The net effect is a forcing function similar to the shot effect in vacuum tubes. The tape itself will respond to this forcing function in a complex way, because of the large number of possible resonances. One analysis [1] shows the possibility of resonant frequencies ranging from the subaudio region to hundreds of kilocycles. In view of the number and wide range of such possible resonances and the probable relatively high damping of many of them, it is not unreasonable to suppose that the tape will not greatly affect the spectral distribution of the forcing function over the range of frequencies normally encompassed in flutter measurements (except for such specific high-frequency responses mentioned in the previous paragraph). As tape transports are improved by elimination of periodic flutter components, it is thus to be expected that a relatively low level of random flutter will remain, distributed almost uniformly over the flutter spectrum range. This is clearly apparent from flutter frequency analyses and the general shape of cumulative flutter curves published by manufacturers of tape transport equipment.

As a corollary of this reasoning, it is clear that a certain amount of this random flutter will not be uniform across the tape and will not be the same (i.e., correlated) for each track. A driving impulse caused by a single particle will set up waves in the tape traveling in all directions; these will be reflected from the edges of the tape and from sections where the tape is in contact with parts of the tape transport. The velocity of such waves will be different in different directions, further complicating the pattern.

Consequently, in a machine so perfect that periodic flutter components are negligible, we should expect a background random flutter with an approximately uniform frequency spectrum. A portion of this flutter would be correlated in adjacent tracks, while the balance would be random.

Figure 5.1 illustrates a moderately close approach to this situation. The straight line represents the cumulative flutter graph (see next paragraph) for a theoretical machine with only random flutter. The peak-to-peak flutter for a 10-kc bandwidth (60-ips speed) is 1 per cent. If we assume the flutter measurement to be such that the measured value is exceeded by peaks only 5 per cent of the time, then the rms flutter is 0.25 per cent over the 10-kc band, and the power spectral density of the flutter (assumed uniform) is 2.4×10^{-6} (ips)^2 per cycle of bandwidth. The circles are points from a representative actual flutter characteristic (they are translated vertically so that they do not represent absolute values). It can be seen that from approximately 500 cps to the band limit of 10 kc the actual curve follows the random flutter graph quite closely. Below 500 cps, a few periodic components, although small, raise the actual measured points above the random cumulative graph. By plots of this type, an estimate can be made of the relative amounts and spectral location of periodic components and the approximate level of random flutter.

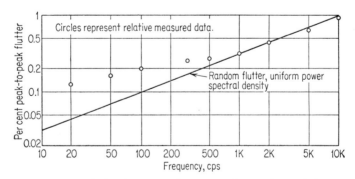

Fɪɢ. 5.1. Cumulative flutter graph, pure random and actual flutter.

The cumulative random flutter graph rises in proportion to the square root of the bandwidth (maximum frequency in this case).

The technical description of flutter for specification purposes is not easy. The effect of flutter depends on the recording technique used, and the parameters of the flutter which determine its effect are different for the different recording methods. Thus, no single technical description of flutter will suffice for evaluation of its effect on all recording systems. In addition, data processing techniques applied after recovery of data from the tape system may be affected by flutter characteristics. This is particularly true in the case of frequency analysis of tape-recorded information.

Specification and Measurement of Flutter. In audio equipment, the rms value of the flutter over a restricted band of frequencies (generally about ½ or 1 cps to 300 cps) is usually used as the flutter specification. This is not adequate for instrumentation equipment because flutter components above 300 cps and up to the maximum frequency covered by the system can be important and because the flutter spectrum of a well-designed machine is a combination of small sinusoidal components and a more or less uniformly distributed noise signal. With this type of flutter waveshape, the peak, or peak-to-peak, value is a more useful description than the rms value and is a better basis for predicting the effects of the flutter on the system.

One form of flutter specification is the so-called *cumulative flutter characteristic*. This is measured by passing the flutter signal through a variable cutoff low-pass filter, measurements of the filter output being made for progressively larger values of the cutoff frequency. Since this characteristic is most useful with respect to FM carrier recording, the filter cutoff frequency is usually extended up to the maximum frequency normally handled by a wideband FM carrier system at the tape speed being measured. Because of the random components of the flutter, such a cumulative curve can be expected to rise with frequency and each sine-wave component would introduce a definite step in the curve as that component comes into the passband of the filter. Actual curves of this type published by tape equipment manufacturers are generally averages for a number of tape transports and do not show the "bumps" that would be introduced by sine-wave components. Also, such average curves do not depict the extreme values which might be encountered in an individual machine. They are useful, however, in giving an approximate picture of the peak noise that the flutter will introduce into FM carrier systems.

For some purposes a detailed frequency analysis of the flutter would be highly desirable, but an adequate analysis of this sort can be obtained only by means of an automatic wave analyzer of the type used in vibration analysis, which is usually not available to the manufacturers of tape equipment. When such an analysis can be obtained, it is valuable for prediction of the effect of the flutter on PDM and digital recording systems and is about the only way to evaluate the tape system with respect to frequency analysis of the output data. A combination of the cumulative flutter characteristic and a frequency analysis would represent a fairly complete technical description of flutter.

Flutter is readily measured by means of a *flutter bridge* or an FM discriminator. In either case, a known stable frequency is first recorded on the tape. On playback, the reproduced tone is passed through the flutter bridge or FM discriminator, and the output of either device is a direct measure of the flutter.

The flutter bridge is a Wien or other similar bridge circuit which has a null at a specific frequency, the null point being adjusted to the frequency of the recorded tone. If the tape speed were exactly the same in reproduction as in recording, and uniform, the reproduced signal would be completely eliminated by the bridge. Any variation in the average or instantaneous frequency of the reproduced tone will result in a bridge output which is proportional to the deviation from the original recorded frequency and hence a measure of average speed change and flutter. The d-c component of the bridge output represents average speed change, while the a-c component represents flutter. The frequency of the recorded tone must be 5 to 10 times the maximum flutter frequency to be measured. For measurements of audio equipment, a tone of 3000 cps is generally used and all components up to 300 cps measured.

For measurement of flutter components up to 10,000 cps at tape speeds of 60 ips, measuring frequencies of 50 kc or more are necessary, and considerable care would be required in bridge design for satisfactory performance at such frequencies. An FM discriminator, of the type normally used for reproduction of signals recorded on tape by FM carrier, can be used to recover the average and instantaneous frequency variations of the reproduced signal. For measurements of flutter in the vicinity of 0.1 to 0.3 per cent peak-to-peak, considerable care must be exercised to reduce noise in the electronic system to a negligibly low value. Normal FM carrier equipment may not be suitable for this use, even though it is entirely satisfactory in its regular application.

Figure 5.2 shows a representative flutter measurement setup. A

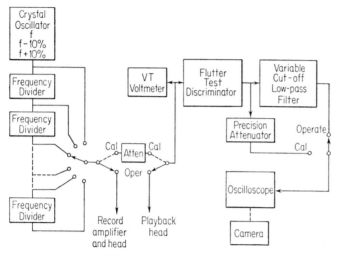

FIG. 5.2. Flutter measuring system.

crystal oscillator and series of frequency dividers are used to generate the stable signals for recording, the frequency divider chain making available a number of different frequencies corresponding to the various tape speeds at which measurements are to be made. The discriminator for playback is likewise arranged for center frequency switching so that it can be adapted to the tape speed. For calibration purposes, two additional crystals are incorporated in the recording-oscillator portion of the system, each displaced by 10 per cent from the center frequency crystal, one above and the other below. For calibration, the precision attenuator in the discriminator output is set to introduce an appropriate attenuation corresponding to the full-scale range desired for the flutter measurement. For example, for 1 per cent peak-to-peak full-scale range, the attenuation would be 20:1, while for 0.1 per cent peak-to-peak range a 200:1 attenuation would be used. If the adjustable low-pass filter does not pass direct current, it must be bypassed for calibration and its gain established by separate checks. The center frequency, plus 10 per cent, and minus 10 per cent crystals are switched in in turn and the resulting calibration lines noted on the oscilloscope, oscilloscope adjustments being made to locate these lines conveniently.

To make a measurement, the desired frequency output from the center frequency crystal oscillator and divider chain is recorded on the tape, saturation recording without bias being the simplest. The tape is then played back through the discriminator, the attenuator in the discriminator output being set to zero attenuation. The oscilloscope pattern is observed, or preferably photographed, for successive values of filter cutoff frequency. Each such observation shows the flutter within the filter band. Its value is determined by reference to the previously made calibration readings.

If the tape transport uses a synchronous motor for capstan drive, this motor should be energized from a constant-frequency constant-voltage power supply during recording and reproducing for flutter measurement. Most power lines have instantaneous-frequency variations in the order of ±0.25 per cent, even though the average frequency over a long period is very precise. These frequency variations cause corresponding speed variations, which contribute to reading difficulties and may at times be confused with true flutter. This point is particularly important if recording is done at a low tape speed and playback occurs at a high speed. In such a case, the frequency multiplication effect may easily bring the power-line frequency variations into the flutter spectrum range and cause erroneous results. If the transport has a "built-in" servo for tape speed control, naturally it should be operated from the normal specified power source during flutter tests.

When a synchronous motor transport can be operated during reproduction under servo control of a signal recorded on the tape, it is highly desirable to measure flutter under both of the possible operating conditions, i.e., with constant-frequency drive on the capstan motor and with servo speed control. The servo may affect the flutter characteristics in the extreme low-frequency portion of the spectrum.

Since the amount of tape on the supply and takeup reels can affect the flutter characteristics, it is good practice to make measurements near the beginning and end of the reel and in the middle. Also, a number of measurements (at least five) should be made in each region and averaged, because the recording and playback speed variations combine in random phase relationships and the average of a number of readings helps to eliminate extreme values which might result from accidental in-phase or out-of-phase combinations.

When sinusoidal rather than random components are predominant, recording with motor drive at 60 cps and reproduction with a motor-drive frequency of 59 or 61 cps will often produce clearly defined beats in the various flutter components. In such a case, careful study of an oscillographic record of the flutter will permit a rather accurate assessment of the true flutter, rather than its over-all record-playback combination. This procedure is particularly useful in design and trouble-shooting work, as it frequently shows up individual flutter components by virtue of their canceling and adding at different times. Of course, a frequency analysis, when feasible, is to be preferred for this purpose.

For measurements in the region of 0.1 per cent flutter, it should be possible to connect the recording oscillator output to the discriminator input (through a suitable attenuator) and attain an electronic-system noise-level reading equivalent to about 0.01 to 0.02 per cent flutter. This noise level is 72 to 78 db below full-scale output for a normal 40 per cent deviation FM carrier system and indicates the care needed in elimination of noise in the crystal oscillator and discriminator circuits. A noise level of -60 db compared with 40 per cent deviation is quite satisfactory for normal use of wideband FM discriminators. The voltmeter shown connected to the playback-head output is used to monitor the discriminator input level to ensure that it is sufficient to maintain adequate noise quieting in the discriminator.

It would be desirable to have a better method of reading the amplitude of the flutter signal than mere visual observation of the oscilloscope's screen or a photograph of it. The magnitude of flutter observed in this way will depend upon the brightness of the oscilloscope pattern, rate of sweep, and in the case of photographs the normal factors that affect the intensity of a photographic image. These factors result in appreciable error in the flutter reading, but careful work with the photographic method will probably give an accuracy in the 10 to 20 per cent region. It is doubtful if visual observations are accurate to better than ±25 to 30 per cent. At tape speeds up to 15 or 30 ips, an oscillographic record of the flutter signal can be made and appears to be the best observational method. For higher speeds, galvanometer frequency response may be inadequate.

Figure 5.3 shows a typical series of photographs of flutter in a high-quality tape transport for several filter cutoff frequencies. These measurements were made using equipment quite similar to that described above.

E. N. Dingley, Jr., [2] and J. F. Sweeney [3] have described a useful method for measurement of time displacement error in a recorded signal produced by tape-velocity errors. The method involves recording a sine wave derived from a precision standard frequency source. When reproduced, pulses are derived from the zero crossings of the sine wave and used to intensity-modulate the electron beam of an oscilloscope, a horizontal sweep being derived from a saw-tooth generator synchronized from the same frequency standard

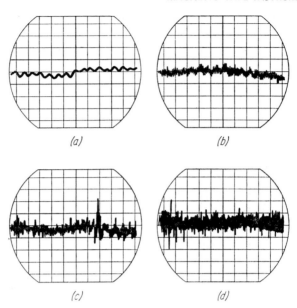

Fig. 5.3.   Typical flutter photographs; vertical scale (all pictures): 0.1 per cent peak-to-peak per division.   (*a*) Filter: 0.2 to 20 cps, sweep 0.1 sec per div; (*b*) filter: 0.2 to 200 cps, sweep 0.1 sec per div; (*c*) filter: 0.2 to 2000 cps, sweep 0.01 sec per div; (*d*) filter: 0.2 to 5000 cps, sweep 0.01 sec per div. Tape speed: 30 ips.   (*Courtesy of Industrial Systems Division, Minneapolis-Honeywell Regulator Company.*)

used to generate the recorded signal.   Timing pulses at 10 times the frequency of the standard are also applied to the intensity-modulation circuit to produce 10 timing marks per sweep and eliminate errors due to sweep nonlinearity.   The oscilloscope is photographed with a continuously-moving-film camera.   The result is a continuous trace showing the instantaneous phase difference between the reproduced signal and the standard.   Average speed error is indicated by a constant drift of this trace across the film, while instantaneous speed variations are indicated by the irregular characteristics of the trace. This method is particularly valuable when cumulative and instantaneous timing errors are important.   As will be shown later, there is a rather complex relation between flutter and the timing error produced by it, so that it is difficult to deduce much information about the flutter from the time displacement error curve.   Conversely, it is difficult to compute time displacement error from flutter data, so that direct measurement of this error is preferable when it is the governing factor in system accuracy.   This is the case in pulse width or pulse position modulation systems.   In digital systems, the timing error may affect pulse spacing.

Several other methods for measuring time displacement due to flutter, as well as differential time displacement due to skew, have been discussed by Skov [4]. The most fruitful of these comprises charging a capacitor at a uniform rate during the time between pulses. The peak voltage to which the capacitor is charged is a measure of the time, and successive charging cycles can be displayed on an oscilloscope and photographed.   Time variations are thus readily discernible.

Measurement of flutter by either of the direct-measurement methods includes true flutter and also velocity variations which are not uniform across the tape, as well as noise that might be introduced into the signal by nonuniformity of the tape coating.   In many cases it is not important to differentiate between these quantities, but when compensation methods for motion irregularities are used, it is helpful to be able to differentiate between the correlated speed variations and the uncorrelated ones.

A few observations along this line have been made by the author; the results show that all the normally observed flutter is not attributable to velocity variations that are uniform across the tape.   A certain amount is due either to uncorrelated and apparently random velocity variations or to noise introduced by nonuniformity and granularity of the tape.

These data were obtained by recording frequency-modulated signals from the same source on two tracks and, in playback, subtracting the outputs of two discriminators, one connected to each track.   By the use of modulation frequencies covering the entire range of flutter measurement, the ability of the system to cancel components which were in phase on the two tracks was established.   Components as high as 5 kc at 30 ips were reduced by at least 20 db when they were in phase on the two tracks.   The cumulative flutter curve was observed from one track only, and a similar curve with the outputs of the two discriminators canceling each other was also taken.   The second curve was at all frequencies lower than the single-channel curve, but in the high-frequency region the reduction of flutter noise was less than the reduction of in-phase sine-wave signals.   That portion of the flutter signal which is canceled might be termed the *correlated flutter*, while that which does not cancel is due either to *noncorrelated* flutter or noise from other sources, possibly tape characteristics.   It would be rather difficult to establish experimentally which of these two possibilities is the true cause or whether they both are contributing factors.

5.2 Skew (Yaw)

The terms *skew* and *yaw* have been applied to explain the fixed and variable time or phase displacements encountered on different tracks recorded by a single head stack. These terms imply that the tape is skewing or yawing as it passes over the head stack. While this certainly causes part of the effect, it seems very likely that tension variations across the width of the tape also enter into the picture. For lack of a better term, *skew* will be used herein.

Fixed relative time or phase errors between two tracks can be introduced by recording and reproducing electronic equipment, by departures from perpendicularity to the direction of tape travel of the line of gaps in a head stack, by departures from exact alignment of individual heads in a head stack, by differences in direction of tape travel as it crosses the head stacks, and by fixed differences in tension distribution across the tape. The effects of the electronic equipment, errors in head-stack alignment, and alignment of head gaps within a stack are naturally fixed for a given set of equipment and can be eliminated by phase or time-delay adjustment in the electronic circuitry if necessary.

Variable skew produced by tape-motion irregularities produces time or phase variations between data recorded on two different tracks and is of considerable importance in some recording-system applications. It is probable that the actual direction of tape motion across the head stacks varies somewhat and such variations would produce skew that would be linearly proportional to the spacing between tracks. A uniform tension gradient across the tape can also produce skew that is linearly dependent upon the spacing between tracks. Finally, tension gradients which are not uniform across the tape, warp or other dimensional nonuniformity inherent in the tape, and uncorrelated flutter components will produce skew effects that are not necessarily closely related to spacing between tracks. All these phenomena contribute to variable timing errors between tracks recorded on a single head stack.

Experimentally, it is quite evident that differential timing errors due to skew are very much more pronounced when tape is recorded on one machine and played back on another. Remarkably good timing correlations can be observed between tracks when the recording and reproduction are both accomplished with the same tape transport. Consideration of the above causes of skew shows that this behavior can be reasonably expected.

Relatively little information is available to indicate the magnitude of skew due to tape-motion irregularities only, in commercial continuous-running equipment. The author's experience has indicated that a rough approximation to the expected skew can be made by assuming that the two extreme edges of 1-in. tape will move differentially by about $\pm\frac{1}{2}$ mil when a recording is made on one machine and played back on another. This applies to continuous-running machines. Because of the strains of fast start-stop operation, digital tape handlers appear to introduce somewhat more variation than this. Since the magnitude of skew appears to be relatively independent of tape speed, its expression in terms of actual displacement rather than timing error provides a basis for estimating timing error at any tape speed. Thus, based upon the above figure, the expected timing error due to skew at 30 ips, between extreme outside tracks recorded on 1-in. tape by a single head stack, would be estimated as ± 17 μsec. This is readily arrived at by dividing the tape velocity of 30 μin. per μsec into the 500-μin. ($\frac{1}{2}$-mil) displacement variation.

The previously mentioned article by Skov [4] discusses some of the causes of skew in a particular machine, as well as several measurement methods.

5.3   Timing Error Due to Interleaved Head Stacks

Another source of timing error between tracks, not directly related to skew, is the spacing between head stacks in equipment utilizing interleaved head arrangements. Here the standard distance between such head stacks is $1\frac{1}{2}$ in., so that the signal recorded at one instant on one track is spaced $1\frac{1}{2}$ in. along the tape from another signal recorded on an adjacent track at the same instant. Unless this physical spacing remains exactly the same between recording and playback, there will be a time error introduced between the two channels. Any stretch or shrinkage of the tape due to environmental conditions encountered between recording and playback, plus relatively minute differences in tension between the recording and playback machines, will introduce corresponding timing errors. A 1 per cent variation in tape dimensions corresponds to 15 mils in a distance of $1\frac{1}{2}$ in. and may correspond to many wavelengths of a recorded signal. A difference in tension in the tape between the recording and playback machines will introduce a fixed timing error, while variations in tension as the tape passes through the machine will introduce variations in the timing. In view of the magnitude of these effects, there seems to be little point in extremely close tolerances on the distance between gap lines in interleaved head stacks.

5.4   Harmful Effects of Flutter and Skew

Flutter and skew in tape transports introduce errors into the data recovered from a recording-reproducing system. The type and magnitude of the error depend upon the method of recording. Flutter causes errors in one data channel; skew introduces relative errors between two data channels.

Noise and Data Errors in FM Systems. Probably the best known deleterious effect of flutter is the noise that it introduces in FM carrier systems. It is quite apparent that a constant frequency tone recorded on tape will be reproduced with a certain amount of frequency modulation, dependent upon the magnitude of flutter during recording and playback. Demodulation of such a signal will result not in the ideal pure d-c signal that should be obtained but in a d-c signal with superimposed noise. When a modulated signal is recorded, the noise due to flutter is added to the output signal, and in addition the demodulated data signal is both amplitude- and frequency-modulated by the flutter.

Mathematical analysis shows that a sinusoidally modulated FM signal, after recording, reproduction, and demodulation, gives an output voltage which has the following form:

$$e_0 = b \cos \omega_3 t - a \cos \left(r\omega_2 t + rb \frac{\omega_2}{\omega_3} \sin \omega_3 t \right)$$

$$- m \frac{\Delta f}{f_0} \left[1 + b \cos \omega_3 t - a \cos \left(r\omega_2 t + rb \frac{\omega_2}{\omega_3} \sin \omega_3 t \right) \right]$$

$$\sin \left[r\omega_1 t + rb \frac{\omega_1}{\omega_3} \sin \omega_3 t - a \frac{\omega_1}{\omega_2} \sin \left(r\omega_2 t + rb \frac{\omega_2}{\omega_3} \sin \omega_3 t \right) \right] \qquad (5\text{-}1)$$

where e_0 = output voltage

b = peak playback flutter as a fraction of average speed

ω_3 = angular frequency of playback flutter

t = time

a = peak recording flutter as a fraction of average speed

r = ratio of playback speed to recording speed

ω_2 = angular frequency of recording flutter

m = recorded signal modulation level as a fraction of full deviation signal

Δf = peak carrier deviation, kc

f_0 = carrier frequency, kc

ω_1 = angular frequency of modulation of recorded signal

The derivation of this equation is given in Appendix I.

For purposes of interpretation, it is very useful to simplify the above equation by assuming that the playback tape transport is perfect $(b = 0)$. Also, we shall not lose any generality by assuming playback at the same speed as recording $(r = 1)$. With $b = 0$ and $r = 1$, the equation becomes

$$e_0 = a \cos \omega_2 t + m \frac{\Delta f}{f_0} (1 - a \cos \omega_2 t) \sin \left(\omega_1 t - \frac{a\omega_1}{\omega_2} \sin \omega_2 t \right) \qquad (5\text{-}2)$$

The first term of (5-2) represents the noise component introduced by the flutter. Since the coefficient $\Delta f/f_0$ is approximately the peak-signal amplitude, the peak-signal-to-peak-noise ratio is $\Delta f/af_0$. The peak noise in per cent of peak full-scale signal is $100(af_0/\Delta f)$. This demonstrates the "noise multiplication" effect, in that the per cent flutter must be multiplied by the ratio of carrier frequency to frequency deviation to determine the peak noise in per cent of peak signal. To put this still another way, peak noise percentage is obtained by dividing peak flutter percentage by peak percentage carrier deviation and multiplying by 100. If the percentage frequency deviation is small, this multiplication factor is rather serious and accounts for the great stress laid on low flutter for tape transports used in FM carrier recording and also for the effort to use as large a deviation as possible in wideband FM systems without compensation.

The term $1 - a \cos \omega_2 t$ represents an amplitude modulation of the data signal by the flutter and can be considered as a second-order effect, since it is dependent on the product of the data signal amplitude and the flutter amplitude. In a sense, it can be considered as a "noise behind the modulation," as it is zero for zero modulation signal. The data disturbance due to this modulation term is equal to the peak per cent flutter times the instantaneous value of the data signal and hence represents an error which is a constant percentage of the *instantaneous* value of the data signal, not of full scale. For reasonable values of flutter (say not over ½ per cent peak-to-peak) this second-order amplitude modulation is essentially negligible in comparison with the electronic system errors.

The second term in the argument of the sine function, $(a\omega_1/\omega_2) \sin \omega_2 t$, represents frequency modulation of the data signal by the flutter. The peak frequency deviation is af_1 and the modulation frequency is, of course, that of the flutter, f_2. The phase deviation is af_1/f_2. This can be fairly large for high modulation frequencies and low flutter frequencies. However, instantaneous phase errors in a reproduced signal are rarely if ever important in themselves; since flutter affects all channels essentially identically, the instantaneous phase error in Eq. (5-2) would not represent any error in relative phase between two signals. Such errors arise from skew rather than flutter. The frequency modulation of the data signal appears to be important only when a frequency analysis is to be performed. This will be covered more fully later.

Pulse Timing Errors Caused by Flutter. It is to be expected that variations in tape velocity will introduce errors in the time relation between two pulses recorded on the tape. Such perturbation of time relationships between pulses can be of importance in PDM systems, digital systems, and others in which precise timing relationships between two or more recorded events are important.

Since the timing error is obviously a function of the integrated value of the flutter over the period of time between the pulses, it will depend upon the frequency composition of the flutter as well as the time interval between pulses. The actual governing parameter for periodic flutter components is the product of flutter frequency and time between pulses, or the ratio of time between pulses to the period of the flutter component. The exact relationship is rather complex, but a very close approximation is given by (see Appendix II)

$$T' = \frac{T}{r}\left(1 \pm a\,\frac{\sin x}{x} \pm b\,\frac{\sin y}{y}\right) \tag{5-3}$$

where T' = time interval between reproduced pulses

T = time interval between recorded pulses

r = ratio of average playback speed to average recording speed

a = peak recording flutter at frequency f

$x = \pi f T$

b = peak playback flutter at frequency f'

$y = \pi f' T / r$

In deriving this equation, the phase angle between the pulses and the sinusoidal flutter component was chosen for maximum error. There is a phase angle which gives zero error; thus, the error in timing between two isolated pulses is a random function having any value between zero and a maximum value given by the above equation. For a pulse train with constant spacing between pulses and a sinusoidal flutter component whose frequency is not integrally related to the pulse recurrence frequency, there will be a sinusoidal variation of the time between pulses, the departure from correct timing varying from zero to the maximum of Eq. (5-3).

It is clear from the above equation that the maximum per cent timing error never exceeds the sum of the peak per cent flutters in recording and playback and is this large only a part of the time. For integral values of fT (or $f'T$) timing error is zero, as these values correspond to the zero crossings of the sin x/x function. For values of fT above 0.8, the maximum error does not exceed one-fifth the peak flutter. Appreciable timing errors from sinusoidal components are, then, only to be expected when the product fT (or the ratio of T to the flutter period) is relatively small. In general, timing error will almost never exceed ½ per cent for machines with 1 per cent or less peak-to-peak flutter.

The effect of random flutter will depend upon the power spectral density of the flutter. If the flutter has a normal (Gaussian) distribution, its rms value will be roughly one-fourth the measured peak-to-peak value, since the rms value is also the standard deviation, and excursions beyond twice the standard deviation occur only 5 per cent of the time. The standard deviation (the rms value) for the speed variation can thus be estimated from peak-to-peak flutter data; power spectral density w can be computed by dividing the mean-squared flutter (square of the rms value) by the bandwidth effective in the flutter measurement (this assumes uniform spectral density).

If two pulses separated by time T are recorded on the tape, the distance between them will be determined by the integral of the velocity over the time T. In playback, a second integration of distance divided by velocity gives the time between the reproduced pulses. As shown in Sec. II.2 of Appendix II, the result of these integrations has a standard deviation given by

$$\sigma^2 = 0.067 \frac{a^2 T}{B} \qquad (5\text{-}4)$$

where σ = standard deviation of the timing error
 a = peak-to-peak random flutter
 B = flutter measurement bandwidth, cps
 T = time between recorded pulses

The factor 0.067 arises from the assumed 4:1 relation between peak-to-peak and rms flutter. The timing error will exceed σ about 32 per cent of the time and will be greater than 2σ only 5 per cent of the time.

It can be seen that the square of the rms timing error is proportional to the flutter power spectral density and to the time between pulses. The time "jitter" will be less for closely packed pulses than for widely separated ones. However, if Eq. (5-4) is divided by T^2 to obtain the timing error as a fraction of the spacing between pulses, then the right-hand side becomes *inversely* proportional to T, and it is thus seen that the *percentage* timing error is greater for closely packed pulses than for widely spaced ones.

In digital recording, relative timing errors between tracks caused by skew are usually more important than the time jitter of a single track produced by flutter. Time jitter on a single track produced by causes other than flutter (such as electronic-system time variations due to amplitude fluctuation) is generally larger than the flutter-induced errors unless there are very large flutter components in the critical frequency region as related to the timing between pulses.

Data Errors in PDM Systems. Pulse durations in PDM systems extend over the range of 60 to 1000 μsec. With this range of pulse lengths, periodic flutter frequencies from very low values up to about 10,000 cps would give fT products in the maximum error regions. However, the standard practice of incorporating two calibration points on the commutator switch compensates for any speed variations having periods appreciably longer than the time taken by the switch to make one revolution. Thus, for normal 30-, 20-, and 10-rps switches, flutter components below approximately 3, 2, and 1 cps are not important.

On the other hand, the calibration once per switch revolution is particularly sensitive to flutter components having frequencies which are small-order submultiples or multiples of the switch rotation rate. Such components, if properly phased with the switch, can produce data errors in some of the channels which are equal to the peak per cent flutter. The exact relationship between flutter frequencies and switch rotation rates depends on the location on the switch of the calibration points. About the worst condition can be readily visualized by assuming the zero and full-scale calibration points to be adjacent, with a flutter component of approximately half the switch rotation rate phased so that the calibration points are contacted at a zero crossing of the flutter wave. Under such conditions, calibrations would occur at average tape velocity and would be unaffected by the flutter, while the data channels connected to switch contacts diametrically opposite from the calibration contacts would be encountered at the peaks of the flutter cycle. Thus, the velocity at these data-channel contacts would be a maximum amount above or below the average speed and these data channels would be in error by the peak percentage flutter at the assumed frequency. Errors on other channels would be intermediate between this value and zero.

For random flutter, Eq. (5-4) gives the mean-squared error in the pulse durations. Now the PDM signal, as a fraction of full scale, is given by

$$M = \frac{T_1 - T_0}{T_2 - T_0} \tag{5-5}$$

where M = signal level as a fraction of full scale

T_0 = duration of zero calibration pulse

T_1 = duration of signal pulse

T_2 = duration of full-scale calibration pulse

If S_M, S_0, S_1, and S_2 are the rms errors (standard deviations) for M, T_0, T_1, and T_2, respectively,

$$S_M{}^2 = \left(\frac{\partial M}{\partial T_0}\right)^2 S_0{}^2 + \left(\frac{\partial M}{\partial T_1}\right)^2 S_1{}^2 + \left(\frac{\partial M}{\partial T_2}\right)^2 S_2{}^2 \qquad (5\text{-}6)$$

Substituting from (5-4) for the values of S_0, S_1, and S_2 and performing the indicated differentiations on (5-5), we obtain

$$S_M{}^2 = 0.067 \frac{a^2}{B(T_2 - T_0)^2} [(1 - M)^2 T_0 + T_1 + M^2 T_2] \qquad (5\text{-}7)$$

Now suppose that we have a tape transport with 1 per cent peak-to-peak random flutter over a 5-kc band at 30 ips (this is a high value as compared with most transports) and assume that a full-scale PDM signal is recorded and reproduced. Then $a = 0.01$, $B = 5000$, $M = 1$, $T_0 = 60$ μsec, $T_1 = T_2 = 600$ μsec. Substitution of these numbers in (5-7) gives $S_M = 0.23$ per cent; then 95 per cent of the data points will have errors not exceeding 0.46 per cent. As M decreases from 1, the rms error also decreases, becoming 0.14 per cent for $M = \frac{1}{2}$, and well under 0.1 per cent for small values of M. If the per cent flutter is the same, but the tape speed is 60 ips and the flutter measurement band 10 kc, the power spectral density of the flutter will be only one-half as great and S_M will be 0.16 per cent for the full-scale signal.

We can see from this that tape transports with random flutter somewhat under 1 per cent over a 5- or 10-kc bandwidth will record and reproduce PDM signals without important error. A cumulative flutter graph in the region of 0.2 to 0.3 per cent in the low-frequency region, and rising to a peak of 0.7 to 0.8 per cent at 5 kc for 30- or 60-ips tape speeds, describes an acceptable flutter characteristic for PDM recording. The same flutter figures, but over a 2.5-kc band at 15 ips, would result in occasional 0.6 to 0.7 per cent errors in signals near full scale.

Since the normal system accuracy for PDM equipment can be expected to be in the vicinity of $\frac{1}{2}$ per cent, it may be safely assumed that a flutter figure of $\frac{1}{2}$ per cent peak-to-peak is not likely to produce appreciable additional error unless the flutter is made up predominantly of components in the most critical frequency region of about 5 to 400 cps.

Relative Timing and Phase Errors Due to Skew. There are numerous cases in analog recording in which it is desirable to retain phase relationships between signals recorded on separate data tracks. In parallel or serial-parallel digital recording it is important that a reasonable degree of simultaneity be preserved among pulses recorded on a line across the tape in several tracks. Since relative timing between tracks recorded by means of separate head stacks with interleaved tracks is likely to be very poor and is completely unpredictable because of the unknown factor of tape stretch between recording and playback, it is pertinent to consider only the relative timing between tracks recorded by a single head stack and reproduced on a corresponding single stack. When relative timing between two signals is important, they should not be recorded on separate stacks of an interleaved pair.

Correlated flutter, as defined previously, produces no relative phase or timing errors. Fixed timing errors introduced by imperfections in head stacks and tolerances of electronic circuit components can be and usually are held to minimum or negligible values by suitable design and quality-control procedures. In extremely critical applications, residual errors due to such fixed system imperfections can be eliminated by time-delay or phase-correcting networks inserted in the proper channels. There remains the variable timing error due to tape skew.

It has already been mentioned that little data have been published regarding the magnitude of the phase and timing errors to be expected from skew. Some information is given in two papers [4, 5]. The author's observations indicate that skew errors can be expected to vary approximately linearly with the transverse spacing between tracks for tape widths up to 2 in. There seems to be no reason to expect that there would be any difference with wider tapes. Observation of the varying phase differences between two signals recorded on widely separated tracks indicates the presence of skew errors varying in frequency from extremely low values having periods of many seconds up to relatively high-frequency values of many tens of cycles per second. This upper limit is probably merely the result of the experimental conditions rather than any actual upper limit on skew phenomena. In fact, the uncorrelated random flutter already mentioned would clearly introduce random time and phase jitter at a rate of thousands of cycles per second.

The previously mentioned "rule of thumb" of $\pm\frac{1}{2}$-mil displacement per inch of tape width produces timing errors at various tape speeds and widths, as shown in Fig. 5.4. The graphs represent peak errors, which may be either positive or negative, between the two edge tracks on the tape; the total peak-to-peak time jitter between these two channels may be twice the values shown. For tracks more closely spaced, the error will be proportionately smaller. The larger errors inherent in fast start-stop digital machines are indicated by the dotted line.

Errors in Frequency Analysis of Tape-recorded Data. It is often desirable to perform a frequency analysis on a data signal which has been recorded on magnetic tape. In fact, tape recording and loop playback are essential in obtaining frequency analyses of some short-duration signals. In such analyses, frequency modulation of the data signal by source instability and flutter in the tape recording and reproducing system is a possible source of error, and it is important to determine the magnitude of this error. The discussion here assumes perfect stability of source data, so that all errors are presumed caused by

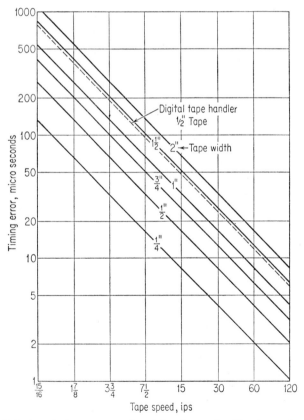

Fig. 5.4. Relative timing error produced by skew of $\pm\frac{1}{2}$ mil per inch of tape width.

flutter. This is rarely true in practice. The permissible instability determined here must generally be allocated partly to source and partly to flutter, in accordance with circumstances in the individual case.

Two types of frequency analyzers are available: the manually operated type and the automatic type. In the manual type, it is necessary for the operator to tune the analyzer to obtain a maximum reading on an indicating meter and then to read and record the meter reading. In such a situation, an important requirement is that a reasonably stable meter reading be obtainable. In both manual and automatic analysis, it is important that flutter should not introduce spurious signals (widely separated from the main signal) which might be interpreted as components present in the original signal. Finally, in automatic analysis, flutter sidebands close to the main signal must not produce "bumps" on the sides of the plotted filter resonance curve which might be interpreted as additional signal components.

A careful qualitative analysis of the problem shows that there are four factors involved: analyzing filter bandwidths, data (or signal) frequency, flutter amplitude, and flutter frequency. These can be reduced to three by normalizing the frequencies in terms of analyzing filter bandwidth, but it is helpful in obtaining a physical grasp of the problem to retain, at first, all four variables.

If f is the data frequency, f_0 the flutter frequency, and b the peak flutter amplitude, expressed as a fraction of average tape speed, the frequency deviation of the reproduced signal is bf, and the phase deviation (or modulation index) is bf/f_0. Now, if f_0 is smaller than the 3-db filter bandwidth BW, the carrier and sidebands cannot be resolved by the filter, and the modulated data signal will be passed rather accurately by the filter if bf does not exceed half the filter bandwidth. Thus, b in per cent must not exceed one-half the per cent bandwidth, or, mathematically,

$$b \leq \frac{BW}{2f}$$

This is readily understood if we consider a flutter frequency of, say, 1 cps and a filter bandwidth of 5 cps. If the value of bf is $2\frac{1}{2}$ cps, the filter output will vary by 3 db at a 2-cps rate, dropping by 3 db each time the signal reaches its extreme frequency swing. The exact way that this is indicated will depend on the dynamic characteristics of the indicating or recording instrument, but under most circumstances it will be possible to read the peak value with acceptable accuracy.

On the other hand, if f_0 is large compared with the filter bandwidth, the filter separates the signal from the spurious sidebands produced by the tape flutter, and the value of bf/f_0 must be limited so that the sidebands will not be interpreted as additional signal components. In order to establish a specific limit, it is necessary to assume a definite dynamic range for analysis. Since well over 40-db signal-to-noise ratio can be obtained in a properly designed FM carrier magnetic tape system and since several commercial analyzers cover at least this range, we shall assume a dynamic range of 40 db for the frequency analysis.

Thus, we establish the criterion that spurious signals must not exceed a level 40 db below analyzer full scale. However, since the wave to be analyzed is a priori a complex wave, it is reasonable to assume that, on an average, the largest single frequency component will be 6 db below full scale, so that the spurious sidebands introduced by high-frequency flutter must not exceed a level 34 db below that of the signal component. This gives a value of bf/f_0 of 0.04, since the first sideband has an amplitude proportional to $J_1(bf/f_0)$, and, for small values of bf/f_0, $J_1(bf/f_0) = bf/2f_0$. For a first sideband equal to 2 per cent of the carrier, then, 0.04 is the limiting value for bf/f_0. This criterion holds, for any analyzing filter selectivity, for $f_0 \geq 10$ BW.

As a result of these considerations we can prepare portions of a graph of permissible flutter amplitude against frequency (see Fig. 5.5), in which the permissible flutter at one bandwidth frequency (using now the normalized frequency coordinates) is one-half the fractional bandwidth, while at flutter frequencies of 10 BW or more the permissible flutter amplitude is 0.04 f_0/f, as indicated by the straight-line portion of the graphs.

For flutter frequencies between 1 and 10 BW, the flutter sideband, if large enough, will appear as a "bump" on the side of the filter selectivity curve. A small "bump" is practically impossible to detect on a manual analyzer, and since the problem in this region must be related to a specific analyzer selectivity, the tolerance has been determined with respect to one commercial Automatic Analyzer.* It is not likely that the graphs would be much different for other analyzers.

An analysis was made to determine the magnitude of a sideband which would be just sufficient to cause the filter skirt to be distorted so that a horizontal "shelf" would occur (zero derivative). The

* Minneapolis-Honeywell Regulator Company.

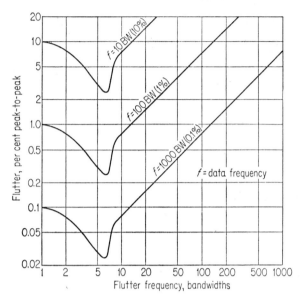

Fɪɢ. 5.5. Permissible flutter when output data are to be subjected to frequency analysis. (*Courtesy of Industrial Systems Division, Minneapolis-Honeywell Regulator Company.*)

results of the analysis were checked experimentally with the analyzer. In the course of this checking, it was decided that this tolerance was too large, as a "bump" of the type defined in the mathematical analysis was quite pronounced when actually plotted by the analyzer. Therefore, sideband levels slightly lower than the theoretical values were chosen empirically, so that the filter resonance curve as plotted by the analyzer was almost unnoticeably disturbed by the spurious sideband. These values were then plotted to give the graph for the region between 1 and 10 BW.

It will be seen from the permissible-flutter graphs that flutter must be held to rather low limits in certain frequency regions, while quite large amounts are permissible in other frequency regions. As the data frequency increases, the permissible flutter at any frequency decreases proportionately. It appears that an attempt to make a frequency analysis too fine, in terms of per cent of data frequency, may be frustrated by the need for unattainable low flutter in the tape equipment and equivalent stability of the initial signal. In general, analysis bandwidths as low as ½ per cent of the signal frequency would be feasible with the best available magnetic tape equipment, provided that the data itself were sufficiently stable in frequency.

Very frequently changes in speed are used to adapt data signals to the frequency range of the analyzer. This is particularly true in connection with speedup in playback to permit the analysis of extremely low-frequency signals. The permissible-flutter graphs, in such a case, can be applied to the playback situation with respect to analyzing bandwidth, data, and flutter frequencies; the frequencies included in the critical region of flutter frequencies should then be divided by the ratio of playback to recording speed to determine the critical flutter frequencies in recording. It will sometimes be found that such frequencies are extremely low so that they might be produced by variations in power-line frequencies or even by variations of temperature and humidity, causing variations in tape dimensions during recording.

REFERENCES

1. Magnetic Tape Study, Second Quarterly Progress Report, Signal Corps, Contract DA18–110–sc–42, June–September, 1958.
2. Dingley, E. N., Jr.: Measuring the Stability of Sonic Recorders, *IRE Trans. on Audio,* vol. PGA–7, p. 20, May, 1952.
3. Sweeney, J. F.: A Method for Measuring the Changes Introduced in Recorded Time Intervals by a Recorder-Reproducer, *IRE Trans. on Audio,* vol. PGA–7, p. 24, May, 1952.
4. Skov, R. A.: Pulse Time Displacement in High-density Magnetic Tape, *IBM J. Research and Develop.,* vol. 2, no. 2, p. 130, April, 1958.
5. Maxwell, D. E., and W. P. Bartley: Synchronization of Multiplexed Systems for Recording Video Signals on Magnetic Tape, *IRE Conv. Record,* part 7, 1955.

CHAPTER 6

COMPENSATION OF FLUTTER
AND SKEW ERRORS

Many methods have been proposed for system compensation to eliminate the effects of flutter, as contrasted with the elimination of flutter itself. Some of these methods have been rather widely applied, mostly in FM carrier systems. Others have found relatively limited application. Methods for compensating for skew errors have also been proposed, but applications of these methods are quite limited.

In carrier recording systems generally, the introduction of a first-order noise component as a result of flutter is the major deleterious effect, as has been specifically pointed out with respect to FM systems. In direct recording, on the other hand, only the second-order amplitude- and time-modulation effects are present. First-order noise due to flutter can be fairly easily eliminated by electronic methods; the second-order effects, particularly the time modulation, are rather difficult to handle electronically but can be eliminated by mechanical expedients. Since skew introduces relative time displacements, its correction by electronic methods becomes rather involved, but it can be at least partially corrected by mechanical methods.

Properly designed electronic compensation offers many advantages, particularly in FM systems. It eliminates the first-order noise introduced by the flutter; makes system performance relatively insensitive to tape-transport performance, thereby lightening maintenance problems with respect to the tape transport; makes the system d-c zero independent of tape speed, so that elaborate and expensive speed control systems can be dispensed with in some applications; and makes possible the achievement of good performance in extreme design regions, including very low tape speeds and ultracompact equipment for operation in extreme environmental conditions [1].

In some extreme situations compensation may permit recovery of data which could not otherwise be obtained. For example, certain

122

types of motion of a recorder (particularly rotation about an axis parallel to that of the capstan) are almost certain to produce tape-speed fluctuations, and if such motion unavoidably occurs at the time of recording it will seriously influence the data. Compensation can be used in such cases to eliminate the effects of the speed variations.

6.1 Electronic Compensation in FM Systems

The simplest form of compensation, applicable to wideband FM carrier recording, comprises the recording of a stable-frequency reference signal on one tape track, recovery of the flutter signal by FM demodulation of the reference signal on playback, and subtraction of the flutter signal from all data channels. To the extent that signal and compensation channel gains are equal and phase relations are maintained, this procedure cancels the first-order noise signal introduced by the flutter. Equality of gain and phase characteristics in signal and compensation channels is not particularly difficult to establish and maintain, because the channels are identical from the terminals of the recording heads to the outputs of the discriminators. Thus relative gain and phase drifts are minimized. Additionally, exact unity gain and 180° phase relationships are not critical; a phase shift as large as 30° still permits a noise reduction of 2:1 (6 db), and a departure from the proper gain relationship simply corresponds to an equivalent shift of the exact compensation point from the carrier frequency.

For wideband FM systems the compensation signal frequency is most conveniently made equal to the carrier center frequency and may be used as a control signal for playback servo speed control. A single compensation discriminator can furnish a compensating signal to a large number of signal channel discriminators. Discriminator circuitry should incorporate simple gain and phase adjustments so that the discriminators can be matched as to gain and phase characteristics throughout the operating signal frequency range. A concurrent advantage of such adjustments is that all signal channels are made alike in both gain and phase characteristics (not including the low-pass output filter) and thus provide the maximum relative signal equality attainable in a given system. The stability of adjustment in well-designed discriminators is excellent; such equipment can be operated for days, and frequently weeks, without amplitude adjustment of the compensation. Phase adjustments are required only when resistors and capacitors change through aging.

Relative phase errors between tracks on wide tape limit somewhat the efficacy of compensation at high flutter frequencies. Experience with such equipment, however, shows that a central location of the compensation track permits effective use of this technique for all tape widths up to 2 in. The $\pm\frac{1}{2}$-mil skew displacement mentioned in Chap. 5 indicates 30° phase shift at the maximum possible flutter frequency in this situation. It is desirable, of course, that all heads be in a single stack when compensation of this type is used. With double-stack interleaved head arrangements, a separate compensation track for each head stack is most efficacious; however, a single track in one head stack can be used if only very low-frequency components are predominant in the flutter characteristics of the machine. The stability of d-c level and some of the other advantages of compensation are not fully achieved in such an arrangement, however.

The d-c stabilization effects of compensation are often overlooked. Consider, for example, a recording and reproducing system operating from an ordinary power line with instantaneous frequency stability of $\pm\frac{1}{4}$ per cent, a figure which is reasonably representative of what is to be expected in most portions of the United States (integrated error over reasonable time periods is much less than this, of course). Neglecting any other speed errors, the tape speed during recording will vary by $\pm\frac{1}{4}$ per cent from its normal value because of line frequency variations, and the same thing will happen in playback. In an uncompensated system with 40 per cent deviation, these speed variations will produce errors up to $\frac{1}{2}$ per cent in the reproduced frequencies and d-c zero drifts of varying magnitude up to $\pm1\frac{1}{4}$ per cent of full scale, with corresponding data amplitude errors. In a compensated system, the speed variations resulting from line frequency would produce negligble d-c zero drift; the residual effect of the speed variations would be an equivalent drift in system gain of a maximum of $\frac{1}{2}$ per cent and a variation in frequency of the reproduced signal, as related to the recorded frequencies, of up to $\frac{1}{2}$ per cent (the frequency error is not affected by compensation). Since the gain drift of $\frac{1}{2}$ per cent maximum applies to the instantaneous amplitude of the data signal and is not a "percentage of full scale" factor, it may well be tolerable; if the frequency deviation is likewise tolerable, the use of servo speed control equipment would not be necessary.

In order to achieve all the advantages of compensation, the compensation channel must pass all frequencies down to direct current and up to the maximum data frequency that can be handled by the signal channel. The d-c response of the compensation channel need not introduce any additional d-c zero drift into the signal channel; in fact, certain sources of drift can be made to cancel each other so that a slight improvement in d-c zero stability can be attained.

A graphic picture of the effect of compensation is shown in Fig. 6.1, which is a group of signals reproduced from tape and recorded by a direct-writing recorder (frequency response to 50 cps). A strip of plastic adhesive tape was attached to the transport capstan to introduce severe flutter during reproduction only, measured as 1 per cent peak (2 per cent peak-to-peak). The tape speed was 30 ips, and the capstan rotation rate 10 rps, giving a major flutter component at 10 cps. The two upper traces show the reproduction of an 11-cps signal, recorded by wideband FM carrier, without and with compensation. Carrier deviation was only 2 per cent, corresponding to 5 per cent of full-scale signal in a 40 per cent system. The difference between the left and right portions of the traces is due to a 10:1 increase in output recorder-paper speed. The cleanness of the compensated signal is evident, in spite of the fact that the peak flutter is 50 per cent of the peak data signal. Theoretically [Eq.(5-2)], there should be a 1 per cent disturbance of the instantaneous value of the data signal by virtue of the second-order effect of the flutter. This is just barely discernible at the peaks of the signal cycle in the original recording but is lost in the reproduction.

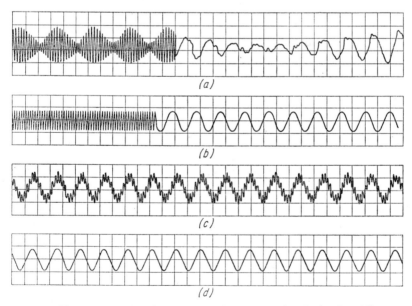

(a)

(b)

(c)

(d)

Fig. 6.1. Uncompensated and compensated tape-reproduced signals. (*Courtesy of Industrial Systems Division, Minneapolis-Honeywell Regulator Company.*)

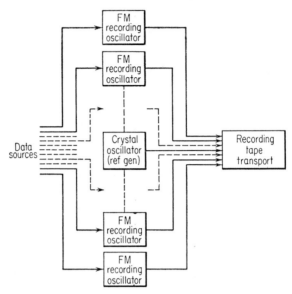

Fɪɢ. 6.2. Wideband FM recording system with compensation.

The two lower traces of the figure also show uncompensated and compensated reproduction; all conditions are the same except the data frequency, which here is 1 cps.

Discriminator design should permit insertion of the compensation signal ahead of the low-pass filter used in the discriminator output. In this fashion, phase shift errors occasioned by the low-pass filters are avoided. If the frequency of the compensation signal is not equal to the carrier frequency of the FM data-recording oscillators, the relative gains of the compensation and data channels, after demodulation, must be in proportion to the signal and compensation frequencies. Because of this the compensation signal should not be appreciably lower in frequency than the FM carrier frequency, as additional gain would then be required in the compensation channel. Such additional gain could contribute to differential drift. If the compensation frequency is higher than the carrier frequency, identical circuitry can be used in the two channels with stable resistive attenuation to reduce the compensation channel gain appropriately. Figures 6.2 and 6.3 show block diagrams of wideband FM recording and reproducing systems with compensation.

Adjustment of the relative gains of the signal and compensation channels permits adjustment of the point at which complete compensation is effective. If the compensation signal frequency is equal to the carrier frequency and if the channel gains are equal, compensation occurs at the carrier frequency which corresponds to zero data signal. This is the adjustment normally used. However, if a signal of particular interest occurs at one-half of full-scale signal in a 40 per cent deviation system, a shift of the relative channel gain by 20 per cent will move the compensation point to the data signal value, thus eliminating both the noise signal and the second-order amplitude modulation of the data. This technique has been particularly valuable in situations in which unavoidable recorder motion caused tape-speed variations at the time of recording.

Elimination of the second-order amplitude modulation of the data signal is also possible by electronic methods. The most commonly used way of doing this is variation of the energy content of the discriminator output pulse (in cycle-counting discriminators) by the flutter compensation signal. This is equivalent to varying the gain of the signal channel in accordance with the flutter signal, and other methods of accomplishing this could obviously be used.

In the multiplex recording of subcarriers, flutter requirements become almost prohibitive and compensation is very valuable to maintain signal-to-noise ratios and hold stable d-c zeros. The 7½ per cent deviation used with many of these subcarriers results in a 13 to 15 times multiplication of the flutter. Without compensation, for a 40-db rms-signal-to-rms-noise ratio, the rms flutter cannot exceed 0.05 per cent; for 40-db peak-signal-to-peak-noise ratio the peak-to-peak flutter

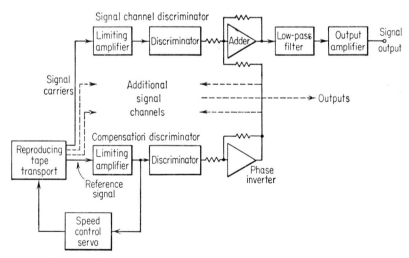

FIG. 6.3. Wideband FM reproducing system with compensation.

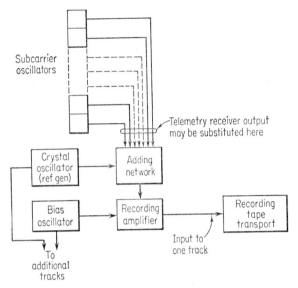

Fig. 6.4.   Subcarrier recording system with compensation.

cannot exceed 0.15 per cent.   These figures assume full use of the 7.5 per cent deviation capability of the channel, which rarely occurs. Therefore, lower flutter figures are necessary even if the 40-db signal-to-noise ratios are satisfactory.   If these low flutter figures are not consistently maintained, system performance will suffer.

Unfortunately, compensation circuitry for subcarrier discriminators is somewhat more complex than that for wideband FM.   On the other hand, the compensation signal can be multiplexed on the same track with the data signal carrier, thereby eliminating any random phase errors between tracks and improving the precision of the compensation signal.   Figures 6.4 and 6.5 show block diagrams for recording and reproducing systems.

The circuit complications are required by the differences in time delays of the bandpass filters used to single out the individual carriers from the multiplexed signal.   These filters have passbands which are a fixed percentage of the center frequencies, and the time delay is inversely proportional to the absolute bandwidth.   Consequently, the highest-frequency channel has a relatively small time delay, the delay increasing progressively to the lowest-frequency channel which has a minimum bandwith and maximum delay.   The compensation signal for each channel must be delayed by an amount equal to the signal delay in the bandpass filter for that channel.   Thus, it is necessary to provide for a series of time-delay networks in the compensation channel, the total delay of these networks being equal to the difference between the delay of the lowest-frequency signal channel and that of the compensation channel. Taps at various delay points provide compensating voltages for the other signal channels. The bandpass filter used to separate the compensation signal from the remaining carriers on a track must have an absolute bandwidth at least as wide as the maximum bandwith filter used on any signal channel.

The time-delay networks in the compensation channel do not add greatly to its complexity or cost, but the necessity for them can introduce operational complexities when changes are required in the system discriminator setup. For example, a change in a high-frequency channel from 7½ to 15 per cent deviation requires a change of the bandpass filter for that channel and a corresponding change in the time delay in the compensation channel. Once the time delay is adjusted for a specific signal channel filter, it should rarely if ever require readjustment until the signal-channel characteristics are changed.

Since up to 18 signal channels can be accommodated on one tape track, one compensation discriminator is needed for each bank of 18 or fewer signal discriminators in a normal subcarrier system. Some special systems use fewer than the full complement of 18 subcarriers per track, and in such cases the proportion of compensation dis-

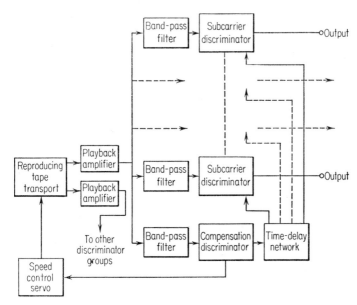

FIG. 6.5. Subcarrier reproducing system with compensation.

criminators to signal discriminators may be larger if a compensation signal on each track is consistently used with the signals on that track. If the system is such that this arrangement creates undue cost increases, it is quite practical to use the compensation signal from one track for data signals on several adjacent tracks, so long as all tracks are recorded and reproduced from single head stacks.

The cost of compensation in terms of the original equipment cost and somewhat more complex adjustment procedures in subcarrier systems must be weighed against the very considerable system-performance advantages which accrue, and the cost of maintenance of low flutter in an uncompensated system. To a considerable degree, compensation can be compared to inverse feedback in amplifiers; it reduces the effect on system performance of variations in system components.

Compensation methods discussed to this point do not affect the time-delay or instantaneous phase errors introduced by flutter into the data signal. It would theoretically be possible to do this by insertion of a variable time-delay network in the signal path, the network delay being controlled by the flutter signal. In fact, such a network interposed in the FM carrier playback channel before demodulation could theoretically eliminate all effects of flutter. Practically, however, time modulation of the data signal by flutter has not appeared to be of sufficient importance to warrant the cost of such compensating networks.

6.2   Flutter Compensation by Mechanical Methods

If the relative velocity between tape and the playback head can be made to conform exactly at each instant to the relative velocity between tape and the recording head, then all velocity variations and their effects will be canceled and the reproduced signal will be identical, except for a gain factor and electronic errors, to the recorded signal. At least two methods have been suggested for accomplishing this.

E. N. Dingley, Jr. [2] proposed to move physically the reproducing head, in a direction parallel to the tape travel, to produce an instantaneous playback velocity equal to the relative tape-head velocity during the recording. Variations in average speed would cause the head to move either against or with the direction of tape travel. This motion would adjust the driving mechanism to correct the average speed and bring the head back to its neutral position. Speed fluctuations that were too rapid to be followed by the drive-speed correction would be followed by the head itself.   The resultant oscillations of the head back and forth in the direction of tape travel would produce the desired instantaneous tape-head velocity.

Dingley's method uses a precisely controlled frequency recorded on the tape along with the signal, in the manner indicated in Fig. 6.2 or 6.4.   This may be recorded separately on one track or multiplexed with the signal, depending on the equipment characteristics.   The reproduction arrangement is indicated in Fig. 6.6 and applies to the multiplexed recording situation.   If separate recording tracks were used, the bandpass filters would be eliminated and an additional amplifier would be required.   If the reference signal recovered from the tape is not identical in frequency and phase to the signal derived from the timing oscillator, there will be an output from the balanced modulator which, by means of the electromagnetic drive system, will cause head motion in the proper direction to cancel the frequency or phase difference.   The feedback inherent in this system forces the reference signal reproduced from the tape to match at all times the signal from the timing oscillator, within the limits of error of the servo system.   To the degree that the timing oscillator used in the reproduction process has the same frequency as that used during recording, the data or other recorded material reproduced will also be equal to that recorded.

The Dingley system controls average and instantaneous speed and thus completely eliminates the effect of speed variations over the range of frequencies from zero to the upper frequency limit of the mechanical servo system.   It is hardly to be expected that such a mechanical

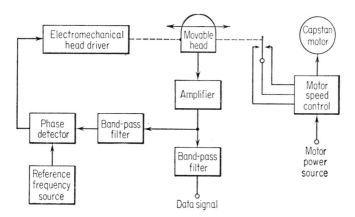

Fig. 6.6.   Reproducing system for movable-head compensation.

system could be designed to respond to more than a few tens of cycles per second, particularly in a multitrack data system that would require a rather bulky head stack with correspondingly large mass.

A variation of this system has been devised for use in a recorder for color television signals [3]. The playback head is rotated about its axis, rather than translated linearly. Such rotation must be limited to a rather small arc, so that the head motion itself cannot be used to generate the correction signal for average speed control. This function is taken over by an electronic servo system. Flutter frequencies too high to be eliminated by the speed control servo are applied to the rotating head assembly. The servo in this case also acts to make the effective instantaneous head-tape playback speed equal to the instantaneous recording speed, thus eliminating the flutter effects.

Figure 6.7 shows the magnitude of the relative tape-head motion, velocity, and acceleration at various flutter frequencies and percentages. The amplitudes, velocities, and accelerations are normalized for a tape speed of 1 ips and must therefore be multiplied by the tape speed to give actual figures at other speeds. The units are inches for

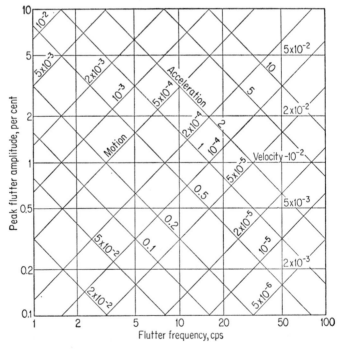

FIG. 6.7.   Normalized motion, velocity, and acceleration from flutter.

displacement or amplitude, inches per second for velocity, and inches per second per second for acceleration. The amplitude decreases as flutter frequency increases, the velocity is independent of the flutter frequency, and the acceleration increases with flutter frequency. For a flutter amplitude of 1 per cent peak at a tape speed of 30 ips, the amplitude is $30 \times 1.6 \times 10^{-3}$, or 0.048 in. at 1-cps flutter frequency, 4.8 mils at 10 cps, and proportionately smaller at higher frequencies. The velocity is $30 \times 10^{-2} = 0.3$ in. per sec, regardless of frequency. The peak acceleration would be about $0.6 \times 30 = 18$ in. per sec^2 at 10-cps flutter frequency and 180 in. per sec^2 at 100-cps flutter frequency. In view of the fact that flutter values well below the assumed 1 per cent peak (2 per cent peak-to-peak) are rather easily attainable, it seems quite likely that mechanical flutter compensation can be made effective to at least 500 cps and perhaps into the kilocycle region. This response would take care of all normally encountered sinusoidal flutter components and would be fairly effective in reducing the random background flutter.

The previously noted application of mechanical flutter compensation [3] is the only one known to the author. It was apparently successful in reducing effective flutter to a value of about 0.008 per cent peak-to-peak, something more than an order of magnitude better than the best ever claimed for "brute force" flutter reduction technique and almost two orders of magnitude better than the performance which can be expected from the best production equipment. It seems quite likely that a portion of the tremendous engineering effort expended in stubborn attempts to reduce flutter itself would have paid off far more handsomely, in actual performance useful to the user, if it had been used to perfect the available flutter compensation methods. Mechanical compensation almost requires a single-stack head assembly, and this is another of the numerous reasons supporting the statement that such an arrangement is technically preferable to the dual-stack assembly.

6.3 Skew Compensation

In so far as the relative timing error between tracks due to skew is linearly proportional to the distance between tracks, it can be compensated by rotation of the playback head about an axis normal to the plane of the tape and passing through the center of the line of head gaps. Two tracks on the opposite edges of the tape must carry reference signals which, by phase comparison, will give a signal proportional to the skew error which may be used to actuate the head

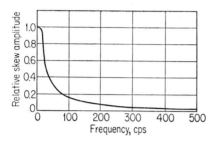

FIG. 6.8. Frequency spectrum of skew. (*Courtesy of Institute of Radio Engineers.*)

motion. The frequency response of the head control should extend to direct current and up in frequency as high as possible. The maximum peak-to-peak angular motion required can be estimated to be not more than $\frac{1}{1000}$ radian, or about 4 min of arc.

Such a mechanical method for skew compensation has been described by Maxwell and Bartley [4]. In tape machines running at speeds of 100 to 200 ips they found maximum skew angles of the order of $\pm 0.02°$ (0.35 milliradian). The frequency spectrum of the skew is shown in Fig. 6.8, and a block diagram of the skew correction servo is given in Fig. 6.9. The improvement obtained by the use of this servo is indicated by the two oscillograms in Fig. 6.10. It can be seen from this figure that the servo very considerably reduces the skew error.

Skew correction by all-electronic means is possible by several methods. Variable time-delay circuits, controlled by the skew error voltage derived from outside reference tracks, could be used in each playback channel. The signal voltage applied to each time-delay network would be adjusted in magnitude in accordance with the position of the track. This system has been suggested by several people but is somewhat complex equipment-wise and hardly seems economically feasible. Maxwell and Bartley, dealing with short sampling pulses of varying amplitude, mention the possibility of stor-

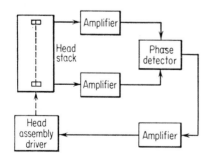

FIG. 6.9. Skew correction servo. (*Courtesy of Institute of Radio Engineers.*)

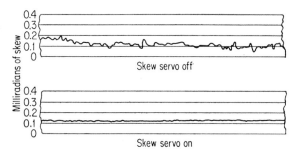

Fɪɢ. 6.10. Improvement due to skew correction servo. (*Courtesy of Institute of Radio Engineers.*)

ing these samples in boxcar storage circuits and reading them out in the correct time sequence and spacing. They do not discuss this method further.

In parallel and serial-parallel digital systems, several methods are used for elimination of the effect of skew, although they are not strictly classifiable as skew compensation devices. One such method makes use of the clock or sprocket track to generate a sharp pulse delayed by somewhat less than half the time between successive pulse groups. The data signal pulses, whenever they occur, open gates which remain open approximately half the time between pulse groups. The short pulse generated from the clock track passes through these gates at the instant of its occurrence so that all the pulses of the output group occur at the same instant and their timing is not dependent upon the times of occurrence of the individual data signal pulses.

Another system comprises a group of storage elements, such as flip-flops or magnetic cores, one for each of the data tracks. These storage elements are set by the data track pulses whenever they occur and are reset and simultaneously read out by a delayed pulse derived from the clock track or other source.

These methods used in digital systems produce a simultaneous group of output pulses for each character on the tape, regardless of the times of occurrence of the individual pulses from the tape. They do not, however, reduce the skew, and timing errors due to skew must be less than half the time between pulse groups. Therefore these methods for obtaining pulse simultaneity do not really alleviate the skew problem in digital recording, and with no other skew compensation arrangements the relative timing error due to skew is the major factor limiting pulse packing in the direction of tape travel in such systems.

REFERENCES

1. Davies, Gomer L.: Magnetic Recorders for Data Recording under Adverse Environments, *IRE Trans. on Audio,* vol. AU–2, no. 5, p. 133, September–October, 1954.
2. U.S. Patent no. 2,656,419, Reissue no. 24,182.
3. Olson, H. F., W. D. Houghton, A. R. Morgan, M. Artzt, J. A. Zenel, and J. G. Woodward: A Magnetic Tape System for Recording and Reproducing Standard FCC Color Television Signals, *RCA Rev.,* vol. 17, no. 3, September, 1956.
4. Maxwell, D. E., and W. P. Bartley: Synchronization of Multiplexed Systems for Recording Video Signals on Magnetic Tape, *IRE Conv. Record,* part 7, 1955.

CHAPTER 7

SPEED CONTROL SYSTEMS

There are many recording situations in which a stable-frequency a-c source is not available for capstan drive of the tape transport. In such cases it may be desirable to incorporate in the recording system some apparatus to hold the tape speed within tolerable limits.

Since it is not always feasible to hold recording speed accurately and because tape may shrink or stretch between recording and reproducing the data, speed control systems are very frequently used in tape playback systems to make the average playback speed equal to the average recording speed. These are servo systems which include in the control loop the capstan-drive mechanism of the tape transport. Since considerable inertia is desirable in the capstan drive to reduce flutter, average speed control systems generally cannot respond to speed variations at frequencies greater than 1 or 2 cps.

Two basic methods have been most commonly used for playback speed control: One of these converts, by means of a discriminator, a reference frequency from the tape to a d-c control voltage; this is inherently a rate servo, and while it controls the speed and thus the reproduced frequencies with reasonable accuracy, the accumulated timing error can become rather large. The second method uses a phase comparison between a signal reproduced from the tape and a local standard to generate the required control voltage; this is inherently a positional servo, counting each reference cycle on the tape against a cycle from the local standard source, and is capable of precise speed control and excellent integrated timing accuracy. Each type has its advantages and disadvantages.

7.1 Speed Control in Recording Systems

Some tape-speed-control device is required in a recording system whenever there is not available a capstan-motor power source of sufficiently stable frequency. The term "sufficiently stable frequency" is not susceptible to absolute definition, as it depends upon the frequency and timing accuracy with which the data must be reproduced and hence upon the type of servo that will be used in reproduction of the data from the tape. Conversely, the accuracy of recording speed control that can be achieved under a given set of recording environmental conditions will determine the type of playback speed control servo that must be used and thereby establishes the frequency and timing accuracy that can be achieved in the reproduced data. Since it is usually fairly easy to record accurate timing signals on the tape, such timing signals can often be used to establish timing in the reproduced data, thereby eliminating the necessity for precise reproduction of time intervals.

Typical situations which require recording speed control devices include those in which the available power is d-c, or a-c of variable frequency. These situations frequently arise in airborne and missile recording and in portable recording systems not operable from controlled-frequency power sources. Most laboratory systems can be operated from the normal 60-cps power lines, and the frequency accuracy of the vast majority of these lines is good enough to permit tape drive by a hysteresis synchronous motor operating directly from the line.

There are two general classes of recording tape speed controls, those which use a hysteresis synchronous motor for capstan drive and rely on frequency control of the power supply to this motor, and those which use some form of servo in the drive system itself to establish proper tape speed. When a synchronous-motor drive is used, the normal technique is to furnish power to this motor by means of a stable frequency source and a power amplifier. The source may be a stable electronic oscillator or a tuning fork or crystal-controlled oscillator when maximum precision is required. Since frequency-control crystals are not usually available to operate directly at the normal drive frequencies of 400 or 60 cps, a series of frequency dividers is generally used with a crystal operating in the range of 1 to 5 kc. Tuning forks are suitable at 400 cps, but for a 60-cps power source a higher-frequency fork and frequency dividers are generally used to reduce the size of the fork and render it less susceptible to disturbance by environmental conditions.

Precision frequency supplies and power amplifiers are generally available for driving the 60-cps capstan motors of standard laboratory-type tape transports. Some of these use forks and some use crystals as the stable frequency element. The power amplifiers must be capable of delivering 75 to 125 watts, depending upon the requirements of the capstan motor. Such precision frequency supplies are generally used when the primary power source for the system is 60-cps a-c derived from a converter or motor generator operated from batteries or from a gasoline- or diesel-engine generator system.

A stable 60-cps resistance-capacitance oscillator and power amplifier are used in at least one type of airborne recording system to furnish capstan-motor power. A crystal oscillator and frequency divider chain delivering 400 cps have been used to synchronize a power transistor inverter to drive a 400-cps hysteresis synchronous motor from a d-c source in other airborne equipments.

The speed accuracy that is obtained with the precision frequency power source and hysteresis-motor drive is sufficient for any application, particularly if a fork or crystal is used as the frequency-determining element. A self-excited oscillator as a stable frequency source may be borderline in a few cases requiring extreme integrated timing accuracy in reproduction but is entirely satisfactory in the great majority of applications. In such systems, the capstan speed will be as accurate as the source frequency, and tape slippage would be essentially the only factor introducing speed error. The major disadvantages of such speed control systems are size, weight, and relatively low efficiency resulting in high power drains. These disadvantages are particularly present in the 60-cps systems. Transistorized 400-cps systems can be made quite compact, lightweight, and efficient, but the high speed of 400-cps synchronous motors introduces some complications in the tape-drive system because of the large speed reduction necessary between motor and capstan.

Several servo devices have been used for control of recording speed for equipment which must be operated from d-c or unstable a-c power sources. For d-c-operated equipment, the simplest speed control device is a governor-controlled capstan motor. If environmental conditions are not unduly severe, it is possible to attain speed accuracy of ½ to 1 per cent with such a motor. Variations in supply voltage, temperature, and torque will produce speed changes in the motor. Certain combinations, such as low voltage and high temperature, tend to produce additive effects and thus increase the speed error. Something in the order of 2 to 3 per cent maximum speed error under widely varying environmental conditions can be expected with most governor-controlled motors. Small-size d-c motors must operate at high speed to develop sufficient power and introduce the same speed-reducer problems as the 400-cps motors.

Higher accuracy in tape speed can be obtained by more elaborate

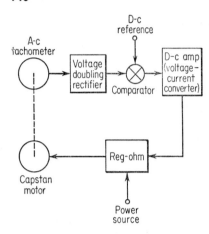

Fig. 7.1. Tachometer-generator speed control. (*Courtesy of Department of Defense.*)

servos which sense the capstan or tape speed itself and include some gain in the servo loop. In one system, a tachometer generator associated with the capstan-drive mechanism provides speed sensing which is used in a conventional rate servo arrangement to control capstan-motor speed (Fig. 7.1). The output of the a-c tachometer generator is rectified, filtered, and compared with a stable d-c reference. The error signal is amplified by a single vacuum tube whose plate current actuates a Reg-Ohm. This in turn controls the line-frequency power applied to the capstan motor to control the tape speed. Adjustment of the d-c reference sets the tape speed to the desired value.

Another system (Fig. 7.2) uses a tone wheel on the capstan shaft

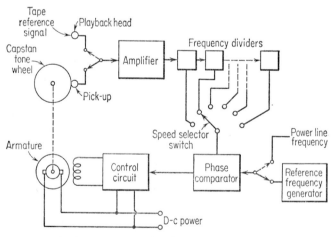

Fig. 7.2. Tone-wheel speed control servo. (*Courtesy of Mincom Division, Minnesota Mining & Manufacturing Company.*)

to generate a relatively high frequency. This signal is then passed through a chain of frequency dividers and the resultant submultiple of the tone-wheel frequency is compared with a standard frequency source. When these two signals are locked in phase, the capstan speed is constant. In this particular system, the speed control is effected by variation of field current in a shunt-wound d-c capstan motor, thus requiring relatively little control power. The entire frequency divider chain, phase comparison circuitry, and field current control elements are transistorized. As has been mentioned, such a phase comparison device is essentially a positional servo rather than a rate servo and gives control as precise as the reference frequency. With this arrangement, it is easy to change tape speed by altering the number of frequency dividers in the chain between the capstan tone generator and the phase comparison circuit. The greater the frequency division used, the higher the capstan speed will be. This particular speed control system is adaptable for both recording and playback control, the reference signal being taken from the capstan tone wheel in recording and from the tape for playback control.

In another system [1] the arrangement for speed control comprises phase comparison of the tone wheel or prerecorded frequency with a standard, use of the d-c output from the phase comparison circuit to control the frequency of a voltage-controlled oscillator, and amplification of this oscillator signal to drive a hysteresis synchronous capstan motor (Fig. 7.3). This system is employed in seismic recording equipment, which uses a wide sheet of tape wrapped on a drum; the speed sensing signal may be obtained from a tone generator mechanically associated with the drum or from a prerecorded signal on the sheet of tape. The latter method is used under conditions of extreme

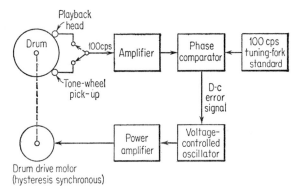

FIG. 7.3. Another tone-wheel speed control. (*Courtesy of Southwestern Industrial Electronics Company.*)

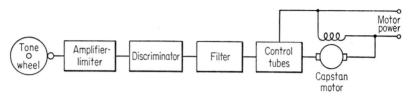

FIG. 7.4.   Rate servo for recording speed control.   (*Courtesy of Mincom Division, Minnesota Mining & Manufacturing Company.*)

variation of humidity or temperature which might cause dimensional variations in the tape sheet.

Figure 7.4 shows a discriminator-type rate servo used with a shunt-wound d-c capstan motor.   Because of the better control characteristics of the d-c motor, as compared with the hysteresis synchronous type, higher loop gain, and thus closer speed control, can be achieved than is possible in the servo discussed later (Fig. 7.7).   A speed accuracy of ±0.1 per cent over an input voltage range of 95 to 135 volts is feasible, and power-source frequency is immaterial.   The discriminator is novel; it uses only one tuned circuit and furnishes a correctly polarized output control voltage for input frequencies from extremely low values up to the maximum frequency that can be passed by the circuits.   This characteristic is quite different from that of most tuned-circuit discriminators, the output of which rises to a peak on each side of and rather close to the center frequency and then falls to zero at greater departures of input frequency from center frequency.   The single tuned circuit is advantageous, since center frequency and tape speed are changed simply by switching capacitors. The tone-wheel frequency is about 4000 cps at 60 ips and correspondingly lower at lower tape speeds.   Application of this system to playback speed control is discussed in a later paragraph.

Occasionally it is not desirable to maintain a specific uniform speed in the recording system but rather to cause the tape to move in synchronism with some other mechanical motion.   In such cases, a self-synchronous motor and generator combination can be used to slave the tape drive to the external mechanical motion.   In some few cases, a direct mechanical coupling may be used.   In one such application, it was desired to correlate the motion of the tape in the recording machine with the motion of a truck.   A self-synchronous generator was driven from the truck wheels and the motor used to drive the tape in the recorder.   The same system was used for playback by driving a self-synchronous generator from a hysteresis synchronous motor and supplying the generator output to the tape recorder motor.

This gave constant-speed playback. A drive system of this sort is also very useful for slaving a tape loop to a conveyor belt or other moving device.

7.2   Playback Speed Control Servos

Regardless of the accuracy of speed control in recording equipment, precise reproduction of recorded frequencies and time intervals can be achieved only by use of a speed control servo in playback, to eliminate the effect of dimensional changes in the tape between recording and playback.

The precision of speed control necessary in recording is generally determined by the pull-in range of the playback servo, since the recording speed must never depart so far from nominal that the playback servo cannot correct for the departure. Thus, if a servo with wide pull-in range is to be used in playback, a relatively coarse speed control device may be used in recording. On the other hand, if the pull-in range of the playback servo is small, then close control of recording speed must be maintained.

Phase Comparison Servos. Figure 7.5 shows the block diagram of one type of phase comparison servo. The reference signal on the tape is a carrier amplitude-modulated by a stable and precise 60-cps signal derived from a local standard during recording. Almost any reasonable carrier frequency can be used, depending on the system charac-

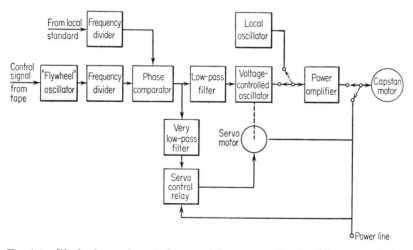

Fɪɢ. 7.5. Playback speed control servo (phase comparison). (*Courtesy of Department of Defense.*)

teristics; in telemetry recording, 17.0 kc has been established as a standard value as it can be multiplexed on one track with mixed subcarriers. After amplification of the modulated carrier and demodulation, the resulting 60-cps signal is fed to a phase comparison circuit, to which is also supplied the output of a precision frequency local oscillator. The d-c or very low-frequency a-c output from the phase comparison circuit controls the frequency of a 60-cps voltage-controlled oscillator whose output serves to drive the synchronous capstan motor by way of a power amplifier. The servo loop acts to control the tape speed so that the reference signal recovered from the tape is locked in phase with the local standard frequency. Once this lock is achieved, the tape is, in effect, "metered," a length of tape corresponding to one cycle of the recorded reference frequency being passed through the machine for each cycle of the local frequency standard. As long as the phase lock is maintained, frequency and integrated timing accuracies are very good, depending only on the frequency difference between the recording standard frequency and the playback standard frequency. With precision generators, this difference can be held to a very small value. The servo motor acts to correct accumulating errors, so that the demand on the electronic correction circuits is a minimum, to avoid loss of control due to small transients.

In some cases the recording standard frequency is used for capstan-motor drive, in which case the playback servo must correct only for variation in tape dimensions between the time of recording and the time of playback. However, this is not essential, as some speed variations in recording are permissible provided that they are not large enough or sudden enough to disturb the phase lock in playback. Generally, capstan-motor drive from normal power lines is suitable. If the recording speed varies slightly, there may be a small amount of "rocking" in the playback phase relationship to provide the necessary corrective signal to the voltage-controlled oscillator of the servo system. This can introduce very small and usually negligible variations in reproduced frequencies but will not affect integrated timing accuracy.

The pull-in range of a servo of the type shown in Fig. 7.5 is somewhat limited. When the playback speed is different from the recording speed, the output of the phase comparison circuit is a very low-frequency a-c signal. During one half cycle of this a-c output, the polarity is such as to cause the tape speed to change toward the correct value. However, if the proper speed is not reached during this half cycle, the reversal of phase comparator output voltage in the next half cycle will drive the tape speed away from its correct value. The result is a speed oscillation without lock-in. Thus, the combination of recording-speed errors and tape dimensional changes between recording and playback must not introduce too large an error. The output frequency from the phase comparison circuit must be low enough so that the servo can pull in during one half cycle. If the pull-in time is ½ sec, the error signal frequency must not exceed 1 cps, and the error in recording speed plus tape stretch cannot exceed about 1.7 per cent when the control frequency is 60 cps. As a consequence, recording tape speed must be quite closely controlled to permit initial lock-in and proper maintenance of control during playback.

Another phase comparison servo is shown in Fig. 7.6. The reference signal from the tape and the local standard are supplied to two phase detectors, the local standard being shifted 90° in one case. If the tape speed is correct, the output of phase detector 1 passes on through phase detector 3 to the voltage-controlled oscillator, and phase lock is maintained as in the system of Fig. 7.5. Since the outputs of phase detectors 1 and 2 are fixed, or changing very slowly, the differentiated output of phase detector 2 is essentially zero and has no effect. However, if there is a difference between the recording and playback speeds, the outputs of phase detectors 1 and 2 are very low-frequency a-c signals, ±90° out of phase. This 90° phase shift, plus the phase

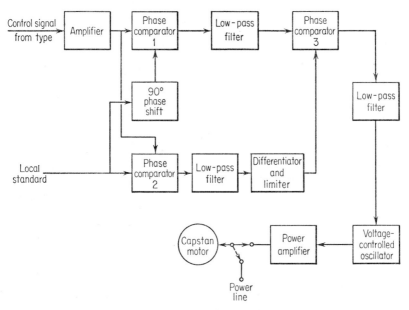

Fig. 7.6. Playback speed control servo (phase comparison). (*Courtesy of Industrial Systems Division, Minneapolis-Honeywell Regulator Company.*)

shift due to the differentiator, causes the inputs to phase detector 3 to be in phase or out of phase, depending on the sign of the tape speed error. Phase detector 3 then produces a d-c output of the proper sign to correct the tape speed, even when the speed error is so large that the output of phase detectors 1 and 2 is an a-c signal with a frequency of several cycles per second. When the speed comes within the lock-in range of phase detector 1, the auxiliary branch including phase detector 2 becomes inoperative. This system is capable of pulling into phase lock when the recording-speed error is as large as 5 per cent or more. Also, severe transients in velocity, from whatever cause, can result in only a brief interruption in the phase lock.

As previously mentioned, the systems shown in Figs. 7.2 and 7.3 may be used as well for playback speed control as for recording. The only difference is that the speed indicating signal is obtained from the tone wheel during recording and from the tape during playback. They are, consequently, "universal" speed control systems. In addition, the system of Fig. 7.2 controls line power for the capstan motor, rather than generating this power by an oscillator-amplifier technique. It is therefore far more efficient from the over-all power-consumption standpoint and makes the system essentially independent of power-supply frequency.

The system of Fig. 7.4 may be used in three ways for playback servo control. First, with the speed reference signal derived from the capstan tone wheel as shown in the figure, it can be used exactly as in recording. No correction is introduced for variation in tape dimensions, and the total error will be the sum of this variation and the recording and playback servo errors. Second, the speed reference signal can be obtained from the tape; in this case it becomes a discriminator rate servo of the type discussed below. The speed error is the tape stretch plus recording-speed error, divided by the servo loop gain. Because of the d-c motor, as previously mentioned, the loop gain can be somewhat higher than when a hysteresis synchronous motor is used, giving greater speed reproduction accuracy. Finally, for maximum accuracy, the system is converted to a phase comparison servo by the addition of a local standard frequency, a phase comparator, and a reference signal from the tape. The output of the phase comparator is applied through the discriminator to the control tubes and takes over control when the speed is nearly correct, the rate servo loop gain being simultaneously reduced. In this operating mode, and with the rate servo controlled by the tone wheel, the pull-in range is somewhat greater than that of the system shown in Fig. 7.5 because of the d-c motor characteristics and the use of a wide-range phase comparator. With the rate servo controlled by a reference from the tape, the system becomes comparable to that of Fig. 7.6 and is capable of pulling into phase lock despite large errors in recording speed.

For telemetry subcarrier recording, the recorded tape speed control signal is obtained from a 17-kc crystal oscillator, amplitude modulated by 60 cps derived from a 3.84-kc crystal oscillator and a six-stage binary divider. The same 3.84-kc oscillator and divider furnish the 60-cps reference for the playback phase comparison system. Clipping the 17-kc signal to remove the amplitude modulation and division by 4 produce a 4250-cps signal usable as the rate servo control signal.

The phase comparison servo was initially developed for recording of broadcast programs where it is essential that integrated timing accuracy be very high, in the order of a very few seconds in 30 min. It is most useful in instrumentation work when exceptionally high accuracy of frequency reproduction is necessary or when long time intervals between recorded events must be precisely preserved. When a phase comparison servo is used in playback, the recording speed must be controlled within the limits imposed by the playback servo, both with respect to average speed and rate of change of speed.

Discriminator Servos. The frequency of a reference signal derived from the tape may be sensed by a discriminator to furnish a d-c signal for control purposes. Speed control can be effected by the voltage-controlled oscillator, amplifier, and synchronous capstan motor, or by field current control of a d-c motor. A block diagram for this type of servo with a synchronous capstan motor is given in Fig. 7.7. A reference frequency is recorded on the tape and in reproduction is amplified by a limiting amplifier and supplied to the discriminator circuit to produce a d-c output control voltage. In the system of the figure, the output voltage controls the frequency of the 60-cps oscillator, whose output is amplified to drive the capstan motor. The discriminator used is generally a tuned-circuit one to achieve maximum rate of change of d-c output for a given input frequency change. A high degree of linearity is not necessary, and the steep slope characteristic provides system gain without d-c amplification. The center frequency of the discriminator is adjusted to correspond to the frequency of the reference signal recorded on the tape. Tuned-circuit discriminators can readily be constructed to operate over the range of

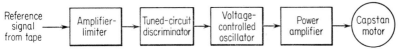

Fig. 7.7. Discriminator speed control servo.

50 or 100 cps to frequencies well beyond those used in tape recording, so that there is great latitude in the choice of the reference frequency. A deviation of the reproduced reference frequency from the center frequency of the discriminator generates an output d-c voltage of such polarity as to shift the frequency of the voltage-controlled oscillator in the proper direction to correct the tape speed. Clamps are necessary on the voltage supply to the controlled oscillator so that, in starting the tape, speed will be brought up to a point at which it is within the control range of the discriminator.

Because it senses frequency rather than phase, this type of system is a rate servo rather than a positional servo. Drift of the voltage-controlled oscillator introduces a small frequency error which corresponds to a speed error in this system, as distinct from the phase comparison servo in which controlled oscillator drift merely causes a shift in phase between the tape-derived signal and the standard. Discriminator drifts would produce the same effect but are negligible in a well-designed unit. This type of servo acts to reduce by a factor equal to the servo loop gain the departure of the recording tape speed from its nominal value. It causes the reproducing speed to be equal to the recording speed within this tolerance. Loop gains of 10 to 15 are readily attained, so that a recording speed 1 per cent off from the proper value will be duplicated within 0.07 to 0.1 per cent. Recorded frequencies are reproduced within the same tolerance limits as the tape speed, but integrated timing error can become rather large over long periods of time. Consequently the discriminator servo is primarily useful when frequency accuracy of a small fraction of a per cent is desired but integrated timing accuracy is not necessary.

The chief advantage of the discriminator servo is that it can be designed to pull in over a wide range of recording-speed error. It is therefore usable when circumstances prevent accurate control of tape speed in the recording system. Fewer components and simpler circuitry are involved in the discriminator system as compared with the phase comparison system.

In the preceding servo discussion only two methods of controlling the speed of the capstan motor have been mentioned. Obviously others can be used, such as a saturable reactor controlling the voltage applied to an induction motor. Such systems have been suggested a number of times to obviate some of the stability difficulties encountered in the system design when the oscillator-amplifier and hysteresis synchronous motor are used. However, the very fact that the oscillator–power-amplifier control systems are bulky and wasteful of power seems to have contributed greatly to their use. The size and weight of the components in the systems of Figs. 7.3 and 7.5 to 7.7, inclusive, make it unthinkable to incorporate the control physically in the tape transport. It follows immediately that a hysteresis synchronous motor drive is desirable so that the transport alone can be used, with capstan-motor power derived from the line, in those situations in which precise speed control is not essential. Only the systems of Figs. 7.1, 7.2, and 7.4, in which the entire speed control system can be physically incorporated in the tape transport without undue increase in size and weight, are entirely suitable for all-round use with servo speed control. The system of Fig. 7.2 is equivalent to synchronous motor drive without servo if the line frequency is used as reference. With a precision reference frequency, control is inherently as accurate as that achieved by any of the other phase comparison systems.

7.3 Control Signal Frequency

Choice of the control signal frequency has an appreciable bearing on system flexibility and to some degree affects equipment complexity. A 60-cps control frequency is suitable in those instances in which the playback speed must always be equal to the recording speed. Telemetry recording is a typical example; there is no reason, in standard FM/FM and PDM systems, for playback at speeds other than the recording speeds. In certain other special-purpose systems, there is the possibility of recording a multiple or submultiple of 60 cps to achieve a definite fixed ratio of recording to playback speed, and in such cases a limited degree of flexibility in speed changing can be achieved.

In general-purpose equipment and in systems which are not permanently committed to a specific application, it is highly desirable to achieve maximum flexibility in speed control. This requires a relatively high reference frequency. Specifically, the reference should be equal to the comparison frequency multiplied by the maximum speed ratio that will ever be used. The comparison frequency should be relatively low because of the pull-in considerations previously mentioned and is usually selected in the range of 30 to 100 cps. Since speed ratios as large as several hundred are quite feasible, reference signal frequencies in the range of 12 to 40 kc are indicated.

Reference frequencies in this region can also be used for flutter compensation, and so the best arrangement would appear to comprise a reference frequency chosen for flutter compensation purposes, with a frequency divider chain reducing this to a suitable value for the comparison frequency in the speed control servo. Switch or push-button selection of the division ratio can then be used to achieve playback servo speed control at any desired speed.

A straightforward series of binary dividers, as indicated in Fig. 7.2, provides a series of speeds in successive 2:1 ratios. The more convenient speed ratios in a 1:2:5:10 series can also be readily established by a combination of 2:1 and 10:1 dividers. Figure 7.8 shows one system which can provide operation over a 2000:1 speed range, using a reference frequency of 54 kc at 60-ips recording speed and proportional values at other speeds. The reference is the same as the normal carrier center frequency for wideband FM recording and can be used also for flutter compensation. Table 7.1 shows the reference frequency, dividers in use, and comparison frequency at a number of tape speeds. While it is not likely that any one system would cover such a wide speed range, the table applies equally well to equipment operating over any portion of the range. Two different comparison frequencies, 54 and 67.5 cps, are used to simplify the reference frequency divider chain. The 8:1 and 10:1 dividers indicated in the local frequency standard chain can actually be a single group of four binary stages, three being used for the 8:1 ratio and the four in any conventional manner for the 10:1 ratio.

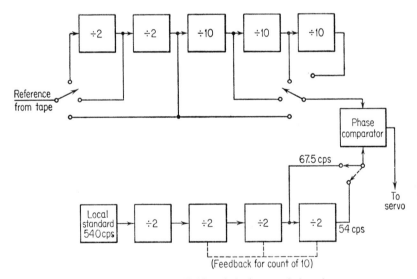

Fig. 7.8.   Frequency divider chain for speed changing.

TABLE 7.1

Tape speed, ips	Reference frequency	Dividers in use	Comparison frequency, cps
120	108 kc	2, 10, 10, 10	54
60	54	10, 10, 10	54
30	27	2, 2, 10, 10	67.5
15	13.5	2, 10, 10	67.5
12	10.8	2, 10, 10	54
7½	6.75	10, 10	67.5
6	5.4	10, 10	54
3	2.7	2, 2, 10	67.5
1½	1350 cps	2, 10	67.5
1.2	1080	2, 10	54
¾	675	10	67.5
0.6	540	10	54
0.3	270	2, 2	67.5
0.15	135	2	67.5
0.12	108	2	54
0.06	54	None	54

7.4 System Speed Control Considerations

It can be seen from the previous discussion that tape speed control is a system problem, and the recording and playback controls must be chosen in the light of the over-all reproduction performance desired and the limitations that may be imposed by power sources available for the recording equipment. When the utmost precision is required, particularly with respect to integrated timing accuracy, a phase comparison servo must be used in playback, if for no other reason than to remove the effect of dimensional changes in the tape. It then becomes necessary to select the recording-speed control in accordance with the capabilities of the playback control system, particularly with respect to its pull-in range. If this is small, then precise control of the recording speed is necessary, and a precision-frequency capstan-motor power supply or a tone-wheel phase-comparison servo is indicated for the recording system.

On the other hand, if system performance requirements are satisfied by reproduction of recorded frequencies with an accuracy of ¼ or ½ per cent or better and if environmental circumstances make close control of recording speed difficult, then the discriminator servo may be used in playback, and recording speed allowed to vary by as much as ±5 per cent or even more from its nominal value. If power supply, recording time, and size and weight restrictions make it difficult or impossible to achieve precise control of recording speed and if best possible reproduction accuracy is desired, then a phase comparison servo with wide pull-in range, such as that of Fig. 7.6, should be used in the reproduction system.

REFERENCE

1. Erath, L. W.: A Magnetic Tape Recorder and Record Analysis System for Seismic Use, Instrument Society of America, paper 55-5-2 (presented at Instrument Conference and Exhibit of the Instrument Society of America, 1955).

CHAPTER 8

ELECTRONIC EQUIPMENT FOR RECORDING AND REPRODUCING

A tape transport with suitable heads is only a part of a recording or reproducing system. In practically every case some form of electronic gear is necessary to transform the data signal into a suitable recording current, and, in playback, amplifiers, demodulators, and other circuit elements are necessary to recover the data signal from the playback head signal. The performance of the over-all system depends just as much, and in some cases more, on the performance of the electronic components as on the tape-transport characteristics. In consequence, the design and quality of the electronic portions of a tape system are at least equal in importance to those of the tape transport. Also, electronic-component design should take into account the normal vagaries of the reproduced signal which result from the characteristics of tape and transport mechanisms, particularly with respect to level fluctuations.

8.1 Direct-recording Equipment

While the actual power that must be delivered to the head for direct recording is extremely low and might well be furnished directly from many signal sources, the necessity for bias injection, proper head driving impedance, and preemphasis, when used, makes a special recording amplifier advisable in practically all cases. Likewise, in playback, the requirements for equalization of the head-tape frequency characteristic and facilities for changing this characteristic with tape speed make the use of specially designed playback amplifiers mandatory.

Recording Amplifiers. In data recording, as contrasted with voice and music recording, there is no predetermined relationship between power level and frequency. Therefore, the preemphasis of low and high fre-

153

quencies often used in audio equipment cannot be applied in data-recording systems, and a first approximation to the correct recording arrangement is that which produces constant current in the recording head regardless of the frequency. This means that the equivalent generator impedance as seen from the head should be very high, so that variations in head impedance with frequency will not affect the recording current.

It has been previously mentioned that self-demagnetization, penetration or spacing losses, recording demagnetization, and head losses cause a reduction in the remanent flux in the tape at short wavelengths or high frequencies. Stewart [1] points out that self-demagnetization and penetration losses cannot be made up by high-frequency preemphasis of the recording current but that recording demagnetization and head losses can be partially or fully compensated by preemphasis, thus maintaining a more nearly constant tape flux than would be achieved by strictly constant-current recording. Preemphasis by more than the amount necessary to compensate for recording demagnetization and head losses is not desirable, as the limiting action which would result can introduce intermodulation products.

Thus, in direct recording for instrumentation applications, two techniques are feasible: constant-current recording or constant-current with high-frequency preemphasis to make up for recording demagnetization and recording head losses. The latter makes maximum use of the medium by achieving the closest approach possible to constant tape flux.

Figure 8.1 shows a typical circuit diagram for a constant-current recording amplifier, while Fig. 8.2 illustrates the circuit of a recording amplifier with high-frequency preemphasis. The feedback path of Fig. 8.1 is purely resistive, while that of Fig. 8.2 comprises an RC T network. This reduces feedback at high frequencies, with a consequent increase in over-all gain.

Commercially available recording amplifiers require input signals ranging from 0.1 to 1 volt rms. Input impedances are 100,000 ohms or more. A gain control is normally incorporated so that the recording-current level can be adjusted to its proper value, as specified by the equipment manufacturer. In some cases, a meter is included in each recording amplifier for measuring recording and bias currents, while in other cases a separate meter panel is furnished for this purpose. Since the bias current is much larger than the recording current, it is often necessary to shut off the bias oscillator while measuring signal recording current; to avoid this requires the use of filter circuits to eliminate the bias signal from the current measuring circuitry.

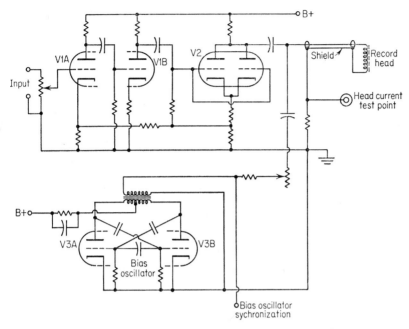

FIG. 8.1. Constant-current recording amplifier. (*Courtesy of Department of Defense.*)

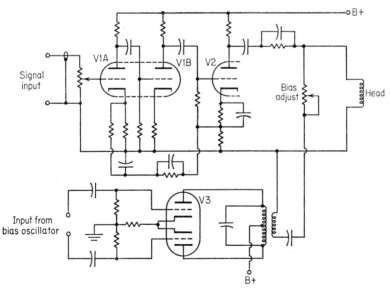

FIG. 8.2. Recording amplifier with preemphasis. (*Courtesy of Industrial Systems Division, Minneapolis-Honeywell Regulator Company.*)

Since one of the major applications of direct recording is the handling of FM/FM telemetry subcarriers, recording-amplifier input-level requirements are more or less tailored to this application. Consequently, if the output from a microphone or other transducer must be handled by direct recording, some form of a-c preamplifier or a special amplifier must be added. If the low-frequency subcarriers are not used, it is feasible, though not very desirable, to multiplex voice on the same track. A low-pass filter must be used in the voice circuit to eliminate high-frequency components, and automatic gain control or clipping circuits are preferably incorporated to prevent overloading.

Bias Sources and Injection. Bias injection in multitrack instrumentation systems is somewhat more complex than in most audio systems. A single bias oscillator to supply all recording heads results in the imposition of rather high power requirements on the bias oscillator, and suitable circuit isolation methods are necessary to avoid introduction of crosstalk between channels by way of coupling through the bias oscillator. One technique which has been used for multitrack bias injection from a single bias oscillator is indicated schematically in Fig. 8.3. In this arrangement, the ground returns of all heads are connected together and then to ground through a low-impedance winding on the bias-oscillator transformer. The bias injection transformer winding presents negligible impedance to the recording current so that no significant crosstalk is introduced between signal channels. The

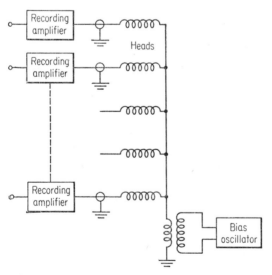

Fig. 8.3. Multitrack bias injection.

bias current flowing out of the high side of each head returns to ground by way of cable capacitance, or, if necessary, by a capacitor connected between the high side of the head and ground. The value of the cable or added capacitance is adjusted to approximately series-resonate the head inductance to the bias frequency, and thus the capacitive reactance is quite high at signal frequencies.

This arrangement requires a minimum number of vacuum tubes but has one serious drawback in that it is difficult to adjust the bias current individually for the different tracks. For best results, such individual adjustment is desirable to make up for inevitable small production variations in individual head characteristics. Also, in an actual equipment, the lengths of all cables connecting the heads to the recording amplifiers are not likely to be the same, and it is necessary either to install equal-length cables or provide padding capacitors for the short-cable connections. Making all cables of equal length generally results in added bulk, weight, and cost. Adding capacitors to make up for the shorter-length cables involves tailoring each circuit to fit the installed cable length. This is sometimes satisfactory but is often undesirable.

Separate independent bias oscillators for each track are not feasible, because there is sufficient coupling between tracks to produce beats between the various oscillator frequencies which would fall in the signal frequency band and be recorded. Coupling between bias oscillators can be introduced to cause them to synchronize (Fig. 8.1). A single low-power bias oscillator, in conjunction with an individual bias amplifier associated with each recording amplifier, provides an excellent arrangement for bias injection, although more components are necessary than in circuits in which all heads are driven directly from one bias oscillator. The bias amplifiers for each track provide a convenient means for individual adjustment of bias current. If these amplifiers are single-ended, particular attention must be paid to linearity, so that no appreciable even harmonic distortion is introduced. The recording amplifier circuit of Fig. 8.2 includes a bias amplifier $V3$.

Playback Amplifiers. The playback amplifier is the most critical element in a direct-recording system. The signal recovered from the playback head at minimum frequency is generally in the order of a fraction of a millivolt, so that very high gain in this frequency region is necessary. Noise in the first stage of the playback amplifier is a major factor in determining over-all signal-to-noise ratio and hence must be held to a minimum. To equalize the nonuniform tape-head frequency characteristic, the playback amplifier gain must rise at approximately 6 db per octave from a midfrequency turnover point to the minimum signal frequency of interest. Usually this means that the amplifier gain is at or near its maximum value in the region of the normal 60- and 120-cps hum components, so that great care must be exercised to keep hum sources at an extremely low level.

The frequency response required of the channel, and in particular the lower limit of the flat frequency range, has a great bearing on playback amplifier design. For telemetry FM subcarrier recording, frequencies below 300 cps are not used, and noise due to hum pickup can be greatly reduced by allowing the frequency response of the tape recording channel to fall off below 300 cps. Of course, the roll-off below 300 cps must not introduce an excessively nonlinear phase characteristic in the 360- to 440-cps region, where the lowest-frequency subcarrier is located.

When the lower limit of flat frequency response is required to be below 300 cps, meticulous attention must be paid to hum sources, and the attainable signal-to-noise ratios are often lower than those in systems with a 300-cps minimum.

In all cases, it is essential that both leads from the playback head terminals be carried to the input terminals of the playback amplifier and that only a single ground connection be used for the head and input circuit. Naturally, head leads must be shielded, and in some system assemblies this requirement makes necessary the use of pre-amplifiers located close to the heads, or double-shielded cable with a driven inner shield, to avoid head-cable resonance within the signal frequency band. Sometimes head resonance is used to assist in high-frequency equalization; if this is done in an FM subcarrier recording system, the head resonant frequency must be well above the maximum frequency FM carrier band to prevent the introduction of phase non-linearities.

Equalization for the nonuniform frequency characteristic of the head-tape combination must, as already mentioned, be accomplished primarily in the playback amplifier. Equalization networks may be incorporated in the normal forward path of the amplifier, in feedback networks, or both. A single RC integrating network in the forward path or a corresponding differentiating network in a feedback path will take care of the 6-db-per-octave rise of signal in the low-frequency portion of the head-tape frequency characteristic. Additional circuit elements in this portion of the equalizing network are usually desirable to stop the rise in gain of the playback amplifier below the minimum signal frequency to be handled. Another way of handling this problem consists in proportioning the normal interstage coupling elements so that the gain falls off below the minimum signal frequency desired, although this technique cannot be used with low-frequency feedback equalization because of the phase shift introduced.

If extremely flat frequency response to the upper frequency limit of the system is required, a single RC circuit is not sufficient for high-frequency equalization, even when preemphasis is used in the recording amplifier. Two RC circuits, or one RC plus a peaking coil arrangement, will permit equalization to a wavelength of 0.5 or 0.6 mil with a playback head having a 0.25-mil gap. Equalization to 0.5 mil (120 kc) at 60 ips may be difficult because of head self-resonance, particularly if over-all system considerations such as low-speed playback dictate the use of the maximum possible number of turns on the playback head. In some instances this problem has been dodged by the use of different heads for high-speed and low-speed playback. This is primarily a matter of head design and system application, rather than playback amplifier design per se.

One typical example of a playback amplifier using the driven-shield technique is shown in Fig. 8.4. A double-shielded coaxial cable connects the head to the playback amplifier, and the inner shield is connected to the cathode of the first stage. Since the cathode resistor is unbypassed, the inner shield is at essentially the same potential as the tube grid and cable inner conductor, so that no cable capacitance is effective across the head winding. Capacitance between the inner and

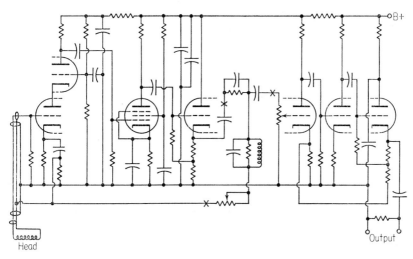

Fig. 8.4. Playback amplifier for direct recording. (*Courtesy of Department of Defense.*)

outer cable shields is shunted across the cathode-to-ground impedance and thus has negligible effect. Equalization circuits are switched by relay contacts at points marked "x" so as to provide for two tape speeds. The relay is controlled by the tape speed switch on the tape transport, which in this case provides for only a 2:1 speed change by a front-panel electrical switch.

Figure 8.5 shows a transistor preamplifier and vacuum-tube amplifier combination for tape playback. The preamplifiers are mounted in the tape transport close to the head stacks so that cable capacitance is held to a minimum. The impedance level at the output of the preamplifier is quite low so that capacitance in the cable connecting the preamplifier to the remainder of the system is relatively unimportant and long cable runs can be tolerated. This arrangement permits the use of single shielded cable throughout, simplifying connections and particularly alleviating the patch-panel problem when such a panel is needed in the system. In this equipment, equalization for various tape speeds is selected by means of a front-panel rotary switch, up to six settings being possible to correspond to six tape speeds. The equipment is designed to operate with a tape transport which has front-panel switch selection of two to six speeds.

For hum reduction, at least the first one or two stages of a vacuum-tube amplifier must have d-c heater supply. In the case of transistor amplifiers or preamplifiers, circuit part values and head inductance

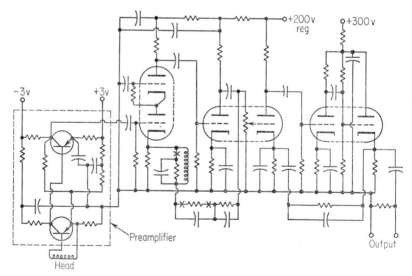

Fig. 8.5. Playback amplifier with transistor preamplifier. (*Courtesy of Industrial Systems Division, Minneapolis-Honeywell Regulator Company.*)

should be properly matched for minimum noise, as pointed out by Middlebrook [2].

The normal output signal delivered by commercial playback amplifiers is in the range of 1 to 4 volts across a 600-ohm load. A gain control is usually provided and is convenient for adjusting output level. These amplifiers are generally designed in plug-in form and a group of them operated from a common power supply.

8.2   FM Carrier Equipment

For FM carrier recording, it is necessary that the original data signal be converted to a modulated FM carrier prior to recording on the tape and that the signal recovered from the tape be demodulated or discriminated to recover the original signal. If electronic flutter compensation is used, an additional fixed frequency must be recorded and provision made in the playback discriminators for injection of the flutter compensation signal.

FM Recording Oscillators.   The ordinary component for wideband FM carrier recording comprises a signal amplifier, an oscillator whose frequency varies in accordance with a signal voltage applied to it, and an output amplifier or impedance changer as a head driving source. Nomenclature for this assemblage is not uniform in the industry, but the term *FM recording oscillator* will be used herein. For multiplexed FM recording, it is common practice to use the frequency-modulated oscillators developed for telemetry purposes, which are almost universally termed *subcarrier oscillators*.

Wideband FM Recording Oscillators.   These oscillators are used for the recording of one signal channel per tape track, and frequency deviations of 20 to 40 per cent are most common, although deviations as large as 75 per cent are used. Several types of vacuum-tube circuits have been used commercially for these oscillators, typical ones being the multivibrator, the modified phantastron oscillator, and another type which achieves an operating cycle similar to the phantastron by means of different circuitry. Circuits using transistors and saturable magnetic cores have been developed.

The multivibrator has been treated fairly extensively in the literature [3–5] and, while still used as a subcarrier oscillator, has been generally replaced by other types in wideband applications. Linearity is difficult to attain in the multivibrator for large-percentage frequency deviations.

The phantastron was first introduced as a time-delay circuit, and its use in this connection is discussed in the literature [6]. Like the multivibrator, it may be operated as a "one-shot" device or as a continuous-running oscillator. Figure 8.6 shows an elementary diagram of the phantastron as a free-running oscillator, using a standard pentode. In such a circuit, the control grid potential determines the cathode current, while the suppressor grid and relative plate-screen potentials determine the division of cathode current between screen and plate. When the suppressor is at ground potential (or above) and the plate above the screen potential, normal plate current flows; if the suppressor becomes appreciably negative, plate current is cut off and the entire cathode current is diverted to the screen. As the plate potential drops below that of the screen (suppressor at ground), the proportion of cathode current taken by the screen rises, while that passing through to the plate falls.

Now, with normal electrode potentials, the circuit acts as an integrator, with the plate potential decreasing at a rate proportional to the input voltage E. When the plate voltage falls to a point somewhat below the screen voltage, screen current begins to increase, causing a drop in screen potential which is conveyed to the suppressor by the suppressor-screen coupling capacitor. The drop in suppressor potential further reduces the plate current and increases the screen current. This cumulative action causes a rapid switching of current from plate to screen, resulting in plate-current cutoff and a rise in plate potential to the plate supply voltage. The screen current and voltage are now stabilized momentarily, and the suppressor rises toward ground potential. When the suppressor voltage rises sufficiently, plate current begins to flow, and screen current decreases with a resulting rise in screen and suppressor potentials, causing a further increase in plate current and another switching action which restores the normal division of current between plate and screen. The integrating action, with plate voltage rundown, is now resumed.

The rundown of plate voltage due to the integrating action is quite linear, and so long as the triggering voltages are constant the time required for the rundown is inversely proportional to the applied

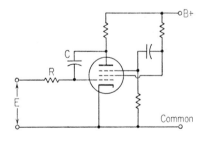

Fig. 8.6. Simplified phantastron oscillator.

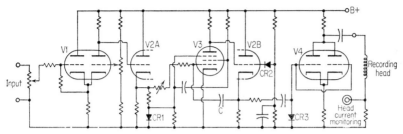

Fig. 8.7. Phantastron FM recording oscillator. (*Courtesy of Department of Defense.*)

voltage E. The total period is the integrating time plus the "flyback" time, which is mostly the time required to recharge capacitor C. If the flyback time can be made negligible as compared with the integrating time, then the total period becomes inversely proportional to the input E, and the frequency is directly proportional to E. Thus, large-percentage frequency deviations are possible with good linearity.

The flyback time is not small in the simple circuit of Fig. 8.6, and so practical circuits use special methods to recharge the integrating capacitor C quickly. Two such circuits are shown in Figs. 8.7 and 8.8. The first of these makes use of a cathode follower in the manner shown in the previous reference [6]. $V3$ is the phantastron oscillator, and when its plate voltage rises the cathode follower conducts heavily to charge C quickly. In Fig. 8.8, the screen-suppressor coupling is omitted, the transformer serving to couple the screen voltage pulse to the cathode follower to cause recharging of the integrating capacitor. In both circuits diodes are used to clamp the maximum plate potential to a fixed value. In both circuits also a large d-c

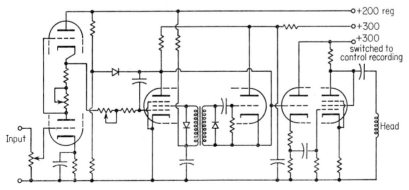

Fig. 8.8. Modified phantastron FM recording oscillator. (*Courtesy of Industrial Systems Division, Minneapolis-Honeywell Regulator Company.*)

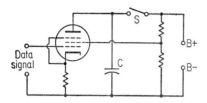

Fɪɢ. 8.9. FM oscillator,
simplified schematic.

voltage is applied to the input resistor of the integrator. This improves center frequency stability but makes necessary a sizable signal voltage to produce large frequency deviations. Thus, a d-c amplifier is used in each case to provide 1-volt input signal sensitivity for 40 per cent deviation.

A change in the d-c component of input voltage affects both the center frequency and the percentage deviation for a given modulating voltage, as does a change in the resistor R (Fig. 8.6). Consequently, they are not entirely suitable as center frequency adjustments because they affect the deviation sensitivity as well. The integrating capacitor C, however, can be adjusted to change the center frequency without changing the percentage modulation produced by a specific input signal. Thus, for complete independence of center frequency and sensitivity adjustments, the capacitor C should be used for center frequency adjustment, and a gain control at the input to the preceding d-c amplifier should be used for sensitivity adjustment. At low carrier frequencies such control may not be feasible, however, because of the limitations of trimmer capacitors.

Another interesting frequency-modulated oscillator [30] is shown in extremely simplified form in Fig. 8.9. If the switch S is closed momentarily, capacitor C will be charged to the supply potential and will then discharge through the pentode at a constant current rate determined by the instantaneous amplitude of the data signal connected to the pentode grid. When the capacitor voltage falls to a predetermined fixed level, the switch S is again momentarily actuated to recharge the capacitor. It will be readily seen that the performance of this circuit will be quite similar to that of the phantastron oscillator, the time required for the capacitor voltage to run down from its maximum to minimum values being inversely proportional to the magnitude of the data signal, thus resulting in a frequency that is directly proportional to this magnitude. The recharging time of the capacitor must be kept small in comparison with the discharge time if the proportionality between frequency and input voltage is to be accurately maintained. The high effective plate impedance of the pentode, increased by the unbypassed cathode resistor, assures constant current discharge and resultant linear rundown of capacitor voltage.

The actual switching circuit is shown in more detail in Fig. 8.10 and utilizes tubes $V2$ and $V3$. When the capacitor C is charged, the cathodes of $V2A$ and $V3B$ are at fairly high potential and these tube sections are cut off. $V3A$ is conducting and holds the grid of $V3B$ at a point below the cathode potential. Since the plate of $V3A$ is low, the cathode follower $V2B$ holds the grid of $V2A$ below its cathode potential to maintain the cutoff condition of this tube. Capacitor C discharges through the pentode $V1$, and when its potential falls sufficiently, tube section $V3B$ begins to conduct. The fall of plate potential on $V3B$ carries the grid of $V3A$ negative, and the interconnections between $V3A$ and $V3B$ cause a regenerative action which rapidly cuts off $V3A$, causing its plate to rise to $B+$. Through cathode follower $V2B$, the grid of $V2A$ is carried to a high potential, causing this tube section to conduct heavily and recharge capacitor C very rapidly. When the recharging is complete, $V3A$ begins to conduct and again regenerative action brings $V3A$ to its normal conducting condition and cuts off $V3B$, along with $V2A$. The discharge of C through the pentode then proceeds for the next cycle. It will be noted that the grid of $V3B$ is at a higher potential than that of $V2A$, so that $V2A$ does not conduct until after the regenerative triggering of $V3$.

The schematic of Fig. 8.10 covers the oscillator portion only. The oscillator is preceded by an amplifier to furnish 1 volt rms sensitivity at the signal input, and an output amplifier furnishes current to the recording head. In one seismic-recording application for which this oscillator was designed, the center frequency is 4000 cps, and the oscillator is deviated ±75 per cent, the upper and lower deviation limits thus being 7000 and 1000 cps, respectively. Data frequencies up to 500 cps are accommodated.

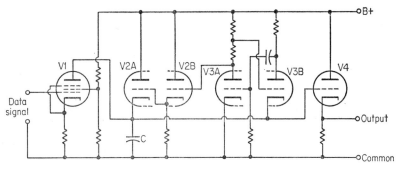

FIG. 8.10.   FM oscillator.   (*Courtesy of Southwestern Industrial Electronics Co.*)

Another capacitor-discharge oscillator has been described by Bengston [7]. This employs a blocking oscillator for capacitor charging, and two triodes in series control the discharge rate in accordance with the modulating signal. No separate d-c amplifier is necessary, as deviation sensitivity of 100 kc per volt input can be obtained.

Subcarrier Oscillators. Many types of subcarrier oscillators have been developed for telemetry use. These are, of course, applicable to multiplexed FM recording on tape. There are three broad classes: inductance-controlled, voltage-controlled, and resistance (or bridge)-controlled. Various vacuum-tube circuits are covered quite extensively in the literature [3, 8].

Inductance-controlled oscillators are used with variable-inductance transducers, in which the quantity being measured varies the inductance of the pickup. This, in turn, changes the oscillator frequency.

Voltage-controlled oscillators are used with transducers giving electrical output signals or for data sources which are electrical in nature. These oscillators may be divided into two groups. One of them comprises a conventional oscillator circuit such as the Hartley or Colpitts, with a control tube to vary the frequency in accordance with the signal voltage. These are used for the lower-frequency subcarrier bands, where it is essential that the oscillator output be quite free of harmonics to avoid introduction of noise and crosstalk into higher-frequency bands. The second group consists of the multivibrator oscillators which are used for the subcarrier bands ranging from 22 to 70 kc. Since the multivibrator output is essentially a square wave and thus rich in harmonics, suitable filters must be used with these oscillators for the bands up to and including 40 kc. Frequency is again varied by means of a control tube which determines the grid voltage of the multivibrator tubes.

Resistance-controlled oscillators are used with strain gauges, pickups using strain-gauge sensing elements, and other types of signal source in which the primary quantity being measured produces a resistance change or a change in the balance of a resistive bridge. These are basically phase-shift oscillators in which the controlling resistive element or bridge varies the phase shift and hence controls the oscillator frequency. The oscillator furnishes excitation to the bridge or transducer.

For multiplexing a number of these subcarrier channels on a single tape track, an arrangement such as shown in Fig. 6.4 is used. The oscillator outputs are combined in a resistive adding network, and the composite signal is applied to the input of a direct-recording amplifier. The values of the various resistors in the adding network are adjusted to set up the proper relative oscillator levels, while the recording level for the composite signal is controlled by the gain control in the recording amplifier or by the use of a potentiometer in place of the fixed resistor of the adding network which is common to all oscillator output current paths.

The maximum subcarrier frequency which can be used and therefore the number of standard channels which can be accommodated on one tape track naturally depend on the tape speed. At 60 ips all the standard IRIG channels including the 70-kc one can be recorded, while at lower speeds the maximum channel frequency must be correspondingly reduced. Figure 8.11 indicates somewhat conservatively the usable channels at various tape speeds; it allows for a reference frequency for flutter compensation.

Because of continuing pressure for reduction of size, weight, and power consumption, transistors have been applied as rapidly as possible to subcarrier oscillators. The circuit of a typical resistance-controlled transistorized oscillator is shown in Fig. 8.12. Other oscillators are described by Politi [9], Foster [10], and Chwastyk [11]. Wilkinson [12] has published a study of the performance characteristics of transistorized subcarrier oscillator circuits. This indicates that most suitable performance in voltage-controlled oscillators

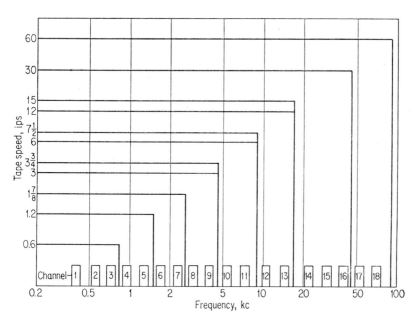

Fig. 8.11.   Usable subcarrier channels at various tape speeds.

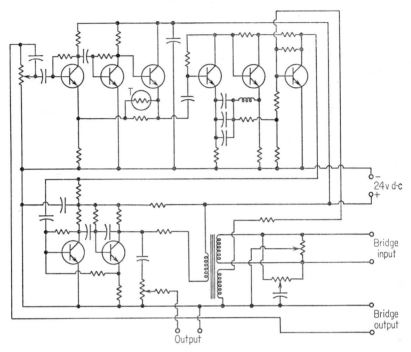

Fig. 8.12. Transistor subcarrier oscillator (resistance-controlled). (*Courtesy of Pacific Division, Bendix Aviation Corp.*)

may be obtainable with emitter-coupled multivibrators and relaxation oscillators using the unijunction transistor [13].

An oscillator utilizing transistors and a saturable magnetic core transformer has been described by Meyerhoff and Tillman [14]. It is said to be capable of operating over the entire range of standard subcarrier frequencies as well as at higher frequencies in the region of hundreds of kilocycles.

Rerecording Amplifiers. It is frequently desirable to transfer a wideband FM carrier signal from one tape to another for data analysis and reduction purposes. Sometimes this is just a matter of insurance, to protect a valuable original data tape; at other times such transfer is necessary for editing purposes or to transfer an originally recorded signal from a reel of tape to a loop for detailed analysis.

Of course, this can be accomplished by demodulation and remodulation, using playback and recording equipment in tandem. Additional errors are introduced into the data signal by this process, however, and direct transfer of the modulated carrier gives higher accuracy. We have seen previously that the head-tape frequency characteristic

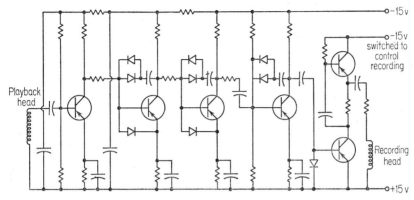

Fig. 8.13. Rerecording amplifier. (*Courtesy of Industrial Systems Division, Minneapolis-Honeywell Regulator Company.*)

introduces amplitude modulation on the wideband FM signal. To avoid compounding this amplitude variation, the signal from the playback head must be completely limited before being delivered to the recording head.

Amplification and limiting of the playback head signal are functions which are also necessary in an FM discriminator; thus, a rerecording amplifier is made up of the limiting amplifier used in a discriminator and a subsequent recording-head driver stage giving sufficient output to saturate the tape. The desirable limiting amplifier characteristics are discussed in the section on FM discriminators.

A transistorized rerecording amplifier is shown in Fig. 8.13.

FM Discriminators. The term *discriminator* is used somewhat loosely in connection with tape recording and telemetering systems to denote an electronic package that includes a limiting amplifier, an FM-AM conversion device which may be called a discriminator or demodulator, a low-pass filter for separating signal from carrier components, output amplifiers, and frequently a power supply. A block diagram is

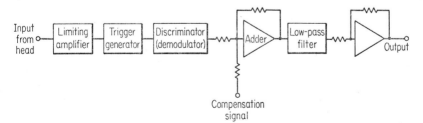

Fig. 8.14. Wideband FM discriminator block diagram.

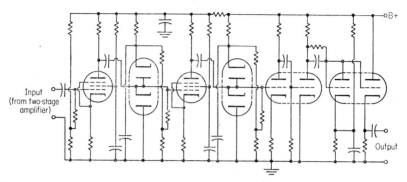

Fig. 8.15.   Vacuum-tube limiting amplifier.   (*Courtesy of Southwestern Industrial Electronics Company.*)

shown in Fig. 8.14.   In the "subcarrier discriminator" there is included also a bandpass filter to select one particular subcarrier from the composite subcarrier signal.

Wideband FM Discriminators.   As the name implies, these are used for the reproduction of wideband FM tape recordings.   They are distinguished from subcarrier discriminators in three respects: They contain no input bandpass filter, require considerably less input signal for full quieting, and are capable of linear demodulation with frequency deviations of 20 to 75 per cent.

The limiting amplifier of such a discriminator must have sufficient gain to accept at its input the minimum expected signal from the tape playback head and deliver at its output a fully limited square wave of sufficient amplitude to drive the demodulator or discriminator proper.   For operation over a wide range of tape speeds, it is desirable that the full limiting action should be attained with an input signal in the region of a few microvolts.   Playback-head signal voltages in the 15- to 60-ips speed range are normally in the order of 5 to 20 mv for tape recorded to saturation.   This signal level will drop by a factor of 20 db (10:1) for a 10:1 reduction in speed.   Since 100:1 speed reductions are neither impractical nor uncommon and since at least 20 db additional leeway is desirable to eliminate any effect from playback-signal-level variations, it becomes apparent that the desirable sensitivity level is roughly 60 db below the maximum signal at top tape speeds.

The amplifier should have linear or zero phase shift over the entire frequency range encompassed by the carrier and its sidebands.   Again, for a wide range of tape speeds, this indicates flat amplitude and linear phase response from a few hundred cycles to about 70 kc.

Finally, limiting should be symmetrical about the zero axis of the input signal, and there should be no d-c shift of this zero axis at any point in the amplifier. These characteristics are necessary to avoid sensitivity to amplitude modulation of the input signal. Such sensitivity may be evidenced by either increased noise or shift of the output d-c zero level.

Figures 8.13 and 8.15 show typical vacuum-tube and transistor limiting amplifiers. The diodes provide limiting.

Performance of a limiting amplifier can probably best be appraised by a noise-quieting and d-c level plot for various input voltages, such as the representative one shown in Fig. 8.16. For the particular discriminator used in this test, the output noise was more than 40 db below full-scale output for a 2-μv carrier input. At 10-μv input the noise was down 50 db and at 50 μv more than 60 db. The d-c zero output level stabilizes at about 2-μv input and changes by less than 0.1 per cent for inputs from 2 μv to 1 mv. Some fragmentary data taken with amplitude-modulated input signals indicates that, with this type of discriminator, the output noise level will rise by 3 to 6 db for amplitude modulation up to 50 per cent and modulating frequencies up to 1 kc. Tests to show the effects of amplitude modulation are desirable but very difficult to make, as the amplitude modulator must

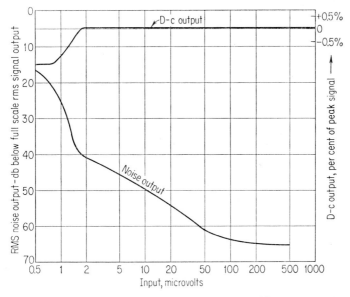

Fig. 8.16. Discriminator noise-quieting characteristic. (*Courtesy of Industrial Systems Division, Minneapolis-Honeywell Regulator Company.*)

not introduce more than about 0.01 per cent frequency modulation if measurements are to be accurate within 1 db to the 60-db quieting level. This imposes severe design requirements on the amplitude modulator.

In discriminators used for wideband or subcarrier reproduction, cycle-counting or locked-oscillator demodulators, rather than tuned-circuit ones, are used to achieve the best possible linearity. The cycle-counting discriminators generate one (or in some cases two) constant-energy pulses for each carrier input cycle. The most common circuit for generating these pulses is a one-shot multivibrator. To maintain constant energy in each output pulse, the voltage swings of the multivibrator are clamped by means of diodes, and careful circuit design is necessary to assure constancy of pulse duration. In so far as the design achieves truly constant energy in each output pulse, the average output of the discriminator is linearly proportional to the number of pulses occurring per second and therefore to the input frequency. Static linearities of 0.1 per cent are not extremely difficult to attain.

Since most one-shot multivibrators prefer to be triggered by pulses rather than a square-wave input, a trigger generating circuit is normally used between the output of the limiting amplifier and the multivibrator. See the discriminator block diagram of Fig. 8.14. Such a trigger generator can be arranged to generate either one or two pulses per cycle of the input carrier. Since multivibrator performance may be affected by the amplitude of the triggering pulses, a Schmitt trigger or equivalent circuit is preferable to simple differentiation of the limiting amplifier output. While this output may be thoroughly limited as far as its maximum values are concerned, the transition time from one maximum to the other will be dependent upon the amplitude of the input signal and therefore simple differentiation gives a train of pulses of varying amplitude.

In some discriminators a Schmitt trigger followed by a differentiator, phase inverter, and full wave rectifier has been used in place of the multivibrator. The available discriminator output with this arrangement is often too small to constitute a useful output signal, and d-c gain is required after the discriminator. With simple d-c amplifier circuits the stability and linearity may be degraded. The multivibrator circuits furnish sufficient energy so that a useful output is still available after filtering to remove the carrier and its sidebands. Thus the circuits following the discriminator need do nothing except accomplish the necessary impedance transformations to fit the filter and output requirements. Since no gain is necessary, these circuits can be feedback-stabilized, and relatively simple arrangements will give adequate zero stability, gain stability, and linearity. Gain stability and static linearity are functions only of the discriminator and output circuits, while zero stability is dependent on the limiting amplifier as well. Dynamic linearity is dependent on the phase response of the limiting amplifier as well as the performance of the remainder of the discriminator.

It has been mentioned that a low-pass filter is necessary in the output circuitry to separate the desired signal from the carrier and sidebands. To a first approximation at least, this filter determines the frequency and transient response of the entire system. The filter must offer a fairly high rejection (in the neighborhood of 80 db) at the effective carrier frequency at the output of the discriminator. Hence, if the discriminator generates two pulses for each input carrier cycle, the input carrier frequency is effectively doubled by the discriminator, and this simplifies to some degree the output-filter design problem. It is well known that, with a given rate of rejection outside the passband, the overshoot and ringing of the filter output will increase as the frequency response in the passband is made flatter. Hence, it is often desirable to tailor the discriminator output filter to the data problem at hand. For this reason plug-in output filters are frequently used so that they can be conveniently changed.

For wideband FM carrier work, the output-filter cutoff frequency, in kilocycles, is generally one-sixth of the tape speed in inches per second. This data signal bandwidth can be doubled with some loss in signal-to-noise ratio.

The *phase-locked oscillator,* or *phase-locked loop,* is another form of circuit suitable for the demodulation of an FM signal. It is shown in block-diagram form in Fig. 8.17. The multiplier or phase detector gives an output dependent on the phase difference between the input signal and the voltage-controlled oscillator. This output is amplified, filtered, and then applied to the voltage-controlled oscillator to force its frequency to follow that of the input signal. The voltage

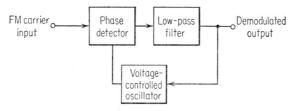

Fig. 8.17.   Phase-locked loop demodulator.

applied to the voltage-controlled oscillator is the modulation on the input signal, and this is the desired demodulated output.

This type of demodulator has been shown [17, 19, 20] to have a lower noise-improvement threshold than the cycle-counting demodulator. Therefore, it can be expected to give improved output accuracy when input signal-to-noise ratio is the limiting factor governing output-signal accuracy. In telemetry, in consequence, there is often an advantage in using this demodulator.

By contrast, the signal-to-noise ratio for a wideband FM carrier recovered from tape is very good except for the brief periods of deep dropouts. In this case, then, noise-improvement threshold is less important than linearity in the demodulator. In the phase-locked loop, the voltage-controlled oscillator is in the feedback path, and any nonlinearities in its characteristic will be present in the output signal. Also, the output of the multiplier or phase detector is linearly proportional to the phase difference, between the input and oscillator, only over a limited range; this range is appreciably less than the $+\pi/2$ to $-\pi/2$ locking range. Holding the phrase error to this smaller linear range imposes additional restrictions on the design of the system.

Compensation. The use of simple subtractive compensation in a system requires that the gain of each signal discriminator be adjusted to the correct value up to the point of injection of the compensation signal and that the phase response be the same in all signal channels and the compensation channel throughout the range of data frequencies. The phase response is normally a function only of passive circuit components such as resistors and capacitors, and if stable units are used in the critical circuit locations, the phase response is a "factory adjustment," requiring readjustment only at very long intervals to compensate for long-term component drift.

Adjustment of gain for compensation purposes is best accomplished by a control in the multivibrator circuit permitting variation of either the amplitude or width of the output pulse. It is desirable to introduce the compensation signal ahead of the low-pass output filter because then there are the fewest components and stages in the two paths which must be matched, and the problem of matching insertion loss, frequency characteristics, and phase characteristics of the filters is completely avoided. A single RC filter is sometimes used between the discriminator and the point at which the compensation signal is introduced. This eliminates compensation inaccuracies that may arise because of differences in high-order carrier harmonics occasioned by minute variations in the multivibrator pulse shapes.

It is to be noted that adjustment of a number of signal channels for correct compensation, as described above, results automatically in standardization of the signal channels with respect to each other, so that each channel has the same sensitivity, in terms of volts output per unit of carrier frequency deviation, and the same phase response over the data signal frequency band. Equality of the final discriminator outputs would then be dependent on the equality of the low-pass filters and the setting of level controls in the output circuits.

Subcarrier Discriminators. The subcarrier discriminator is generally similar to the wideband discriminator just discussed except for the addition of a bandpass filter or other selective device at the discriminator input to separate the desired subcarrier from the composite signal recorded on a single tape track. The subcarrier discriminator is designed to operate from the output of a telemetry receiver or a magnetic-tape-system playback amplifier and therefore does not require the high input sensitivity that is needed to permit the wideband discriminator to operate directly from a playback head. Minimum input signal capabilities, therefore, are in the vicinity of a few millivolts rather than a few microvolts.

The functions and subcircuits of a subcarrier discriminator, outside the bandpass filter, are the same as those of the wideband discriminators. In addition to multivibrator and transistor-core pulse-counting discriminator circuits, phase-locked loops are frequently used as demodulators because of the advantages in threshold level when the input signal-to-noise ratio is small. There are many detailed descriptions of subcarrier discriminators in the literature. A number of references are given at the end of the chapter [3, 8, 15–24], and additional ones are included in a bibliography published by Kiebert [25]. Subcarrier frequencies and data signal bandwidths, along with other telemetry standards, are given in "Telemetry Standards for Guided Missiles" [26].

8.3   PDM Equipment

In Chap. 3 it was pointed out that, for best results, it is desirable to differentiate the PDM signal before recording on tape and that it is then necessary to incorporate special circuitry in the reproduction equipment to reconstruct the original signal. To accomplish this, special recording and playback amplifiers are necessary.

PDM Recording Ampliers. The PDM signal available to the recorder is generally a 1- to 5-volt pulse. The recording amplifier must differentiate this pulse to generate sharp spikes of fairly short duration at the beginning and end of each of the input pulses and then generate from these spikes a current output of sufficient magnitude to saturate the tape. No bias of any sort is necessary. These functions are obviously fairly simple. In many commercial equipments, a switch is provided in the direct-recording amplifiers to permit changing the function to PDM recording. This switch disables the bias source for the track, inserts a differentiator in the circuit, and increases the current supplied to the recording head.

PDM Playback Amplifiers. It will be remembered that the signal derived from the playback head is somewhat similar to a single cycle of a sine wave, although the first rise is somewhat slow, as is the final "tail" of the signal. Crossover in the middle of the signal is reasonably fast. Since the recorded spikes are of alternate polarities, the reproduced pulses are alternately positive and negative, and negative and positive, one of which corresponds to the beginning of the original PDM pulse and the second to the end of the pulse. To reconstruct the original pulse train, it is necessary to generate new sharp pulses from the center crossovers of the reproduced signals and, with these, trigger a flip-flop or one-shot multivibrator whose output then is a replica of the original pulse applied to the recorder amplifier input.

The circuitry for accomplishing this in one way is shown in block-diagram form in Fig. 8.18. The amplifier builds up the head signal to a value sufficient to give a usable output from the differentiator. The output of the differentiator "sets" the flip-flop and also triggers "on" the one-shot multivibrator. The next trigger, of opposite polarity, "resets" the flip-flop, so that the output of the flip-flop is a pulse whose duration is equal to that of the input pulse. The one-shot multivibrator is insurance against dropouts; it is set to return to its normal condition in a time less than the pulse recurrence period but longer than the duration of the maximum full-scale PDM pulse. Therefore, if the trailing edge pulse is lost through a dropout, the flip-flop will remain set until the one-shot multivibrator returns to its

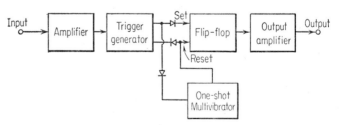

FIG. 8.18.   Block diagram, PDM playback amplifier.

normal condition and resets the flip-flop. This particular output pulse will then be obviously in error because the duration of the flip-flop output pulse will be greater than that corresponding to full-scale signal. Should a dropout eliminate the trigger corresponding to the start of the PDM pulse, the flip-flop will not be set and no output at all will be obtained. In this case the data point in a commutated system is lost. Obviously several other arrangements are possible for reconstructing the output pulse, but all perform the same functions.

If the gain of the amplifier preceding the differentiator is made very high, a point will be reached at which the highest-amplitude noise pulses present at the amplifier input will begin to trigger the reconstruction circuits. It was mentioned in Chap. 3 that it is possible to quiet a high-gain amplifier by the injection of a high-frequency signal. This permits the use of very high gain and limiting before differentiation, and this in turn provides a considerable additional improvement in performance by virtue of the resultant insensitivity to large fluctuations in signal recovered from the tape. This is always desirable in magnetic tape electronic equipment, as has been mentioned.

In the occasional applications of PDM as a carrier system, demodulation is accomplished simply by passing the flip-flop output through a low-pass filter. For reasonably high accuracy of data reproduction in this case, it is necessary that the two flip-flop output voltages corresponding to the set and reset conditions be clamped to fixed reference voltages. This establishes the zero level and pulse amplitude, so that the filtered output is accurately determined by the duty cycle of the pulse carrier.

8.4 Digital Pulse Recording

In the recording of pulses to represent information in digital form, there is no concern about amplitude accuracy, nor is waveshape preservation of particular importance. Maximum playback head voltage is desired. As a consequence, saturation recording without bias is used. Information is recorded in binary form so that only the presence or absence of a pulse, or the polarity of a pulse, need be detected.

Recording Amplifiers. For RZ recording, the recording amplifier can be very simple if the input pulse has a proper duration. In this situation, the recording amplifier is essentially an impedance converter, generating the required tape-saturation head current from the available input voltage. It can be a-c-coupled throughout and, of course, must have a suitable frequency response to pass the requisite pulse shape reasonably accurately.

In RB recording, there is the additional complication of passing a d-c biasing current through the head windings to saturate the tape while no pulse is being recorded. This is quite simple if the head has either a center-tapped winding or two separate windings, so that the bias current can be passed through one winding independently of the amplifier output current. The required amplifier output current is approximately double that used in RZ recording, in order to overcome the bias and saturate the tape in the opposite direction.

In either RZ or RB recording, if the pulse available at the amplifier input is not of the proper duration for recording, then the recording amplifier must include pulse shaping or generating circuits to give the proper pulse duration in the recording head. It was mentioned in Chap. 3 that correct pulse duration can be determined from the rule of thumb that $\frac{1}{2}$ to $1\frac{1}{2}$ mils of tape should pass the head during the recording pulse. Thus, ideally, the pulse should be tailored to the tape speed and would range from $\frac{1}{2}$- to $1\frac{1}{2}$-msec duration at 1 ips and 4 to 12 μsec for a speed of 120 ips. Any one of several standard circuit arrangements can be used for generation of the proper duration pulses.

For NRZ recording, slightly different arrangements are necessary. In this case, the output of the recording amplifier must be sufficient at all times to saturate the tape and must be reversed when necessary in accordance with the input pulse.

The input to the recording amplifier is often a train of sharp unidirectional pulses, from which must be derived the desired recording current. One arrangement for achieving this is shown in Fig. 8.19. The input pulses are amplified and used to trigger a flip-flop so that the latter changes state for each input pulse. The two flip-flop plates are d-c-coupled to a push-pull head-driving amplifier. Head current flows in one direction when the flip-flop is in one state, and in the opposite direction when the flip-flop is in its other state. It is possible to connect the recording head directly into the flip-flop circuit, but the inductance introduced by the head complicates considerably the design of the flip-flop, and it is generally better to use separate circuit elements for head-driving purposes.

Fɪɢ. 8.19. Block diagram, NRZ recording amplifier.

Circuit impedance as seen by the head should preferably be very high; in other words, the amplifier should appear as a constant-current generator. This is desirable to produce maximum rate of change of current in the head. If the amplifier output is low impedance, the head current may rise slowly, which causes the flux change pattern to be stretched out unnecessarily on the tape. For this reason, in a conventional vacuum-tube driver, it is preferable to connect the head in the plate circuit rather than the cathode circuit. Head winding to ground voltage breakdown ratings may have to be considered in such circuits, particularly when the full B supply voltage is applied between head windings and ground before the tubes warm up. An alternative arrangement operates the tube plates at ground potential with a negative supply for the cathodes. Such a circuit may, in turn, create difficulty because of heater-cathode ratings of the tubes.

In transistor head-driving circuits, the inductive voltage developed across the head as a result of the rapid change in current must be controlled so that it does not damage the transistors. The voltage pulse due to head inductance can also give difficulty in some vacuum-tube circuits. One way of controlling this voltage pulse is to connect a series capacitor and resistance across the head to give an approximately aperiodic circuit. Diodes may also be used.

Sometimes the input signal to the recording amplifier has the same form as that desired for the recording current. This occurs, for example, if one specific input level represents a 0, while a different level represents a 1, and it is desired to record with one saturation level representing 0 and the other level corresponding to a 1. In this case, the recording amplifier becomes essentially a d-c-coupled impedance changer and acts simply to transform the input voltage levels to the desired head-current levels. A somewhat unusual circuit to accomplish the desired result has been described by Shaw [27] and is shown in Fig. 8.20. With this amplifier, a 0 input, represented by zero input voltage, produces a saturating head current in one direction, while a 1 input, represented by −10 volts, produces saturating head current in the opposite direction. The input transistor operates as a switch to turn the oscillator on and off, dependent on the input voltage level. When the oscillator is on, its rectified output cuts off the normally "on" output transistor. When the output transistor is on, its collector current is divided equally between the head and resistor R, the head current flowing from the collector to ground. When the output transistor is cut off, current flows from ground through the head and resistor R to the −80-volt supply. With proper resistance values

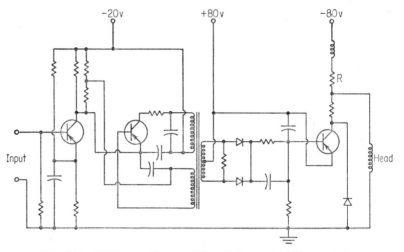

Fig. 8.20. NRZ recording amplifier. (*Courtesy of Electronics.*)

and collector current, the head current can be made the same in either direction of flow.

For recording with the phase-modulation or frequency-doubling methods, both signal pulses and clock pulses must be applied to the recording circuit. Figure 8.21 shows a circuit that will generate the phase-modulation type of NRZ recording current when the input data signal consists of a pulse for each 1 and 0 is shown by the absence of a pulse. Figure 8.22 shows the waveforms at critical points in the circuit. Each signal pulse sets the input flip-flop, overriding the clock pulse. When no signal pulse is present, the clock pulse resets the flip-flop, and it remains in the reset condition until the next signal pulse arrives. The flip-flop consequently changes state only when there is a change from 0 to 1, or 1 to 0, in the signal pulse train. Pulses derived from the flip-flop output signal are applied as inhibit signals to a gate that also receives clock pulses, delayed enough to make them coincident with the inhibit pulses. Clock pulses passed by the gate are further delayed, to make the total delay time equal to

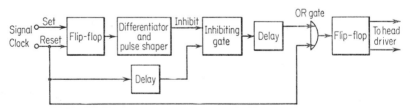

Fig. 8.21. Phase-modulation recording circuit.

half the time between clock pulses. The delayed pulses, combined in the OR gate with the original clock pulse train, trigger the final flip-flop to generate the recording-current waveform shown in the bottom line of Fig. 8.22. A final impedance-changing amplifier to drive the head is not included in the block diagram.

If the input signal consists of fixed voltages, one value representing 1 and another value representing 0, then the input flip-flop can be eliminated. The signal will have the form of the flip-flop output in Fig. 8.22, and its derivative will supply the desired inhibit pulses to control the delayed clock pulse train. The recording current in either case lags the input signal by one clock pulse period.

Recording current in the frequency-doubling method can be in either of two forms. In Fig. 3.17, there is a flux change at each cell boundary and an additional flux change at the center of the cell when a 0 occurs in the signal. For a succession of 1's, the current is a square wave at the bit frequency; for a succession of 0's, the current is a square wave at twice the bit frequency. If the bit frequency is near the maximum that can be passed by the system, the frequency corresponding to 0's will not be reproduced, and an output will be

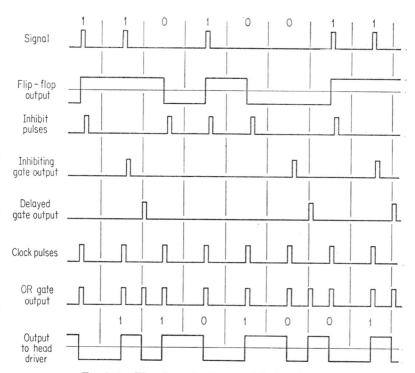

FIG. 8.22.   Waveforms in phase-modulation circuit.

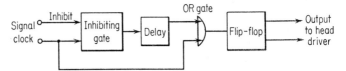

FIG. 8.23.   Frequency-doubling recording circuit.

obtained only for 1's in the signal.   A circuit capable of generating this form of recording current is outlined in Fig. 8.23; the waveforms are shown in Fig. 8.24.   The operation is apparent from the figures. The recording current is delayed by one-half the time between clock pulses.

A second form for the recording current places the center flux change in the 1 cells.   This can be generated by a circuit similar to Fig. 8.23 but with the inhibit gate omitted.   Either the signal or the clock is delayed by one-half the clock period, the two are combined, and the resultant pulse train used to trigger the output flip-flop.   The effect of such a change is readily seen in Fig. 8.24.

If the input signal consists of d-c levels rather than pulses, a slight rearrangement of Fig. 8.23 will produce either form of output current. If the clock pulses occur at the instants of signal level change, the delay must be located ahead of the gate in the clock pulse path.   The 1 level may then be used as an inhibit signal, or the 0 level as an

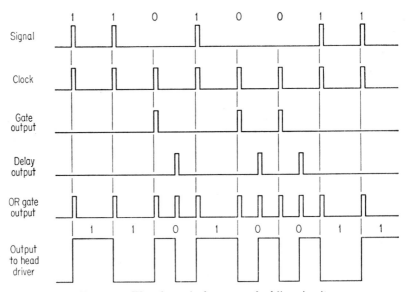

FIG. 8.24.   Waveforms in frequency-doubling circuit.

enabling signal, to produce the output form of Fig. 8.24. If the 1 level is an enabling signal or the 0 level an inhibit signal, then the alternate form of output current is generated.

Playback Amplifiers. We shall consider here as a playback amplifier only that portion of the total circuitry which furnishes output pulses from one tape track. In parallel or serial-parallel digital systems, it is frequently necessary to provide arrangements for synchronizing the output pulses from a number of tracks. Although some or all of such synchronization arrangements are often incorporated physically with the playback amplifier, they will be considered below in the section on pulse synchronization.

With this definition, it is necessary only that the playback amplifier deliver an output pulse of suitable shape for each pulse delivered from the playback head. In the case of RZ recording, it will be recalled that the head output is a dual polarity pulse, a positive-going portion being followed by a negative-going portion, or vice versa. A simple a-c-coupled amplifier with suitable bandwidth for the pulse characteristics will deliver an output pulse of the same shape as the playback head output. Inclusion of an integrator with proper time constant in the amplifier will provide an output pulse having approximately the same characteristics as the recording-current pulse. Clipping above the noise level and pulse amplitude limiting are often incorporated to provide cleaner output pulses.

With NRZ recording, the playback head signal consists of single nonreversing pulses of alternating polarities. The playback amplifier, then, must include a phase inverter and two diodes acting as a full-wave rectifier in order to deliver at the output a train of unidirectional single pulses. Clipping, limiting, or pulse shaping may also be included in the circuit to form a specific type of output pulse. There are certain instances in which an output signal of the same form as the recording current is desirable. In this event, a flip-flop must be included in the playback amplifier, and it may then be possible to dispense with the phase inverter and rectifier. The flip-flop can be triggered directly by the amplified head pulses by suitable steering of these pulses in accordance with their polarities.

With some circuit complication, use can be made of the logic inherent in the NRZ playback signal. This logic arises because each pulse of one polarity must be followed by a pulse of the opposite polarity, and these alternations of polarity must continue as long as the signal is being reproduced. By making use of this logic situation, it is at least possible to determine when a pulse is missed as a result of a dropout. The technique is also applicable to reproduction of a clock or sprocket track in which the pulses occur at regular intervals, and it is relatively simple to insert a pulse when one is missed.

Pulse Synchronization. In parallel or serial-parallel digital recording, a number of pulses are recorded simultaneously on multiple tracks across the tape. When these pulses are supplied from the tape system to other equipment, it is usually necessary that all the pulses recorded simultaneously be reproduced simultaneously. Because of tape skew and other factors mentioned in Chap. 5, a group of pulses recorded simultaneously across the tape will not appear simultaneously at the terminals of the playback heads. Equipment must therefore be incorporated in the system to generate a group of simultaneous output pulses, with the desired characteristics, from the head pulses which are scattered in time.

Each group of pulses recorded in one line across the tape is generally termed a *character*. If a clock track is used, there is always a pulse in this track for each character that might be recorded. If a clock track is not used, then it is necessary to use a character coding that will ensure that there is always at least one pulse in one track for each character, or a parity check bit must be inserted in each character to achieve the same result. Any of these three methods will ensure that there is a pulse recovered from some track for each character recorded, barring dropouts, of course. Consequently, if a clock track is not provided, it is still possible to derive a pulse train that includes a pulse for each possible character time simply by adding the outputs of all playback amplifiers. We may therefore assume the availability of a train of clock pulses for use in pulse synchronization even though there is no specific clock track included in the tape format.

The goal in pulse synchronization circuits is to permit as much time variation as possible between the pulses included in a character. It is clear offhand that, with simple circuits, the total time between the first and the last pulse of the character must not exceed one-half of the mean time between characters; otherwise, a pulse belonging to one character might slip over into another character, producing serious errors. Actually, the total permissible time spread is less than this by the amount of time which must be allotted for switching in the electronic circuits, plus an allowance for tape-speed error.

One method of output pulse synchronizing has been described by Skov [28]. It is shown in Fig. 8.25. This system operates without a clock track. For each tape track there is a playback amplifier and a flip-flop. An OR gate is connected to each flip-flop, and its output triggers a one-shot multivibrator.   The first pulse of the character that arrives sets the flip-flop in its channel, and by way of the OR gate triggers the one-shot multivibrator.   As each succeeding pulse of the character arrives, it sets the flip-flop in its channel.   The delay time of the one-shot multivibrator is adjusted for the desired duration of the *character gate*.   When this multivibrator returns to its stable condition a reset pulse is applied to all the channel flip-flops.   Those which have been set by pulses from the tape deliver output pulses, which are clearly simultaneous.   Thus, an output pulse is delivered on each output line for which a pulse was picked up from the tape, and all the output pulses occur at the same instant.   At this same instant, all the circuit elements are reset to their initial conditions, ready to receive the first pulse of the next character.

Skov points out that the optimum duration for the character gate is given by

$$T_g = \tfrac{1}{2}[P(1 - x) - r]$$

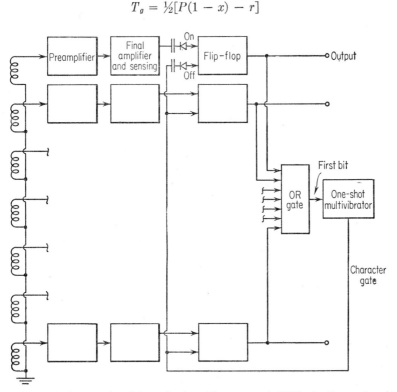

Fig. 8.25. Pulse synchronizing circuit. (*Courtesy of IBM J. Research and Develop.*)

where T_g = duration of character gate

P = nominal time between characters

x = tape-speed error

r = electronic-circuit reset time

He also shows that the minimum permissible time between characters in recording is determined from the equation

$$P_{\min} = \frac{2(T_D + T_S) + r}{1 - 2x}$$

where $T_D = 2d/V$

d = length on tape occupied by character, because of skew

V = nominal tape speed

T_S = playback time displacement from causes other than skew

A reproduction method that can tolerate character overlapping has been described by Gabor [29]. This makes use of what is termed a *circulating buffer*, which can be depicted as a rectangular array of memory elements. The signals from each tape track are supplied to a column of array elements, so that there must be as many columns as there are tape tracks. The number of rows is determined by the maximum anticipated character overlap. The recorded signals must be self-clocking, as the data are stored in each column under control of the clock signal from its track. The clock signal from one track controls the readout, row by row, after a delay sufficient to allow all pulses of a character to be stored in one row. All pulses included in a character are read out simultaneously, so that character pulse synchronization is also effected by the system.

REFERENCES

1. Stewart, W. Earl: "Magnetic Recording Techniques," McGraw-Hill Book Company, Inc., New York, 1958.
2. Middlebrook, R. D.: Optimum Noise Performance of Transistor Input Circuits, *Semiconductor Products*, vol. 1, no. 4, pp. 14–20, July–August, 1958.
3. Nichols, M. H., and L. L. Rauch: "Radio Telemetry," John Wiley & Sons, Inc., New York, 1956.
4. Kiebert, M. V., Jr., and A. F. Inglis: Multivibrator Circuits, *Proc. IRE*, vol. 33, no. 8, pp. 534–539, August, 1945.
5. Bertram, S.: The Degenerative Positive-bias Multivibrator, *Proc. IRE*, vol. 36, no. 2, p. 277, February, 1948.
6. Staff of Radar School, Massachusetts Institute of Technology: "Principles of Radar," pp. 2–58 to 2–64, McGraw-Hill Book Company, Inc., New York, 1952.
7. Bengston, P. S.: Frequency Modulator Covers 25–75 kc, *Electronics*, vol. 31, no. 31, p. 100, Aug. 1, 1958.

8. The Theory and Application of FM/FM Telemetry, Bendix Aviation Corp., Pacific Division, North Hollywood, Calif.
9. Politi, E. Y.: Progress Report on a Solid State FM/FM Telemetering System, *Proc. Natl. Symposium on Telemetering*, Philadelphia, April, 1957.
10. Foster, W. H.: Completely Transistorized Current/Voltage-controlled Oscillator, *Proc. 1958 Natl. Symposium on Telemetering* (published by IRE Professional Group on Telemetry and Remote Control).
11. Chwastyk, A. M.: A Transistorized Voltage-controlled FM Subcarrier Oscillator, *Proc. 1958 Natl. Symposium on Telemetering* (published by IRE Professional Group on Telemetry and Remote Control).
12. Wilkinson, M. M.: Analysis and Performance Characteristics of Transistorized Subcarrier Oscillator Circuits for Airborne Telemetering, *Proc. 1958 Natl. Symposium on Telemetering* (published by IRE Professional Group on Telemetry and Remote Control).
13. Notes on the Application of the Silicon Unijunction Transistor, General Electric Co., Semiconductor Products Dept., ECG–380, February, 1959.
14. Meyerhoff, A. J., and R. M. Tillman: A High Speed Two-winding Transistor-core Oscillator, *IRE Wescon Conv. Record,* part 5, pp. 106–114, 1957.
15. Barnes, G. H., and R. H. Tillman: A New Transistor–Magnetic FM/FM Subcarrier Discriminator, *IRE Wescon Conv. Record,* part 5, pp. 98–105, 1957.
16. Duerig, H. W.: Precision Subcarrier Discriminator for FM Telemetering, *IRE Natl. Conv. Record,* part 1, pp. 70–82, 1956.
17. Gilchriest, C. E.: The Application of Phase-locked-loop Discriminators for Threshold Improvement and Error Reduction in FM/FM Telemetry, *Natl. Telemetering Conf. Rept.,* 1957.
18. Heberling, E. D.: An Improved Subcarrier Discriminator, *IRE Trans. on Instrumentation,* vol. I–6, no. 1, p. 43, March, 1957.
19. McRae, D. D.: Phase-locked Demodulation in Telemetry Receivers, *Proc. 1958 Natl. Symposium on Telemetering.*
20. Preston, Glenn W.: Basic Theory of Locked Oscillators in Tracking FM Signals, *IRE Trans. on Space Electronics and Telemetry,* vol. SET–5, no. 1, p. 30, March, 1959.
21. Rigby, S.: Design of All-channel Ultra-stable FM Discriminator, *IRE Trans. on Telemetry and Remote Control,* vol. TRC–3, no. 1, April, 1957.
22. Sloughter, G. S., and R. T. Ellis: Linear Discrimination for FM Telemetering, *Electronics,* vol. 24, no. 6, pp. 112–115, June, 1951.
23. Sloughter, G. S., R. A. Runyan, W. H. Duerig, and G. E. Tisdale: Telemetry Filters and Their Effect on the Dynamic Accuracy of Multiplex FM Subcarrier Instrumentation Systems, *1955 Natl. Telemetering Conf. Record,* p. 118.
24. A New Standard in FM Discriminators, Bendix Aviation Corp., Pacific Division, North Hollywood, Calif.
25. Kiebert, M. V.: A Bibliography of Telemetry, *IRE Trans. on Telemetry and Remote Control,* vol. TRC–4, no. 1, p. 10, June, 1958.
26. Telemetry Standards for Guided Missiles, IRIG Document 103–56, reprinted in *IRE Trans. on Telemetry and Remote Control,* vol. TRC–3, no. 3, p. 13, December, 1957.
27. Shaw, Robert F.: Universal Tape Amplifiers for Digital Data Systems, *Electronics,* vol. 31, no. 41, p. 91, Oct. 10, 1958.

28. Skov, R. A.: Pulse Time Displacement in High-density Magnetic Tape, *IBM J. Research and Develop.,* vol. 2, no. 2, p. 130, April, 1958.
29. Gabor, A.: High-density Recording on Magnetic Tape, *Electronics,* vol. 32, no. 42, p. 72, Oct. 16, 1959.
30. Erath, Louis W., and Frank C. Smith, Jr.: A Slope Modulator for FM Recording of Analog Data on Magnetic Tape, *IRE Trans. on Telemetry and Remote Control,* vol. TRC–1, p. 20, November, 1954.

CHAPTER 9

HEADS AND HEAD STACKS

Practically all the heads used in tape-recording equipment are of the so-called *ring* types mentioned in Chap. 2. For audio and entertainment equipment, individual heads were used almost exclusively until the advent of stereo recording, which occasioned the introduction of dual and multitrack heads in this field, particularly in motion-picture recording. The requirements imposed on multitrack heads for audio or entertainment work are far less severe than those necessary in the instrumentation field. This chapter is concerned primarily with multihead stacks for data-recording purposes and with the individual head characteristics dictated by instrumentation recording techniques.

9.1 Individual Heads

There are certain points that must be discussed with respect to individual heads before taking up head stacks.

General Construction Requirements. The core of the head is made of high-permeability material and must be laminated to reduce high-frequency losses. Six-mil laminations are common, but 3-, 2-, and even 1-mil laminations are used in some cases when high-frequency characteristics are paramount. Normally each half of the head core carries one-half of the total winding, and the lamination is shaped to accommodate this winding. The shape of the lamination also determines the depth of the gaps and thereby determines the gap cross-sectional area for a given track width. The back gap should have low reluctance, and so the lamination is usually fairly wide at this point. The depth of the front gap should be very small from the performance standpoint, as any flux bridging the gap directly is effectively a short circuit on the active fringing lines that extend out into the tape coating. However, the depth of the front gap is continually decreased by wear of the head surface, and the initial depth must be adjusted as a compromise between performance and long life. This wearing down of the front gap is particularly noticeable in reproducing heads, where the playback voltage increases as the head wears, because of the improving efficiency of the front gap.

For maximum resolution, it is important that the pole faces on opposite sides of the gap are smooth flat surfaces. To achieve such surfaces, lapping of the pole faces is required. Gap spacers, or controlled metal deposition on the pole faces, are used to establish definitely the gap length desired in the head. A nonmagnetic metal with mechanical characteristics reasonably close to those of the core material is desirable for the front gap, and an insulating material is frequently used in the back gap. Eddy currents in the front-gap material help to force the flux out of the gap and increase the fringing effect, thus raising the field intensity in the recording medium. This is particularly true with respect to the bias current used in direct recording, and a metallic front-gap spacer thus reduces the amount of bias current required in the head. A metallic spacer in the back gap is undesirable, because the reluctance of this gap should be a minimum. In some cases no spacer is used in the back gap.

For extremely high frequencies, beyond approximately 100 kc, head losses become rather severe with high-permeability core materials, and ferrites have come into use for some such applications. For those instances in which the head is not in contact with the medium, so that maximum resolution cannot be obtained, ferrite cores are suitable. For contact recording, however, the granular nature of the ferrite prevents the attainment of sufficiently sharp gap definition, and ferrite cores have not been found very suitable. Kornei [1] has designed a head using ferrite cores but achieving good gap definition by attaching small pieces of high-permeability metal to the ferrite to form the actual gap in contact with the tape.

Recording Heads. While there are a few situations, notably in FM carrier recording, in which it is practical to use the same head for both recording and playback, most applications are best handled by the use of different head designs for the recording and reproducing functions.

It will be remembered that the width of the gap in the recording head, within reasonable limits, does not affect the over-all resolution of the system, since recording occurs as the tape leaves the field or at the trailing edge of the recording head gap. In direct recording, it is necessary to use a high-frequency bias signal in the head, and the resonant frequency of the head must be 400 kc or more. In PDM and digital pulse recording, there are rapid changes in head current.

In all these cases, recording amplifier circuit design is simplified if the head inductance is reasonably low, and one of the ways of achieving low inductance is the use of a relatively large gap.

Obviously, low inductance is also achieved by reducing the number of turns. Since the inductance decreases approximately in proportion to the square of the decrease in turns and since the magnetizing force decreases in direct proportion to the decrease in turns, it is possible to achieve quite low inductances without inordinate increase in the recording currents required.

Thus, recording head gaps are generally in the range of 0.5 to approximately 2 mils, and the winding is adjusted to give an inductance in the order of a few millihenries. Typical values range from 2 or 3 to 20 mh. The larger values naturally occur in heads for wide tracks.

For drum and other noncontact recording applications, the larger gaps are used, generally in the range of 1 to 2 mils, in order to extend the range of the fringing flux so that it will adequately penetrate the medium. In some of the drum applications, the same head is used for both recording and reproduction. This requires a compromise design to limit the inductive voltage across the head during recording, and at the same time develop sufficient playback voltage. This is not too difficult in heads used for pulse recording on memory drums, because the relative head-medium velocity is usually quite large and thus provides adequate rate of change of flux in reproduction.

Reproducing Heads. The reproducing head must deliver as much voltage as possible to the input of the playback amplifier and, in general, its resonant frequency must be above the maximum signal frequency encountered. Additionally, it must have a narrow gap to provide maximum resolution.

As gap width is reduced, the maximum available playback voltage decreases, principally because of the shunting effect of the gap. Flux which is picked up from the tape and passes directly through the gap, rather than around the entire core, does not link the head windings and is therefore wasted. The need for maximum voltage and best resolution has resulted in a compromise 0.25-mil gap in most general-purpose instrumentation applications. However, heads with gaps of 0.1 and 0.05 mil have been manufactured to fulfill requirements in which resolution is more important than playback voltage. With such narrow gaps and cores of the usual high-permeability magnetic alloys, head losses prevent the attainment of the maximum resolution capabilities at high tape speeds. Accordingly, such heads are most useful for high-resolution applications at relatively low speeds.

For the high-frequency response achievable with high resolution at high speeds, head losses must be minimized. This calls for core material such as alfenol or ferrite, the use of the latter requiring some form of metal pole tip, as previously mentioned.

For a general-purpose playback head at speeds up to 60 ips, the resonant frequency must be at least 100 kc, preferably somewhat higher. This is the limiting factor on the number of turns that can be used to achieve maximum reproduction voltage. Here again, the gap width enters in, since the inductance increases as the gap is decreased. This is another factor in the common 0.25-mil gap compromise. Playback head inductances generally range from about 30 to 100 mh, the larger values again applying to the wider tracks.

9.2 Head-stack Considerations

A number of conflicting requirements vie with each other in the design of a multitrack head stack. At one and the same time the designer must try to achieve the following goals:

1. Make each track as wide as possible to obtain maximum signal
2. Keep tracks as far apart as possible to hold crosstalk down
3. Minimize the dimensions of the stack in the direction transverse to tape travel, to reduce system skewing problems
4. Find space for windings on the cores and for intertrack shields

Obviously, reconciling all these factors calls for a number of design compromises.

Additionally, the line of gaps in the stack must be held as closely as possible to a perfectly straight line; the line of gaps must be precisely at right angles to a reference mounting surface so that shimming is not necessary when the head is mounted on a tape transport; the area in contact with the tape must be suitably contoured for proper tape wrap to give reasonably long wavelength response; and the surface that contacts the tape must be as smooth as possible, with no cracks or sharp points or edges which might scratch the magnetic coating off the tape. All these requirements must be met by proper processing in assembly and manufacture.

The design compromises have led to head-stack constructions with the number of tracks per inch of tape width ranging from 7 to 20 or more, track widths from less than 20 up to 50 mils, and crosstalk figures ranging from about 25 db to well over 60 db. In general, the wider tracks and greater track-to-track spacings have been used in analog recording where crosstalk is critical and necessarily low recording levels give low playback voltages, and the narrower tracks and closer spacings have been employed in heads designed for digital recording, where crosstalk is less critical and playback voltages are maintained by saturation recording. Track "packing" up to about 14 per inch appears feasible for analog recording, while 20 or more per inch can be achieved when digital pulses only are to be handled.

The precise alignment of gaps is desirable for maintenance of phase relationships in analog recording systems and for minimum time separation of pulses in parallel digital recording. The precision of alignment usually achieved is such that all gaps in a head for 1-in.-wide tape will be within ±0.05 mil of a straight line. This is done by assembling the head in two halves and lapping the pole faces of each half on an optically flat lapping surface. The two halves are then assembled in a special jig with suitable gap spacers, and the whole assembly is generally potted in an epoxy resin. Intertrack shielding must be incorporated for adequate crosstalk rejection between tracks, and the entire assembly is magnetically shielded to prevent pickup from stray fields. Intertrack shields must extend out to the surface of the head in contact with the tape, and they must be continuous across the gap line, particularly if interleaved track arrangements are to be used with two head stacks. If the shields were made in two halves and butted together, the fields induced in them by the head windings would produce a certain amount of recording on the tape at the shield gap, and this would generate crosstalk on the interleaved track lined up with the shield. For this reason, shields cannot be assembled in the two head halves first assembled for lapping but must be inserted in the course of final assembly. Intertrack shields are made up of alternate layers of copper and mu metal, if space permits, or simply mu metal when there is no room for several lamination thicknesses.

Experience has shown that epoxy casting resins will collect oxide from the tape at high tape speeds and particularly in fast start-stop mechanisms in which the tape is shuttled back and forth across the head. The oxide accumulations always occur on the plastic and not on the exposed metal in the tape contact face of the head. Heads with all-metal contact faces were introduced to minimize such oxide buildup.

The complete head assembly includes a precision-machined mounting base with a mounting surface whose plane is accurately perpendicular to the gap line at the contact surface of the head. Tolerances on this perpendicularity are in the order of one part in 5000 to 10,000 in the plane tangent to the tape as it passes over the head and should be in the order of a part in a thousand in the plane normal to this.

This precision with respect to the mounting surface is necessary so that the gap line will lie precisely at right angles to the length of the tape; this is the only way to provide tape interchangeability from machine to machine.

9.3   Crosstalk

Crosstalk between heads in a stack is a major problem in stack design. The necessary gaps in the head cores inevitably cause flux fringing, and complete intertrack shielding is virtually impossible because of the presence of the tape on the surface of the head; shields clearly cannot be extended through the tape.

Basic Causes of Crosstalk.   There are three phenomena that combine to produce the total observed crosstalk level of a recording head, tape, and reproducing head system. These are recording crosstalk, tape field fringing, and playback head crosstalk.

Because intertrack shielding is not complete, there is a certain amount of coupling between adjacent heads in a stack.   In direct or FM carrier recording, there is a continuous magnetizing current in each head, the bias current in direct recording and the carrier current in FM recording.   This current acts as a bias for any small flux induced in one head by the adjacent head or heads and causes it to be recorded on the tape.   In the case of PDM or digital pulse recording, there is no continuous signal present to act as a bias, and the induced flux in one head due to coupling from the adjacent head is usually not large enough to produce noticeable tape magnetization.   This is because of the negligible remanent magnetization produced by very small magnetizing forces in the absence of bias. Thus, recording crosstalk is a pertinent factor in the over-all crosstalk figure for direct recording, FM carrier, and similar techniques in which a signal is continuously present in each recording channel.   Recording crosstalk is nonexistent or negligible as a part of system crosstalk in PDM and digital pulse recording and in other similar systems.

Tape field fringing is a phenomenon associated with long-wavelength signals on the tape and consequently becomes evident only when low-frequency signals are recorded at high tape speeds.   The effectively long magnets in the recorded track may have fringing fields that extend far enough to induce flux in the adjacent head of the playback head stack.   With well-shielded single-stack heads, the intertrack shields appear to short-circuit this fringing flux and the phenomenon is not generally noticeable or at least is not separable from other crosstalk causes. When two head stacks with interleaved tracks are used, however, a track recorded by one head stack is aligned with a shield in the second head stack. It seems that in this situation the shield does not collect and short-circuit all the fringing flux, and it becomes noticeable in the form of rather high crosstalk levels at long wavelengths with interleaved-track dual-head-stack arrangements.

Finally, in reproduction, the coupling between adjacent heads in the playback head stack introduces further crosstalk. This appears to be simply a voltage induced in one head by the flux in the adjacent head.

The total system crosstalk will be the resultant of the recording, tape flux fringing (if any), and playback crosstalk signals in direct, FM, and similar systems, and almost exclusively playback crosstalk in pulse systems. When crosstalk occurs in both recording and reproduction, phase relationships become critical, and the effective over-all level generally varies appreciably from track to track and from one head stack to another. This is particularly true with poorly shielded heads in FM carrier recording.

Measurement. It is quite simple to measure the sine-wave coupling between adjacent heads in a stack; one has merely to drive one head from an oscillator and measure the voltage across the driven head and that induced in the adjacent heads. The ratio of these voltages is a direct measure of the coupling between heads. Unfortunately, such a measurement is not a reliable indication of the system crosstalk when the heads are used for recording and reproduction.

The reason for this is fairly obvious in the case of direct and FM carrier recording, since the addition of recording and playback crosstalk may either increase or decrease the total, as compared with the value measured by the coupling method, or they may combine in the proper phase to produce the same total result. In the case of pulse recording, a single-frequency sine-wave measurement of head coupling may not give the same result as is actually experienced when pulses are recorded and reproduced. Coupling measurements on the head can be made with properly shaped pulses instead of sine waves, but experimentally it is sometimes rather difficult to do this accurately because of external stray coupling at the higher-frequency components of the pulse signal. Very careful attention to shielding and grounding is necessary. Sine-wave measurements over a wide frequency range, covering the total pulse spectrum, permit a reasonable assessment of the magnitude of pulse crosstalk. However, both the phase and magnitude of the coupled signal vary with frequency, and it is generally simpler to measure pulse crosstalk by recording and reproduction rather than by head coupling measurements. Furthermore, normal convenient coupling measuring levels are far higher than actual playback levels, and the coupling may be a function of level.

For measurement of direct-recording crosstalk, signals of two different frequencies are recorded on adjacent tracks with normal bias and recording signal levels. Alternatively, one signal may be omitted, although bias should not be. The tape is then reproduced, and the signal levels in each track at each recorded frequency are measured by means of a wave analyzer or similar tuned voltmeter. In each track, the ratio of the level of the signal recorded on that track to the level of the signal recorded on the adjacent track is the signal-to-crosstalk ratio. For a complete picture, this test should be made at a number of different frequencies covering the normal range of signal frequencies to be handled.

While the above test procedure gives a valid measurement of the crosstalk signal injected in one channel by an immediately adjacent channel, it still may not represent precisely situations which may occur in actual practice. For example, for tracks other than the extreme end tracks of the stack, there are always two adjacent tracks which may couple into the one under consideration. There is also the possibility that the second track away from the one under consideration may introduce additional crosstalk signal, although this factor is negligible in a head which is sufficiently well shielded to be suitable for high-quality direct or FM carrier recording.

A measurement of crosstalk in direct recording as outlined above does not necessarily give a result that is valid for wideband FM carrier recording. In this latter case, the worst possible condition that can occur is one in which d-c input signals cause the carrier frequencies in adjacent tracks to differ in frequency by an amount equal to the maximum data frequency passed by the playback discriminator low-pass output filters. For example, in the commonly used 40 per cent deviation system, at 30-ips tape speed, the input to one channel could be zero volts, giving a 27-kc carrier frequency, while the input to an adjacent channel is a d-c value sufficient to give a 22- or 32-kc carrier frequency. The difference frequency would be 5 kc which is passed by the output filter. The crosstalk observed in this situation represents the worst that can be encountered.

The reason for this is best illustrated by Fig. 9.1. In part a of this figure, there is indicated a large single-frequency carrier vector of magnitude e_0 and two spurious signals each of magnitude e_1, but separated from the carrier frequency by frequency differences f_1 and f_2, respectively. The ratio e_1/e_0 is assumed to be small, of the order of 0.1 or less. Figure 9.1b illustrates the vector diagram for the combination of the carrier vector e_0 and one of the spurious signals, considering first the one closest to the carrier at frequency difference f_1. Since the spurious signal is higher in frequency than the carrier, it rotates counterclockwise in the figure at a rate of $2\pi f_1$ radians per sec. It is seen that the resultant vector is both amplitude- and frequency-modulated, the locus of its terminus being the dotted circle. The extreme phase swings are indicated by the resultants. The magnitude of the phase deviation ϕ is approximately equal to the ratio e_1/e_0, since this ratio was assumed small. The extreme frequency deviation is ϕf_1, or $f_1 e_1/e_0$. Now, the vector diagram for the second spurious signal, separated from the carrier by frequency f_2, will be identical to that shown, and the phase deviation will be the same. However, the frequency deviation for this second signal will be $f_2 e_1/e_0$, larger than that for the first spurious signal considered. Thus, the first spurious signal will produce an output from a discriminator of magnitude $f_1 e_1/e_0$, while the second will produce an output $f_2 e_1/e_0$. Hence, the discriminator output is directly proportional to the ratio e_1/e_0 and to the frequency difference between the carrier and the interfering signal.

The ratio e_1/e_0 is equivalent to the crosstalk, assuming fixed carrier frequencies for the moment. As the frequency difference between the carriers is progressively increased from zero, the actual discriminator output signal due to crosstalk will be a beat frequency equal to the frequency difference between the two carriers, and it will have an amplitude that increases linearly with the carrier frequency difference up to the point at which the low-pass filter begins to cut off. For carrier frequency differences higher than this, the signal due to crosstalk is eliminated by the low-pass filter.

Let us assume that 40 per cent carrier deviation by a normal signal produces a 10-volt d-c discriminator output. Neglecting the low-pass output filter for the moment, a spurious signal separated from the carrier by 40 per cent of the carrier frequency will produce a frequency

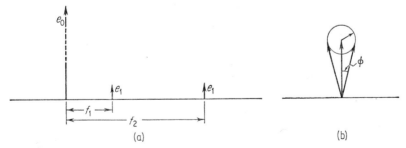

Fig. 9.1. Vector diagram, FM carrier plus small spurious signal.

deviation of e_1/e_0 times 40 per cent of the carrier frequency, or e_1/e_0 times 10 volts in the discriminator output. Thus, in the absence of an output filter in the discriminator, the spurious discriminator output due to crosstalk would rise to a maximum equal to the crosstalk ratio, at a carrier frequency difference equal to the full-scale deviation for the channel. When the low-pass output filter is included, the maximum crosstalk signal is reduced by the ratio of the filter cutoff frequency to the peak full-scale frequency deviation. The inverse of this ratio, however, has previously been defined as the deviation ratio for the channel. Therefore, the worst possible spurious output in a wideband FM channel due to crosstalk is equal to the ratio of the crosstalk signal to the carrier signal, divided by the channel deviation ratio.

Of course, in actual recording situations, it is not at all likely that this worst case will occur for any large fraction of the total time. However, if two modulated carriers are present in adjacent tracks, the critical frequency separation between them will undoubtedly occur at frequent intervals, and at such times the peak crosstalk signal will be that deduced above. Hence the over-all head-stack crosstalk for FM carrier, divided by the deviation ratio, gives a direct indication of the peak noise that may occur in channel outputs due to the crosstalk.

The above argument provides the basis for measurement of crosstalk for FM carrier purposes. Two fixed frequencies, separated by an amount equal to the cutoff frequency of the output low-pass filter, are recorded on adjacent tracks. The signal from one track is reproduced through a standard discriminator, and the output voltage at the beat frequency is measured. This measurement, multiplied by the deviation ratio, is the effective over-all crosstalk. Preferably, one of the recorded frequencies should be the normal carrier frequency, and two measurements should be made, one with the adjacent channel frequency above the carrier and the second with the adjacent channel frequency below the carrier.

For good heads in which crosstalk levels are low, it is usually necessary to measure the beat frequency with a wave analyzer, and if a very narrow band analyzer is used, flutter may make the measurement impossible at the high frequency difference mentioned. In such a case, measurements can be made at several smaller frequency differences and linearly extrapolated to the desired point.

For pulse recording crosstalk, the simplest procedure consists in recording a square wave to produce tape saturation on one track and reading the playback voltage from this track and from adjacent tracks.

The ratio of the adjacent track signal to the recorded track signal is the crosstalk.

It is not safe to assume that a crosstalk figure of, say, 30 db from one track to the next implies a crosstalk rejection of 60 db from the first track to the second one removed from it. In fact, there are instances of head stacks particularly designed for digital recording, in which the crosstalk signal in tracks four or five times removed from the driven track was appreciably larger than the crosstalk signal in adjacent tracks. This phenomenon has not been extensively studied or satisfactorily explained, to the author's knowledge. Those measurements which have been made, however, do show that crosstalk rejection cannot be assumed to be additive from track to track. This factor must be borne in mind in connection with systems that attempt to record on one track of a head stack and simultaneously reproduce on another track. To establish suitability of a head stack for this type of operation, very careful crosstalk measurements must be made under all possible sets of operating conditions. The location in the stack of the driven head, for example, will generally affect the crosstalk pattern in the other heads of the stack.

The conditions prevailing in PDM recording are essentially equivalent to those in digital pulse recording, and effective crosstalk figures can be expected to be the same. Therefore, crosstalk values for digital recording can be applied equally well to PDM systems.

When different types of signals are recorded in adjacent tracks, special care must be exercised with respect to crosstalk. For example, a wideband FM, PDM, or digital pulse signal with saturation recording in a track adjacent to a direct-recording channel will result in far higher crosstalk levels in the direct-recording channel than would be indicated by normal crosstalk measurements on the head. The reason is, obviously, that the recording current for saturation recording is roughly 20 db larger than that used for direct recording, and the crosstalk injected into the direct-recorded track during the recording process is proportionately larger than normal measurements would indicate. A similar relation exists during playback. Conversely, the crosstalk from the direct-recording channel into an adjacent FM, PDM, or digital channel would be appreciably less than normal head measurements would indicate. It is apparent from this that care must be exercised in the system setup when various recording techniques are to be handled simultaneously in a head stack.

Reduction of Crosstalk. Intertrack shielding, to the maximum extent possible in the available space, seems to be the most practical method for reduction of crosstalk in head stacks. In one particular stack design for stereo recording on motion-picture film, small magnetic-coupling members were inserted in the head stack and adjusted to cancel, in so far as possible, the normal crosstalk. So far as the author is aware, no instrumentation head stacks have employed this method.

At a time when well-shielded heads with precision gap alignments were not available, the author spent considerable time attempting to devise networks that could be connected between heads to reduce or cancel the crosstalk. This could be done between two adjacent heads at a single frequency, but even for this simple situation it was not possible to devise a passive network that would be sufficiently effective at all frequencies. Furthermore, it was easy to introduce a network that would completely eliminate at a single frequency the coupling which can be measured in a head; nevertheless, even with complete cancellation of this coupling, recording and reproduction still showed appreciable crosstalk. Efforts to devise a network arrangement to interconnect all heads in a stack were signally unsuccessful. The heads concerned had about 26-db crosstalk rejection from one track to the next adjacent one but still evidenced only 33-db rejection from one track to the second one away. Also, phases were quite different in adjacent tracks and those twice removed, and the inter-connecting network arrangement rapidly became hopeless. It was an inevitable conclusion that adequate intertrack shielding is essential.

It would appear from the available information that crosstalk levels are dependent both on shielding and intertrack spacing. With something in the order of 85 to 90 mils between the head cores, crosstalk figures ranging from 60 to 70 db can be obtained, even for the worst case of FM carrier recording. Such large spacing permits insertion of a considerable stack of shielding laminations, including several layers of mu metal and copper. As the spacing between tracks is reduced, crosstalk tends to increase, but it is difficult to determine what portion of the increase is due to decrease in distance between head cores and what portion is due to the reduction in shielding necessitated by the smaller space available. One cannot obtain a very consistent plot of crosstalk against spacing from published data on commercially available heads. Undoubtedly this is due to the fact that there are many construction variations beside track spacing and shielding that cause considerable scattering of the data. Some data, too, are for direct or FM recording, while other information is for pulse recording, and such figures are hardly comparable with each other.

Those published figures which can be considered to be fairly reliable indicate crosstalk rejection greater than 60 db for heads with seven or eight tracks per inch of tape width, 40 to 50 db for head stacks with 13 or 14 tracks per inch of tape width, and 35 db for stacks of 15 to 20 tracks per inch. Figure 9.2 shows direct-recording crosstalk and direct-coupling measurements for several heads. Elimination of recording crosstalk by removal of bias from one track reduces the over-all crosstalk. The generally poor correlation between coupling measurements and over-all crosstalk is also apparent.

Acceptable Crosstalk Levels. For direct and FM carrier recording, 40 to 45 db is about the minimum acceptable level in most applications, assuming that the crosstalk measurement is based on the worst-case FM carrier situation. Higher rejections are naturally desirable and would become essential if saturation recording is necessary in a channel adjacent to a sensitive direct-recording channel. For wide-band FM carrier, 40-db crosstalk measured in the manner described above will generally result in crosstalk noise at a 50-db or lower level, although the noise peaks may reach 46 db below full scale occasionally.

For PDM and digital pulse recording, 30-db crosstalk rejection appears to be an entirely acceptable level. In some digital equipment, crosstalk levels as high as 20 db have been permitted. Since it is

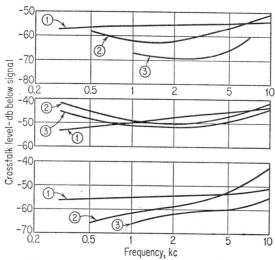

① Induced voltage
② Bias on both channels while recording
③ No bias on pick-up channel

Fig. 9.2.   Crosstalk in head stacks.   (*Courtesy of Clevite Corp.*)

only necessary to recognize the presence or absence of a pulse and since noise-clipping circuits are often used, head crosstalk is generally a relatively minor problem in digital recording. In PDM, it is only necessary that the crosstalk signal be low enough that it will never cause spurious triggering of the pulse reconstruction circuits in the playback amplifier.

9.4   Interleaved and Single-stack Head Assemblies

From the standpoint of general-purpose use and maximum utility of magnetic tape systems, it is certainly desirable that all heads be in a single stack to provide the closest possible time and phase coincidence between all channels. It is indeed unfortunate that, at an early stage in the development of instrumentation equipment, dual head stacks were introduced as an expedient for increasing track "packing" density across the tape, and it is doubly unfortunate that pressures other than technical considerations have encouraged the continued use of this arrangement.

There is no question that the timing accuracy between two tracks in one head stack is several orders of magnitude better than that which exists between tracks recorded on different head stacks at the normal 1.5-in. spacing. Present-day knowledge of the characteristics of tape, and especially what may happen to it as a result of shipment, temperature variations, winding and unwinding on reels, storage, and subjection to the stresses imposed by tape transports, shows clearly that it is easily possible for the length of tape between two head stacks to change by several per cent. The relative timing error normally to be expected between two tracks in a single head stack, even though separated by 1 in., would correspond to well under 0.1 per cent dimensional change in the interhead-stack tape dimension. Even if the tape width were increased to 4 or 5 in., timing accuracy with a single head stack would be considerably better than that between interleaved stacks.

The use of interleaved dual stacks imposes on the user the requirement that signals requiring reasonably close time coincidence be grouped in one stack only. If all the signals require this time coincidence, the track capacity of the tape equipment is cut in half. While it is true that some applications can tolerate large time variations, the general applicability and flexibility of a tape recording system are appreciably diminished by dividing its total capacity into two groups of channels between which there is a large and uncertain timing error.

It is to be hoped that, for maximum utility and flexibility, data-recording systems will eventually be standardized with single-stack heads only.

9.5 Flux Reading Heads

To get around the deficiencies of conventional direct recording with respect to long-wavelength response and dependence of playback voltage on tape speed, a considerable amount of effort has been expended in devising methods of reading the flux on the tape instead of its derivative. These have ranged from mechanical motion arrangements to produce changing flux in the playback head without tape motion, to relatively sophisticated magnetic modulation methods readily adaptable to multitrack recording. Kornei [2] has published an extensive survey of flux-responsive reproducing heads.

We must expect that most of the factors that contribute to amplitude inaccuracy in direct recording will still apply when the playback head responds to the tape flux. Therefore, while flux-sensitive playback methods can be used to extend low-frequency response and provide uniform playback voltage regardless of tape speed, the reproduction accuracy will be comparable to that of direct recording. The over-all utility of flux-responsive playback methods is accordingly somewhat limited, but in certain areas of recording in which wide speed variations and very low playback speeds are desired they are very useful.

Mechanical methods for flux reading involve motion of the playback head itself or motion of magnetic material in the immediate vicinity of the playback-head front gap. Oscillatory motion of the playback head in a direction parallel to the length of the tape will modulate the flux in the playback head at a rate equal to the oscillation frequency of the head. This modulation will generate a voltage in the head windings proportional to the flux from the tape and the rate of motion of the head and will generate as head output a carrier frequency, equal to the head oscillation frequency, having a magnitude dependent on the tape magnetization. Such a signal can be handled by well-known methods to recover a signal proportional to the tape flux. Similarly, a moving piece of magnetic material near the back of the tape and the playback head gap will produce an equivalent modulation of the playback head flux, with a corresponding signal output from the head windings. These methods have found limited use in some special applications.

Rotating heads have been used to reproduce repetitively a limited length of the tape, the particular portion scanned being changed gradually by slow motion of the tape past the rotating head. Usually two or four heads are used in the rotating assembly, and the tape wrap adjusted so that one head contacts the tape as the preceding one leaves it. The length of tape that can be scanned with such an arrangement is obviously dependent on the diameter of the rotating assembly and is limited by the feasible size of the mechanical structure.

An electron-beam flux-responsive head has been described by Skellett, Loveridge, and Gratian [3–5]. This head uses the magnetic field picked up from the tape to deflect an electron beam. The beam is generated in conventional fashion in a small cathode-ray tube and impinges on two plates at the end of the tube. In its normal undeflected position, the beam is adjusted to strike the small gap between the two plates so that the currents received by the two plates are the same. The beam passes through an internal magnetic structure which can be coupled to an external core to pick up the flux from the tape. When flux is present, the beam is deflected from its normal position in one direction or the other, depending on the sense of the flux, and this deflection causes the current in one of the pickup plates to increase, while that of the other plate decreases. Thus the output voltage developed across the two pickup plates is dependent on the magnitude and sense of the magnetic flux.

The frequency response of the cathode-ray tube system itself is flat from direct current to at least 15 kc, and the upper frequency limit could undoubtedly be extended. The external core which picks up the flux from the tape is similar to that of the normal pickup head except that the back gap is the structure inside the tube through which the electron beam passes. Consequently, high-frequency response is limited by all the factors present in normal recording, including gap effect, demagnetization, core losses, and spacing losses. At extremely low frequencies, the dimension of the head in the direction of tape travel again limits the long-wavelength response, and in at least some versions of the head, wings were attached to the core to pick up flux from a greater length of tape. This gave a response flat within ±3 db from 2 to 10,000 cps at a tape speed of 7½ ips. This required two sections of RC high-frequency equalization.

The above performance applies to normal longitudinal recording. With vertical recording, requiring, of course, a different external magnetic structure for the playback head, response to direct current could be obtained but high-frequency response was not as good. At 36 ips this head required 35 db equalization to extend its response to 10 kc.

It may be noted that a static head will not give d-c response with normal longitudinal recording, because the head cannot be extended sufficiently in the direction of tape travel. Also, for very low-frequency response, wings have to be attached to the core pole pieces to extend the head to a dimension of approximately one-half wavelength at the maximum wavelength of response. Because of its nature, the electron-beam head necessarily has a considerable dimension in the direction at right angles to tape travel and does not seem particularly suitable for multitrack operation. Its output is quite large, in the order of 1 volt, and is, of course, independent of tape speed.

A number of methods have been devised to modulate the flux in an otherwise normal ring-type playback head, by variation of the reluctance of the core [2, 6–11]. One of these methods is mechanical, while the others are electrical.

The mechanical method comprises a rotating member in the back gap of the head, so that the effective dimension of this gap is made alternately short and long. When the gap is short, the total reluctance of the head is minimum, and when the gap is long the reluctance is a maximum. With a magnetizing force present at the front gap of the head, the amount of flux present in the core and linking the winding will vary in accordance with the reluctance variation produced by the variable back gap. Thus the output signal from the head windings will vary in proportion to the rate of change of flux and will, in effect, be a carrier whose frequency is determined by twice the rate of rotation of the mechanical member in the back gap. It is rather difficult to attain high efficiency with this type of head structure, because the clearances required for the mechanically rotating system result in a somewhat large minimum back gap, so that the minimum reluctance of the head is considerably higher than that of a conventional head.

A number of ways have been devised for varying the reluctance of the head by electrical methods [2, 7–11]. These depend on intermittent saturation of a portion of the magnetic circuit of the core, which may be achieved in a number of ways. It is essential that the flux generated to saturate a portion of the core be in such a direction that it does not traverse the entire core and thus appear across the front gap of the head. Otherwise, the signal on the tape would be partially or completely erased. Therefore, the core-saturating techniques use either a flux at right angles to the normal flux direction in the core or, by means of wires looped through holes in the core, confine the saturating flux to a limited portion of the core.

Figure 9.3 shows the arrangement proposed by Schurch and Schleif

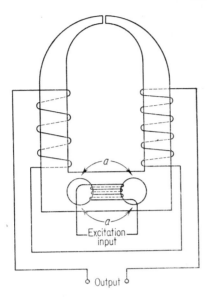

Fig. 9.3. Flux reading head. (*Adapted from Schurch and Schleif, U.S. Patent no. 2,804,506.*)

[7], as it would be applied to a reproducing head for longitudinal recording. The patent referenced shows an arrangement for perpendicular recording. The holes in the back part of the core reduce its effective cross section, the four narrow sections indicated by *a* being the minimum cross-section points. A current in the excitation coil wound as indicated produces a flux that must circulate around the two holes, half of the total flux passing through each of the narrow sections *a*. These sections can easily be made the minimum cross-section portions of the excitation flux path and can thus be caused to saturate when the exciting current becomes large enough. When they are saturated, the core reluctance is high and very little flux will pass through it, owing to a magnetomotive force across the front gap. When the exciting current drops to zero, the core reluctance becomes very low and a magnetomotive force at the front gap causes a large flux in the core which links the pickup windings on the core legs. If a high-frequency excitation current is used, the sections *a* are saturated twice during each cycle of the exciting current; a flux generated by a magnetomotive force at the gap is thus modulated at twice the excitation frequency and produces an output at the doubled frequency in the regular windings. This can be amplified and then rectified or phase-detected to produce a d-c output approximately proportional to the magnetization of the tape. It will be noted that the excitation flux circulates around the holes in the core and does not produce any

flux across the gap which might erase the tape. For the same reason, there is little or no coupling between the excitation winding and the pickup or output winding.

An arrangement disclosed by Kornei [8] is particularly adaptable for multichannel heads and is shown in Fig. 9.4. A magnetic core passes through the back gap of each of the ring-type heads and is formed itself into a complete ring core in the plane normal to the planes of the individual pickup heads. A magnetizing winding is put on this core so that a periodic flux can be generated in the core by passing current through this winding. With the extra core not magnetized, the heads are essentially normal ring-type heads. If an exciting current is applied to the winding on the extra core, this core may be periodically saturated, effectively opening the back gaps of all the heads in the stack each time saturation is reached. It will be seen that the flux in the extra core is at right angles to the normal flux in the pickup heads and hence does not appear at the front gaps of the heads to affect the tape signal. The reluctance of the pickup heads is modulated at a frequency of twice the excitation frequency, and thus an output voltage is generated in the normal head windings whenever a magnetizing force appears across the front gap.

These reluctance-variation heads designed for pickup of longitudinally recorded signals are subject to the limitations pointed out above

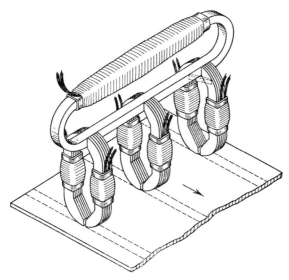

Fig. 9.4.   Multitrack flux reading head.   (*From Kornei, U.S. Patent no. 2,704,789.*)

in the discussion of the electron-beam head, with respect to d-c and long-wavelength response, and, of course, have the same high-frequency characteristics as ordinary heads.   The over-all response of such a flux-responsive head is thus similar to that of the normal head except that the base line for the response, instead of sloping upward at 6 db per octave, is horizontal with respect to frequency.   Departures at long and short wavelengths for the reasons already discussed will occur from this horizontal line rather than from the upwardly sloping line of the normal head.

Ferber [11] has shown that orienting the recording and playback head gaps at an angle of 45° to the direction of tape travel permits response down to direct current and eliminates the long-wavelength effects normally encountered.   The head orientation introduces transverse magnetization in addition to the normal longitudinal magnetization and provides a pattern in the tape which generates a magnetomotive force across the playback head gap for d-c recording current. Some resolution is lost at the high-frequency end, but the increased low-frequency response results in a greater frequency range in terms of octaves.

The Hall effect is also employed in flux-sensitive heads.   If a current is passed through a flat conducting strip and a magnetic field traverses the strip at right angles to the current sheet, a voltage is developed at opposite edges of the strip; this is termed the *Hall effect.* Its magnitude in many materials is too small to be useful, but in some semiconductors the voltage produced is relatively large.   A small strip of such material can be inserted in the back gap of a conventional head core; when a suitable direct current is passing through the semiconductor strip, a flux in the core will produce a voltage at right angles to the current.   This voltage will be a direct function of the flux; no carrier frequency is involved.

One of the principal advantages of a flux-responsive head would appear to be in the field of digital recording, to give a response independent of tape speed.   In this type of recording, there is no long-wavelength signal, and so normal head dimensions are suitable, and with the flux-responsive head, playback can be accomplished at any desired speed with always the same playback voltage independent of speed.   Since the playback signal from the head is a modulated carrier, there is an upper frequency limit on the pulse rate that can be reproduced, which in turn limits the maximum speed of reproduction. However, if this limit is within the desired range of operating speeds, it is only necessary to turn off the excitation to the head and use it as a normal head at higher speeds.

REFERENCES

1. Kornei, O.: Magnetic Head Has Megacycle Range, *Electronics,* vol. 29, no. 11, p. 172, November, 1956.
2. Kornei, O.: Survey of Flux-responsive Magnetic Reproducing Heads, *J. Audio Eng. Soc.,* vol. 2, no. 3, p. 145, July, 1954.
3. Skellett, A. M., et al.: Electron-beam Head for Magnetic Tape Playback, *Electronics,* vol. 26, no. 10, p. 168, October, 1953.
4. Gratian, J. W., and Norman Cole: U.S. Patent no. 2,725,430.
5. Gratian, J. W.: Magnetic Tape Pickup Has DC Response, *Electronics,* vol. 27, p. 156, September, 1954.
6. Schurch, E. C., and F. R. Schleif: Magnetic Tape Oscillograph for Power System Analysis, *Elec. Eng.,* vol. 70, no. 11, p. 993, November, 1951.
7. Schurch, E. C., and F. R. Schleif: U.S. Patent no. 2,804,506.
8. Kornei, O.: U.S. Patent no. 2,704,789.
9. Anderson, M. E.: Magnetic Head Reads Tape at Zero Speed, *Electronics,* vol. 32, no. 10, p. 58, Mar. 6, 1959.
10. Daniel, E. D.: A Flux-sensitive Reproducing Head for Magnetic Recording Systems, *J. Inst. Elec. Engrs. (London),* paper 1856R, July, 1955.
11. Ferber, L. W.: Flux-responsive Magnetic Heads for Low-speed Read-out of Data, *IRE Natl. Conv. Record, part 4,* vol. 6, p. 279, 1958.

CHAPTER 10

MAGNETIC TAPE SYSTEMS

We have used the term *magnetic tape systems* throughout this book; actually, however, the systems described herein are almost invariably subsystems of a larger data acquisition and reduction system. The tape subsystem performs the operation of storing an electrical signal so that it may be reproduced at a later time, and often repetitively, for detailed analysis and further processing. For a complete data system, additional items beyond the tape equipment are generally necessary. Since the input signal to the tape system must be electrical in nature, translation devices are necessary when other physical quantities are to be measured and recorded. Additional equipment is necessary at the output of the tape system to convert the electrical signal there present to a form suitable for ultimate use by the human data consumer. Some other adjuncts are useful to increase the operating speed and convenience of the system.

10.1 Representative Applications

Magnetic tape recording and reproducing equipment has been applied in so many ways that it is difficult to do more here than point out a few of the outstanding large-scale uses. These major fields include telemetry, aircraft flight test, jet and rocket engine testing, and vibration studies, among others.

The need for recording telemetered data in the aircraft, missile, satellite, and space-vehicle fields is obvious. A great many channels are necessary to convey sufficient information regarding the performance of the complex structures involved, and additional channels of command signals and responses thereto are also required. The total duration of a test is frequently quite brief, and it would be essentially impossible for any organization of observers to gather all the necessary information during the test. Recording of the data in visual form by means of direct-writing recorders or photographic methods presents an insurmountable work load in the later processing of the information so recorded. As a result, magnetic tape recording is an essential part of any but the simplest telemetering system. Because of the large number of recording stations which have been established for telemetry work and the use of the recorded data by an even larger number of organizations, it has been necessary to establish standards for equipment used in this area. These "Magnetic Recorder/Reproducer Standards" [1] have been determined by the Inter-Range Instrumentation Group, an organization composed of representatives from a number of aircraft and missile test ranges.

In flight testing of both manned aircraft and missiles, on-board tape recorders have been used to augment the total data-handling system capacity and simultaneously relieve congestion on the radio-frequency telemetering channels. Because of the severe environmental conditions encountered and limited space available, special equipment has been developed for these applications. Rather obviously, the requirements are different for use in manned aircraft and in missiles, and different types of equipment are used. All the main recording methods previously described—wideband FM, multiplexed FM, PDM, and digital (PCM)—are used in these applications to handle the wide range of data that must be recorded.

Magnetic tape equipment has been extensively applied in jet and rocket engine testing, using both analog and digital systems. In such test work, again, a great deal of information must be gathered during the test and preserved for later analysis. In the case of rocket engine testing, the test duration is also very short, increasing the need of recording the available information in rapidly reproducible form. For jet engine work, laboratory-type equipment is usually assembled on a cart or in racks mounted on wheels, so that it may be readily moved from one test cell to another. Playback and data reduction equipment is a fixed installation. For rocket engine testing, both the recording and reproducing systems are fixed installations of laboratory equipment.

Magnetic tape provides the most powerful tool yet available for vibration recording and analysis. For this purpose it has been used in manned aircraft, missiles, rocket sleds, automobiles, and trucks, as well as in stationary applications. Vibration measurement is an important part of jet engine testing, particularly in development and research work. Because of the high-frequency response necessary in vibration work, wideband FM carrier is the most common recording method. Frequency analysis of the recorded data is one of the major data-reduction processes, and a number of special automatic analyzing devices have been developed and manufactured as accessories to the tape-recording systems. In most cases, frequency analysis is performed by transferring a data sample from the original tape to a tape loop which is then repetitively reproduced while the analysis is made by an automatic analyzer. Multiple analyzing channels are frequently used to speed up this process. Madsen [2] describes two other methods of obtaining the power spectral density plot for random data initially recorded on tape.

In the study of radio-signal transmission phenomena, much of the equipment developed for vibration recording and analysis has been found useful. Many of the variations in transmission characteristics are random, with statistical properties essentially the same as those of random vibration, although the frequency ranges are widely different. By recording at very slow tape speeds and playback at much higher speeds, the frequencies involved in the radio transmission phenomena have been translated into the range covered by automatic frequency analyzers, and power spectral density plots are thus obtained. This tape speedup facility has also been applied in other instances to the frequency analysis of very low-frequency data, such as ocean-wave motion and ship rolling and pitching.

Tape loops and drums have been used to provide time delays larger than those which can be easily achieved by purely electrical or electronic delay methods. Such delays can readily be made variable and are useful in analog computation of autocorrelation functions and, as an accessory to an analog computer, for the simulation of large "transit delays" which are common in heat-exchanger and industrial-process applications.

This list of applications of magnetic tape is far from exhaustive. A partial bibliography is given at the end of this chapter; some early applications are referenced in Chap. 1.

10.2   System Limitations and Accessories

We have mentioned that a magnetic tape system is usually the storage portion of a larger data acquisition and reduction system. This section points out some of the components that must be added to a tape system to accomplish the over-all purpose.

Analog Systems.   The input signals required for analog recording are as follows: approximately 1 volt for wideband FM carrier and 5 volts for voltage-controlled subcarrier oscillators, 0.1 to 1 volt for mixed FM subcarriers or other signals to be direct-recorded, a width-modulated pulse of at least 1-volt amplitude for pulse duration modulation. For the measurement and recording of the ordinarily observed physical phenomena such as pressures, temperatures, velocities, positions, and other similar quantities, transducers are necessary to transform the observed quantity into an electrical form. There are many such transducers, developed over a long period of time, to supply signals to various types of electrical equipment. However, few transducers supply the output voltages listed above as required for the inputs to the tape recording equipment. Therefore, d-c and a-c amplifiers are a very common required accessory to provide satisfactory recording. For multiplexed PDM recording, a commutator and PDM keyer are necessary for each tape track on which a PDM signal is to be handled.

Entirely aside from the data channels, other auxiliary equipment may be desirable. Some form of timing signal is almost always necessary; this may be a special signal giving time of day or "range" time, or it may be a simple sine wave or pulse tone as a relative time base during the data-recording period. If a flutter compensation signal or a speed control signal is recorded on the tape, it is frequently possible to make use of this as a relative time signal during playback. A voice-logging channel is useful in many applications to permit voice comments to be recorded on the tape to indicate calibration signals, beginning and end of special test conditions, and any other information pertinent to the test performance. Other forms of signals may also be used to denote special events or conditions during the recording period.

It is in reproduction and data-processing systems that the greatest variety of accessory equipment is generally used. It is not possible to see the information on the tape or detect its presence and character by any simple means. Therefore a number of devices are used to assist in locating data. In addition, it is usually necessary or advisable to record appreciably more data than is actually to be subjected to detailed analysis. As a consequence, equipment is often needed for taking a "quick look" at the entire information content of the tape and selecting those portions that are to be analyzed in more detail.

The nature of such equipment varies somewhat with the type of recording used. For FM carrier, either multiplexed or wideband, discriminators will of necessity be included in the playback setup, and their outputs can be applied to photographic or direct-writing oscillographs to plot a time history of the data on each channel. For PDM signals, the regular decommutation equipment provides analog output voltages which may likewise be applied to direct-writing recorders.

For frequency-analysis work, a tape loop transport is normally used, and suitable equipment must be incorporated in the system to facilitate transfer of data to this loop. For wideband FM, rerecording amplifiers are useful for this purpose to avoid the additional data errors introduced by demodulation and remodulation. For multiplexed FM subcarriers, the entire group of subcarriers can be transferred by use of conventional playback and recording amplifiers in tandem, or a single desired subcarrier can be demodulated in the proper discriminator and the output signal applied to a wideband FM recording oscillator to put the signal on the tape loop.

In any of these transfer arrangements, controls must be included to turn on and off the signal supplied to the loop recording heads at proper times. It is undesirable to record over a portion of the loop already recorded, and so the transferred signal should be adjusted to fill the loop exactly. Any appreciable unrecorded portion on the loop should be avoided unless the loop playback discriminators are designed to give zero output when there is no input present; otherwise the usual noise output from the discriminators would distort the analysis. Sometimes the operating conditions are such that the original tape can be cut into sections and formed into loops for analysis, but most frequently it is desirable to preserve the original tape and transfer the data.

Most often, data to be frequency-analyzed is edited simply by oscilloscope observation or an oscillographic record. Sometimes, however, more sophisticated methods are desirable, particularly in selecting sections of random data. It is possible to pass the entire tape information through a group of relatively broad filters and record the filter outputs with a multichannel direct-writing recorder or oscillograph. This gives a rough picture in terms of the time history of the energy in each filter band during the run and is of considerable assistance in selecting the section or sections that are to be subjected to detailed analysis.

Analog processing of random data by methods other than frequency analysis has been used [3]. This included statistical plots of peak amplitudes and cross-spectral density plots, in addition to the normal power spectral density. Special equipment was designed for this processing. In a number of cases processing has been accomplished by means of an analog computer. This may require several computer inputs from one or more tape tracks. To maintain proper phase relationships between such computer inputs it is essential that all tracks used be recorded and reproduced with a single head stack. Frequently slowdown of the tape during reproduction is desirable to match the recorded data frequency band to the bandwidth of the computer. Occasionally, tape speedup may be used for the same purpose.

Many analog magnetic tape systems are adapted to automatic data reduction by means of a digital computer. Editing is mandatory in most such systems. After editing is accomplished, it is generally desired that the remainder of the operation be entirely automatic. For this purpose, a number of *search and control* devices have been built. The portions of data selected in the editing process for further reduction are designated by suitable numbers related to the timing or other reference signal which must be present on the tape. The tape carrying the data is then scanned, either at maximum normal operating speed or at a special higher search speed, for the number designating the starting point of the first section of data to be transferred for processing. When this number is reached, the tape is slowed down automatically to the proper reproduction speed, and data transfer occurs until the signal corresponding to the desired end of the transfer is reached, which stops the transfer operation.

For transfer of the analog data to a digital computer, conversion of the information to digital form is obviously necessary, and sometimes additional translation is necessary to arrange the data in a format suitable for the computer. Therefore, transfer of analog data from the original tape to a computer input tape is common practice; such "off-line" conversion does not tie up computer time and permits most efficient entry of data into the computer.

Several methods are available for the conversion of data to digital form, depending on the form of the data on the tape. Obviously, a converter capable of digitizing analog voltages can be used at the final demodulated output of the tape system. Sometimes, however, it is more economical in equipment and may also be more accurate to convert the tape signal directly to a digital form. PDM signals can be digitized readily by using the signal as a gate for a high-frequency pulse train, the number of pulses being counted by standard electronic counters. The contents of the counter after each pulse represent the digitized value of the pulse. Special equipment can be included to apply the corrections from the zero and full-scale calibrating pulses, or the entire data sequence can be fed to the computer and the corrections accomplished therein as an initial processing step. Another method of digitizing PDM signals has been described by Chambers [4]. This comprises reading a high-speed digital clock at the beginning and end of each pulse and taking the difference of these times to determine the pulse duration.

FM signals can be digitized in several ways. A time gate can be established from a timing or reference signal on the tape, and the number of cycles of the carrier frequency passing through this gate will give a digitized value of the FM signal. Unfortunately, this relatively simple arrangement severely restricts the effective frequency response of the FM channel because only the average frequency during the gate time is available in the digitized output. A different arrangement involves multiplication of the reference frequency to a very high value and passing it through a gate whose duration is determined by counting one or more cycles of the FM carrier. This gives a digitized value that is dependent upon the period of the carrier signal and hence is an inverse function of the data value. When the data are to be processed in a digital computer, however, this inverse relationship may not be a serious drawback.

If the duration of the digitized signal is such that the number of digital values produced is greater than the number which the computer can accept at one time, because of limited quick-access memory, then some form of buffer storage is necessary to permit arranging the data in blocks on the computer tape with suitable unrecorded gaps between the blocks. Such buffer storage may also include additional circuitry to arrange the data in the proper format on the computer tape, introduce parity check bits, and generate and record desirable computer control signals. Also, if data are digitized directly from the analog tape by methods such as the representative ones discussed above, the relative timing between the output digitized samples may not be as stable as would be desired for computer input. In such a case, auxiliary timing circuits would be required to retime the digitized data uniformly.

Digital Systems. We have seen that digital recording is used to avoid degradation of high-accuracy data; also, in most cases the use of a digital computer for data reduction can be assumed with digital tape systems. As a consequence, the final entry of data into the computer can and generally should be taken into consideration in all phases of the system.

Voltage-operated analog-digital converters are expensive and fairly complex devices. It is therefore very rarely justifiable to use such a converter for a single data channel, and a multiplexer or commutator is the usual companion piece to permit time multiplexing of a number of input channels to the analog-digital converter. The necessary digitizing speed is then determined by the product of the number of input channels and the number of samples per channel per second. The latter figure determines the frequency response and transient characteristics of each data channel. Because very low-speed systems, digitizing at the rate of 1 to perhaps 20 or 30 samples per second, can be handled relatively simply by means of standard punched-card or punched-paper-tape equipment, digital magnetic tape systems generally operate at much higher speeds, in the range of several hundred to tens of thousands of samples per second. If the sampling rate is somewhat lower than the transfer rate to the ultimate computer, it is possible to record the initial data in the proper tape format so that the original tape may be used directly for computer entry. Generation of the necessary gaps between blocks of data can be accomplished by simply interrupting the data flow for the necessary period of time, thereby losing a fraction of the information, or by utilizing a buffer storage to accumulate the incoming data while the interblock gap is generated and transferring the data to the tape as the beginning of the next block. If the second arrangement is used, tape recording must take place at a rate greater than the sampling rate of the digitizer so that the recording does not fall behind the digitizer while the interblock gaps are generated. With either of these arrangements, continuously running tape can be used, the interblock gap being generated on a time basis.

In some situations, it is necessary to collect digitized data only for brief periods of time, the system then idling until another batch of data is to be recorded. In such situations, it is usually feasible to arrange each group of data points into a block on the tape suitable for computer entry. The recording tape transport would then be a fast stop-start unit and be operated only while a block of data is being recorded. In this type of system, it is almost always quite practical to prepare the initial tape in such a manner that it can be used for direct computer entry.

In systems such as we have just been discussing, no special reproduction or translation equipment is necessary. However, in the absence of such equipment, editing of the data can be accomplished only in the computer programming. Thus, such systems are applicable primarily when all data collected are to be fed to the computer and little or no selection or editing is necessary.

When the sampling or digitizing rate is equal to or higher than the feasible computer input rate, it is necessary that a second computer input tape be prepared from the original data tape. The tape format required by the computer is then not a restriction on the format used for the original data tape, and the latter is usually set up in the best manner to accommodate the information to be recorded. There are some cases in which the rate of generation of digitized data is lower than the feasible rate of recording on tape, making it possible to put the information on tape in blocks, with blank spaces between. This arrangement will generally simplify the reproduction and translation equipment and will not affect the recording equipment complexity if the gaps can be generated by merely ignoring the fraction of the input data represented by the gaps. However, if buffer storage is necessary in the recording system to preserve all input data while gaps are being generated, the resultant complication of the recording equipment may be quite undesirable. This would dictate continuous recording with equipment for interblock gap generation associated with the reproducer.

Uninterrupted recording with continuous-running tape must be used when the system sampling rate approaches the maximum feasible recording rate, or when, as in the instance cited above, no interruption of the data flow is permissible and buffer storage is not desirable in the recording system. There may be other economic, space, or weight factors which also dictate such a recording method. For example, if a number of recorders are to be used with a single reproduction and translation system, the over-all cost will be minimized by keeping the recorders as simple as possible. Similarly, for airborne and other applications in which recorder volume and weight must be minimized, simplicity at the recording end is again desirable. In these cases, it is usually best to use continuous-running tape in the recorder and to dispense with block arrangement and interblock gaps.

Since digital signals almost always represent high-accuracy data, at least 10 or 11 binary bits are required for storage. At maximum sampling rates all the bits representing one data sample must be recorded in a single line across the tape, and additional tracks are necessary for a clock signal, if used, parity bit, and multiplexer frame and channel identification. Track requirements for such signals, therefore, range from 12 to 16, which must be in a single head stack. If pulse packing is pushed toward the maximum feasible limits, more than one timing track may become necessary to alleviate the problems introduced by tape skewing.

Because of the relatively lower information capacity of tape for digital data as compared with analog information, very high-speed digital systems often run into difficulty with respect to recording time. One way of improving this situation by a factor of 2, suggested by the author, involves doubling the total number of tracks in the system and recording alternately on each half of the total tape width. With a 15-track system, for example, a 30-track head would be used, and the first data point would be recorded on tracks 1 to 15, the second on tracks 16 to 30, the third on tracks 1 to 15, and so on. For a given sampling rate and packing density, this permits halving the tape speed and doubling the recording time for a given-size reel of tape. Another way of expanding total recording time is the use of two tape transports with automatic switchover when the tape is exhausted on the first-used machine. A fresh reel of tape can be installed in the first transport while the second is recording.

High-speed multiplexers and voltage-operated analog-digital converters, which must be electronic devices because of the speed considerations, normally operate in the range of 1 to 10 volts input. This means that data signal amplifiers, which generally must be d-c amplifiers, are necessarily incorporated in most of the input data channels to match the transducer output level to the multiplexer input. This requirement represents a considerable complication in the recording system and increases costs materially. Transducers producing digitized outputs, or a satisfactory low-level multiplexer, would alleviate this situation. Unfortunately, the voltage and/or current uncertainties and temperature drifts inherent in the magnetic and semiconductor devices usable for high-speed switching pose extremely difficult problems in low-level high-speed multiplexing.

In addition to the amplifiers, multiplexer, and analog-digital converter, which must be added to the basic tape recorder comprised of tape transport and recording amplifiers, a digital system also needs an electronic clock for timing and numerous other circuits for pulse generation, counting, and miscellaneous switching functions. It is thus appreciably more complex than a commutated analog system such as PDM. However, in return for the additional complexity and cost, the digital system provides appreciably higher accuracy and greater total effective bandwidth by virtue of the much higher total sampling rates achievable.

When the system is such that the initially recorded tape is not suitable for direct computer entry, a playback, editing, and translation system is required to prepare a suitable tape for the computer. A "quick look" for editing purposes can be accomplished in several ways; common to all of them is some form of decommutator to single out the desired channel or channels. This may be a simple preset counter triggered by frame identification pulses and actuated by the timing pulses to select by gate actuation the desired channel in each frame; it may be a complete demodulation system permitting simultaneous readout of all channels; or it may be any compromise between these two extremes. The complexity required in the decommutator depends on the number of channels that must be read out for editing purposes and the time that can be allocated to such readout.

The decommutated signal from the original tape is a succession of numbers in parallel digital pulse form. A graph of the data may be obtained from this signal by means of a digital-analog converter and a conventional direct-writing recorder, oscillographic recorder, or oscilloscope. If the samples occur slowly enough or if it is feasible and permissible to make them do so by a slowdown of the tape, a digital point plotter may be used to plot a graph of the data signal. Finally, a multistylus digital plotter may be used to produce the desired graph. We have mentioned here only methods of producing a graphical representation of the recorded signal; the process of editing to select the proper portions of the data for computer entry is almost always best accomplished by such a representation. It is rarely if ever feasible to edit efficiently a large volume of data by means of a printed numerical tabulation of data values. Also, graphical representations can be produced much faster than printed numerical tabulations with equipment of reasonable cost and complexity.

When the data are edited and appropriate portions selected for computer entry, it is then necessary to reproduce the original tape again, preparing from it a second tape suitable for computer input. The selected data must be arranged in suitable-size blocks with proper interblock gaps and such other specific arrangements and signals that may be required by the computer and its program. Several functions must be performed to make this operation automatic or semi-automatic. These include:

1. Manual entry of numbers to identify the portion or portions of the signal to be transferred to the computer tape

2. Circuits to compare the appropriate signals from the data tape with the manually inserted information and effect data transfer upon recognition of the proper signals

3. Translation equipment to rearrange the information from the data tape into the proper format for the computer tape

4. A parity-bit generator if required by the computer and not present on the data tape

5. Buffer storage or other arrangement for the generation of suitable interblock gaps on the computer tape

Each of these several functions can be accomplished in a number of ways. The system designer must choose among these to provide the necessary system capabilities within reasonable cost and operating time limitations. Numerous solutions to the problems involved have been described in the referenced literature.

Combination Analog-Digital Systems. Because no one method of recording is applicable to all types of input signals and because many systems must cope with a wide range of input signals, some tape systems are set up so that they can use analog or digital recording interchangeably and sometimes in combination. Practically all commercially available systems are designed so that the electronic recording components are plug-in elements. Thus a given recorder tape track can be set up for direct recording, PDM, or wideband FM, and sometimes digital recording. Because of head-stack considerations previously mentioned, however, it is most often preferable to use a different head stack for digital recording than is used for analog work. Thus in systems designed for interchangeable analog or digital recording, the choice is made by selection of the head stacks to be mounted on the tape transport and the housing and power supply for the electronic equipment. Such an arrangement permits a reasonably quick changeover from an analog recording system to a digital recording system in accordance with the dictates of the test to be run.

Sometimes it is desirable to record a combination of analog and digital signals, data sources of relatively low accuracy with high-frequency content being handled by analog methods while those with small bandwidth but high accuracy being recorded by digital techniques. This can be accomplished by using two separate head stacks, one carrying the digital tracks and the other the analog tracks. Since the digital information represents quite low-frequency data, the lack of timing coincidence between the data recorded on the different stacks is not of great consequence. Tracks could be interleaved, but if digital pulse packing densities are high, better time coincidence is obtained among the digital tracks by grouping them on one side of the tape with the analog tracks on the other side. In this latter case, each of the head stacks requires an extension beyond the actual head structure to support the full width of the tape. There is no basic reason why a single head stack cannot be constructed with some tracks particularly designed for digital recording and others for analog recording. Such an arrangement is less flexible than the two-stack method with respect to choice and location of direct-recording tracks, because of crosstalk from the high-signal-level digital tracks.

10.3 System Operational Considerations

Operational considerations have considerable bearing on the manner in which recording systems and reproducing systems should be designed and assembled. In the case of recording systems, the setup of the tape equipment is a part of the total work involved in setting up a test. Since magnetic tape is most frequently justifiable in connection with complex tests, the over-all setup and preparation for the test is likely to be quite complex and time-consuming. If tests of widely varying nature requiring general-purpose tape equipment are performed, there is still no great premium on extremely rapid and easy changeover of tape equipment from one condition to another. It is entirely practical to select tape speeds by belt changing or equivalent methods and to plug in the appropriate electronic recording components as a part of the over-all test setup. Even changing head stacks is quite feasible in some instances. Selection of the signal to be recorded on each track can be made by connecting the appropriate input cable to the electronic recording component.

In contradistinction to the recording situation, playback systems should be as flexible as possible and adaptable to very rapid changeover in all respects. Tape-speed changing should be accomplished by a front-panel switch. Ideally, all playback components should be permanently mounted in the system and connected to appropriate playback heads by patch-panel arrangements. All electronic gear should have power on whenever the system is in use, so that it is not necessary to wait for a newly plugged-in unit to settle down after warmup. If it is necessary to reproduce tapes made with different head configurations, the investment in additional transports, one with each of the required head configurations, will often pay for itself in time saved. Such additional transports, of course, should be associated with suitable patch panels so that the electronic equipment can be readily connected to any transport. Since the electronic equipment generally represents a very high percentage of the total system cost, additional transports do not represent a sizeable percentage increase in the investment in the system.

When the data-processing situation calls for transfer of signals from an original tape to a tape loop, it is practically imperative that adequate control means be included for the transfer operation. In this situation, the additional investment in rerecording amplifiers for the transfer of wideband FM signals is frequently justifiable in view of the greater system flexibility and operating convenience achieved thereby. In addition, of course, errors incident to demodulation and remodulation are eliminated.

The ease with which patchboard facilities can be utilized for head-to-electronic-equipment connections is considerably dependent upon the design of the equipment. Driven-shield techniques for eliminating the effect of cable capacitance on head resonance introduce appreciable patchboard complications. From this standpoint, therefore, head pre-amplifiers located in the tape transport are highly desirable.

Patchboard and front-panel patchcord facilities are desirable and useful in making necessary interconnections between the outputs of the various tape-system electronic units and the inputs of other equipment used for monitoring, recording, or data processing. This indicates that playback equipment should have output terminals on the front panel and at the rear of the chassis (assuming the usual rack-mounted equipment), so that it may be wired permanently behind the rack or patched from the front.

If a complete rack-mounted system incorporates both recording and reproducing components, it is frequently desirable to have recorder-circuit output signals available on the front panel for patching through attenuators to the playback components, as an aid in over-all adjustment and calibration. This is a distinction from the normal situation for separated recording and reproduction facilities in which recorder component outputs and reproduction component inputs are normally needed at the rear of the chassis only.

10.4 System Specifications

The same basic principles hold in preparing specifications for magnetic tape systems as they do in specifying any other type of system; that is, the over-all requirements that the system must meet should be specified, and the internal system details by which these requirements are met should be left to the system manufacturer.

Too often, unfortunately, this basic principle of specification writing has been more honored in the breach than in the observance. The author has seen one purchase specification in which tape-transport flutter was the only technical point of the entire specification. The balance called for a system "equal to Model A of manufacturer XYZ." Unfortunately, manufacturer XYZ did not specify either d-c drift or gain stability for Model A systems. The purchaser was, therefore, at least in theoretical danger of obtaining a very good tape transport (his specification was tighter than that for Model A of manufacturer XYZ), together with associated electronic gear of such poor stability that the over-all system would be completely useless. There would have been no technical or legal grounds on which the purchaser could have refused such an unstable system, provided that the tape-transport flutter requirement was met.

Admittedly, this is an extreme case but it illustrates the predisposition to be concerned above all else with tape-transport flutter, which has been instilled in actual and potential users of tape equipment by numerous factors, not the least of which is the great American pastime known as the "hard sell."

It should be apparent from what has been said previously that low flutter is not by any means the only important characteristic of a magnetic tape system. Let us repeat here that, in a properly designed and coordinated system, the over-all performance is dependent more upon the perfection of the electronic equipment than upon low flutter in the tape transport. Furthermore, low flutter achieved at the expense of other important tape-transport characteristics is actually detrimental with respect to the over-all tape handling problem. And finally, straining for minimum flutter in transport design can result in a machine which, like a thoroughbred race horse, requires constant grooming and attention to produce its admittedly fine results. It is far better for the system to produce consistently fine results with reasonable disregard of the transport performance.

Therefore, in specifying a magnetic tape system, one should specify the inputs to the system, the desired outputs, the permissible errors in the relationship between inputs and outputs, environmental requirements, power supplies, physical configuration desired, and such other external, physical, and electrical performance requirements as are dictated by the application. Copying specifications from one manufacturer's data sheets may be risky; important items may be omitted. Combining specifications from the data sheets of several manufacturers in an attempt to get the best possible equipment consistent with the "state of the art" is very likely to result in an impasse: No one can build it.

The best course by far is to put down all over-all performance requirements and require each bidder to state his degree of compliance with each one. If all cannot be met by any one supplier, it is fairly easy to determine which items of performance degradation are least injurious.

In the preparation of over-all specifications, the author believes that considerably more attention than is usual should be directed to the matter of operating convenience. Magnetic tape equipment is a sizeable capital investment in itself and is almost always associated with a larger system. Such an investment must pay off in terms of lower man-hour costs per unit of data output. Ease and convenience in operating the equipment are important factors in attaining this end. Such ease and convenience are not necessarily achieved just by making everything plug-in.

REFERENCES

1. Magnetic Recorder/Reproducer Standards, IRIG Document 101–57, reprinted in *IRE Trans. on Telemetry and Remote Control,* vol. TRC–3, no. 3, p. 19, December, 1957.
2. Madsen, R. G.: Telemetry Data Processing at Convair Astronautics, *Proc. 1959 Symposium on Space Electronics and Telemetry* (published by IRE).
3. Smith, Francis B.: Analog Equipment for Processing Randomly Fluctuating Data, *Aeronaut. Eng. Rev.,* May, 1955.
4. Chambers, F. T.: A Novel Technique for Direct Digital Conversion of Pulse-width Multiplexed Data, *Proc. Natl. Symposium on Telemetering,* paper 1.1, 1958.

BIBLIOGRAPHY

Applegate, B. E.: A Unique Digital–Analog Data Acquisition and Processing System for Flight Testing, *Proc. Natl. Symposium on Telemetering,* paper 5.2, 1958.

Arcand, A. T., S. G. Cohen, and J. Lebid: Digital Airborne Tape Recording, *IRE Wescon Conv. Record,* part 5, p. 168, 1958.

Arsenault, W. R.: A PDM Converter, *Proc. Western Joint Computer Conf.,* 1956.

Batsel, C. N., Jr., R. E. Montijo, Jr., and E. J. Smuckler: The RCA Flight Data System, *IRE Natl. Conv. Record,* vol. 6, part 5, p. 3, 1958.

Begun, S. J.: Magnetic Tape Improves Geophysical Recordings, *Electronics,* vol. 28, no. 1, p. 152, January, 1955.

Bell, W. S., and C. W. Schultz: Shipboard Telemetering for Terrier Missiles, *Electronics,* vol. 29, no. 6, p. 134, June, 1956.

Bohnstedt, L.: An Improved Method of Calibrating FM Magnetic Tape Transports, *IRE Natl. Conv. Record,* vol. 7, part 9, p. 160, 1959.

Chambers, F. T.: Automatic Data Reduction System for Pulse-width Telemetry, *Natl. Telemetering Conf. Rept.,* 1956.

Costrell, L.: FM Data Reduction from Magnetic Tape Recordings, *Rev. Sci. Instr.,* vol. 24, no. 1, p. 76, January, 1953.

Dannals, G. C.: Magnetic Tape Playback and Digital Conversion of Telemetered Flight Data for Entry into Digital Computers, *IRE Natl. Conv. Record,* vol. 5, part 5, p. 31, 1957.

Davies, Gomer L.: Magnetic Recorders for Data Recording under Adverse Environments, *IRE Trans. on Audio,* vol. AU–2, no. 5, September–October, 1954.

Davies, Gomer L.: Accuracy of Airborne Measurements and Calibration Techniques of Magnetic Tape Recording Instruments, *Proc. First Natl. Symposium on Flight Test Instrumentation,* p. 72, 1955.

Davies, Gomer L.: The Role of Magnetic Tape in Data Recording, Processing, and Analysis, *Natl. Telemetering Conf. Record,* p. 182, 1955.

Erichsen, H. W., and D. J. Ettelman: A Subminiature Self-recording Accelerometer for High Shock Duty, *IRE Trans. on Instrumentation,* vol. I–6, no. 3, p. 178, September, 1957.

Fanwick, C., J. S. Lanza, and J. Ottobre: A Digital Data-gathering System, *IRE Trans. on Instrumentation,* vol. I–5, June, 1956.

Fisher, L. L.: A Magnetic Recording System for Precision Data, *IRE Natl. Conv. Record,* part 1, p. 66, 1953.

Fister, B. J., and C. A. Woodcock: Dynamic Data System, *IRE Trans. on Instrumentation,* vol. I-7, no. 1, p. 48, March, 1959.

Foster, W. H.: Airborne Data Acquisition System, *IRE Natl. Conv. Record,* vol. 4, part 1, 1956.

Gabriel, W. J.: An Exploration in Magnetic Tape Recording for Aircraft Flight Testing, *Proc. First Natl. Symposium on Flight Test Instrumentation,* p. 99, 1955.

Gabriel, W. J.: Some Considerations Regarding Versatile Applications of Magnetic Tape Recording, *Proc. Second Natl. Symposium on Flight Test Instrumentation,* p. 49, 1956.

Gabriel, W. J., H. R. Darby, D. A. Johnson, and J. B. Browder: B-58 Magnetic Tape Recording Experience, *Proc. Fourth Natl. Flight Test Instrumentation Symposium,* p. 30, 1958.

Googe, J. M.: An Analog Data Handling System, *IRE Trans. on Instrumentation,* vol. I-5, June, 1956.

Guttwein, G. K., and J. M. Leslie, Jr.: Magnetic Recording for Vehicular Research, *Electronics,* vol. 27, no. 2, p. 154, February, 1954.

Hadady, R. E., and S. Gilman: Telemetry Magnetic Tape Recorder/Reproducer, *IRE Trans. on Telemetry and Remote Control,* vol. TRC-3, no. 1, April, 1957.

Hall, G. O.: Digital Electronic Data Recording System for Pulse-time Telemetering, U.S. Dept. of Commerce, Office of Technical Services, PB-111294, 1953.

Harrison, M. E., and E. P. Brandeis: Some New Techniques in Airborne Data Acquisition, *Proc. Natl. Symposium on Space Electronics and Telemetry,* paper 5.2, 1959.

Holmes, J. N., and J. M. C. Dukes: A Speech-waveform Correlator with Magnetic Tape Delay and Electronic Multiplication, *Proc. IEE,* part III, vol. 101, p. 225, July, 1954.

Howard, D. D.: Instrumentation for Recording and Analysis of Audio and Subaudio Noise, *IRE Natl. Conv. Record,* vol. 6, part 5, p. 176, 1958.

Jabitz, A. E.: Magnetic Recording Systems in Product Design, *Elec. Mfg.,* vol. 45, p. 74, 1950.

Jeske, H. D.: Extension of FM/FM Capabilities, *IRE Trans. on Telemetry and Remote Control,* vol. TRC-3, no. 1, April, 1957.

Johnson, R. A.: A High Speed Digital Data-handling System, *IRE Natl. Conv. Record,* vol. 5, part 5, p. 28, 1957.

Kaplan, L. M.: The Design of Electronic Correlating Equipment to Be Used in Medical Research, *IRE Wescon Conv. Record,* part 5, p. 206, 1958.

Klein, M. L., and R. B. Rush: Techniques for a High Speed, High Quantity, Data Processing System: Idiot II: *IRE Natl. Conv. Record,* part 1, p. 143, 1956.

Knight, J. P.: A PCM Data Acquisition and Processing System for Solid-propellant Engine Testing, *Proc. Natl. Symposium on Space Electronics and Telemetry,* paper 5.1, 1959.

Knight, P.: PCM Data Collecting and Recording System Designed for Airborne Use, *IRE Trans. on Telemetry and Remote Control,* vol. TRC-3, no. 1, April, 1957.

Kramer, Reginald, and William Glass: Instrumentation for Airship Flight Test, *Proc. Natl. Symposium on Telemetering,* 1958.

Kroll, W.: A High Speed, High Accuracy, Automatic Digital Data Conversion System for FM and PWM Telemetered Information, *Natl. Telemetering Conf. Report,* 1956.

Lathrop, P. A.: Data Recovery—New Approaches Required for Re-entry Vehicle Instrumentation, *Proc. Natl. Symposium on Space Electronics and Telemetry,* paper 3.1, 1959.

Lindfors, Paul O.: Project Datum Operational Problems, *Proc. Fourth Natl. Flight Test Instrumentation Symposium,* 1958.

Magida, John M.: Summary of Laboratory Environmental Testing of Three Airborne Magnetic Tape Recorders, *Proc. Second Natl. Symposium on Flight Test Instrumentation,* 1956.

Michelson, R. W.: Magnetic Tape on the Convair F-102, *Proc. Second Natl. Symposium on Flight Test Instrumentation,* 1956.

Mooney, G. F.: Ratrase, A High Capacity, Low Level Automatic Data Handling System, *IRE Natl. Conv. Record,* vol. 7, part 9, p. 167, 1959.

Nirenberg, A., S. Perlman, and R. Burfeind: A High Speed Radar Signal Measurement and Recording System, *IRE Natl. Conv. Record,* vol. 6, part 5, p. 150, 1958.

North, John: Use of Telemetry to Make Magnetic Recordings on the Ground, *Proc. First Natl. Symposium on Flight Test Instrumentation,* p. 132, 1955.

Oscar, I. S., and W. J. Popowski: Automatic Reduction of Large Volume Test Data, *Proc. Natl. Symposium on Telemetering,* 1958.

Pettingall, C. E.: Airborne Data Automation, *Proc. Third Natl. Symposium on Flight Test Instrumentation,* 1957.

Pettingall, C. E., and F. O. Davis: Progress Report on Development of Automatic Data System for Douglas Aircraft Company Testing Divisions, *Proc. Fourth Natl. Flight Test Instrumentation Symposium,* 1958.

Revesz, G.: An Autocorrelogram Computer, *J. Sci. Instr.,* vol. 31, p. 406, November, 1954.

Roman, Steve: Seamaster Digital Data System—Its Progress and Problems, *Proc. Fourth Natl. Flight Test Instrumentation Symposium,* 1958.

Romano, George F.: A Digital Data Recording System, *Proc. Second Natl. Symposium on Flight Test Instrumentation,* 1956.

Royce, H. W.: An Improved System for Collecting and Processing Flight Test Data, *IRE Natl. Conv. Record,* vol. 4, part 1, 1956.

Sargeant, H. I.: The Role of Magnetic Tape in a Systems Approach to Instrumentation of Shock and Vibration, *Proc. Second Natl. Symposium on Flight Test Instrumentation,* 1956.

Selsted, W. T., and R. H. Snyder: Magnetic Recording—A Report on the State of the Art, *IRE Trans. on Audio,* vol. AU-2, no. 5, September–October, 1954.

Shaw, G. S.: High Capacity Pulse Code Telemeter and Data Reduction System, *IRE Natl. Conv. Record,* vol. 4, part 1, 1956.

Shaw, G. S., et al.: The AN/AKT-14 Telemetry System, *IRE Trans. on Telemetry and Remote Control,* vol. TRC-3, no. 1, March, 1956.

Sink, R. L.: An Integrated System for the Recording of Precision Data on Magnetic Tape, *Proc. First Natl. Symposium on Flight Test Instrumentation,* 1955.

Smith, F. C., Jr., and R. R. Pittman: A Twenty-four Channel Cathode-ray Oscilloscope for Monitoring Magnetic Tape Records, *IRE Trans. on Instrumentation,* vol. I-5, June, 1956.

Snyder, A. T.: Report on Development and Flight Experience with a Low-speed Low-level PWM System, *Proc. Second Natl. Symposium on Flight Test Instrumentation,* 1956.

Snyder, A. T.: Experience with Magnetic Tape Recording and Digital Computer Data Processing on the KC–135 and 707 Flight Test Programs, *Proc. Fourth Natl. Symposium on Flight Test Instrumentation,* 1958.

Snyder, A. T., and R. M. Strassner: A Flight Test Instrumentation System for the Acquisition and Reduction of Quasi-static Data, *Proc. First Natl. Symposium on Flight Test Instrumentation,* 1955.

Snyder, R. L.: A Precision Digital Data Acquisition System for Instrumentation Radars, *IRE Wescon Conv. Record,* part 5, p. 41, 1958.

Stone, R. S., and R. A. Dandl: Variable Function Delay for Analog Computers, *IRE Trans. on Electronic Computers,* vol. EC–6, no. 3, September, 1957.

Telander, E. J.: Automatic Digital Readout System for Telemetry, *Proc. Natl. Symposium on Telemetering,* paper 5.1, 1958.

Thompson, Boyd: Data Processing with Magnetic Tape Recorders, *Proc. Natl. Symposium on Telemetering,* 1958.

Veenhuyzen, N. A.: A New Airborne Data Recorder, *IRE Wescon Conv. Record,* part 5, 1959.

Wasserman, R., and P. Hurney: Tones Find Data in High-speed Tape Systems, *Electronics,* vol. 31, no. 47, p. 92, Nov. 21, 1958.

Wiener, F. M.: Time and Frequency Scaling in Magnetic Recording, *IRE Trans. on Audio,* vol. AU–6, no. 4, p. 81, July–August, 1958.

Williams, F. K.: Requirements of a High-speed, All Electronic, Fully Automatic Data Handling System, *IRE Natl. Conv. Record,* vol. 4, part 1, 1956.

Wolber, W. G.: A High-performance Multichannel Instrumentation System, *IRE Natl. Conv. Record,* vol. 6, part 5, p. 158, 1958.

Wynn, J. B., Jr., and S. L. Ackerman: Guided Missile Test Center Telemetering System, *Electronics,* vol. 25, no. 5, p. 106, May, 1952.

CHAPTER 11

MAGNETIC DRUMS, DISKS, AND OTHER DEVICES

Magnetic drums, and to a lesser extent disks, are extensively used for a number of purposes, common to all these purposes being the aspect of short-term storage or storage with reasonably rapid access to any part of the information stored. In most cases the heads used with drums and disks are not in actual contact with the magnetic recording medium, so that no wear is involved and dropouts will not occur unless there are fairly large-scale serious flaws in the magnetic medium. Because of the spacing between head and recording surface, resolution is less than is available with tape in contact with the head, and relative head-surface velocities must be higher in drums and disks to record satisfactorily a given frequency band. In other words, minimum usable wavelengths are greater by a factor of 2 to 4 than those used with tape.

Drums and disks are applied in three major fields:

1. For digital storage with medium-fast access time, in computers, and as buffer storage in data transformation and translation equipment

2. As delay devices

3. As temporary storage for the purpose of time and frequency expansion or compression

11.1 General Description

The magnetic coating on a drum or disk is applied either by plating or by coating with an emulsion of magnetic oxides. The development of oxide coatings that are hard enough and adhere strongly enough to permit precision grinding of the surface after coating has virtually eliminated use of the plating process. Also, the drum material need not be one that is suitable for plating.

Recording and reproducing heads are mounted at desired points around the periphery of the drum and distributed axially along its length in accordance with the requirements of the application. While multihead stacks such as are used in tape recording can be applied to drum applications, the use of individual heads is much more common. If the heads are in contact with the recording surface, the lower mass of the individual head materially simplifies the problems that arise with respect to bounce and uneven contact. If the heads are not operated in contact, then it is generally easier to adjust individual heads to the proper distance than it would be to adjust a multiple stack.

Because of the rapid reduction of field with distance between the head gap and the recording surface, noncontacting heads must be located as close as is feasible to the active surface. This places a premium on precision in a drum, since any eccentricity will vary the head-surface spacing. Such variation produces a large variation in the recovered signal level, which is undesirable. In consequence, great care must be taken in the design and manufacture of a drum so that it will run as true as possible. In addition to eccentricity, allowance must be made for thermal expansion of a drum and for mechanical expansion due to centrifugal force in high-speed drums.

In some applications "air bearings" have been used to assure minimum spacing between head and drum and yet prevent contact. This has been accomplished in two ways. In the case of high-speed drums, the film of air carried along with the drum at the surface will produce a small outward pressure on the head and, with suitable head mounting arrangements, can be employed to prevent actual contact and yet maintain very close spacing [1]. Another method utilizes a small tube to blow air from the head toward the recording surface, thus maintaining a small area in which air pressure is higher than atmospheric pressure, thereby cushioning the head [2, 3].

In some cases the same head is used for recording and reproduction, while in other cases separate record and reproduce heads are used. When required, a number of heads can be located at various points around the circumference of the drum, all operating on the same track. For computer and similar storage applications particularly, a large number of heads are located axially along the drum to provide a large number of tracks.

11.2 Storage or Memory Systems

This area of use represents by far the largest application of drums and practically the only application of disks and other devices. While the total amount of information that can be stored on a drum or single disk of reasonable size is rather small compared with the amount that can be recorded on a 10½-in. reel of tape, any of the information stored on the drum or disk can be recovered in a time not greater than the time of one revolution, whereas recovery of information from a reel of tape may require, in the extreme case, traverse of the entire reel. Thus the access time for information stored on a drum is very much smaller than the access time for information on reels of tape, and this is the reason for the extensive use of drums in computers and other similar storage applications.

While the maximum access time to a piece of information on a drum is the time required for one revolution of the drum, the minimum time may be very small, and on a statistical basis the average time is one-half the rotational period. This applies to simple recording with a single head or with one recording and one reproducing head per track. Access time can be reduced by special techniques, however. For example, if four heads are located at 90° around the drum circumference on one track, and the same information is recorded on all four heads, then the average access time for this information is only one-eighth of the rotational period. However, storage capacity has been lost in direct proportion to the reduction in access time. A better arrangement utilizes one recording head and four playback heads on the same track. In this case the information will appear at one of the playback heads in one-quarter the time it would appear if only a single head were used. Naturally such an arrangement would require more complex circuitry than would be needed with a single playback head. A number of other arrangements have been devised for reduction of access time. Particularly important among these is computer programming to obtain minimum access time.

Because of the desire for reasonably short access time, storage drums are operated at as high a speed as possible. This places some limits on drum diameter because of mechanical considerations, and capacity can then be increased only by increasing the length of the drum and the number of tracks. Again mechanical problems are the limiting factor. Drums which are available or have been used range in diameters from a few inches to several feet, in length from a few inches to 2 or 2½ ft, and in speed up to 30,000 rpm for ball-bearing drums and 100,000 rpm for air-bearing drums. Naturally, only the small-diameter drums can be operated at the higher speeds.

Any of the varieties of digital recording used on magnetic tape—RZ, NRZ, etc.—can be and are used with drums. New information is simply written over the old information, the old data being erased in the process. The combination of high speed and maximum storage capacity results in high peripheral velocities which, in turn, produce relatively large playback voltages; as a consequence, signal levels are generally fairly good, and playback circuit noise is not a severe problem, as it frequently is in tape applications. However, the frequency spectrum of the recorded and reproduced information comprises rather high frequencies, and the equipment must be designed to handle the necessary bandwidth. Ferrite heads are useful in high-pulse-rate applications with noncontact heads. The loss in resolution due to spacing between head and surface overrides the relatively poor gap resolution obtainable with ferrite heads.

A clock signal derived from the drum is almost always associated with drum systems. A clock track may be recorded on the drum initially to provide a timing signal, or a fine-toothed gear may be used as a tone wheel to establish a timing reference. The resolution obtainable on a recorded timing track is considerably greater than that obtainable from a tone wheel, so that the output of the latter requires frequency multiplication to equal the resolution of the former. Use of such a timing signal derived from the drum eliminates problems that would be encountered were it necessary to drive the drum in synchronism with an external timing signal. Nevertheless, some drums have been servo controlled from an external clock. Information seems to be frequently stored in serial form on drums, although there are a number of instances of parallel recording. Because of the rigidity of the drum surface, there is practically no time jitter between adjacent tracks, as there is with tape. The only sources of time jitter would be mechanical vibration of the heads and time variations resulting in the electronic circuits from variations in the amplitude of the playback voltage.

With return-to-bias recording, it is possible with proper circuit design to read the information at a specific spot on the drum and record or erase that information with the same head without waiting for the drum to go through a complete revolution [4–7]. This is because the playback voltage is made up of two pulses of opposite polarities, with the crossover between them occurring when the center of the magnetization change is directly under the head gap. The peak of the first playback pulse occurs before the center of the magnetized spot is under the head and therefore before the time for recording or erasing to occur. Thus, with sufficiently fast-acting circuits, it is possible to detect the presence or absence of a pulse at a specific point and, depending on the information so obtained, determine to write, erase, or leave unchanged that particular spot on the drum.

The decision with respect to one track may be influenced by information on other tracks. The principle may also be usable for checking information just after it is written. This requires faster decay of writing transients in the head.

The storage capacity of a drum is a function of pulse density in the track, diameter, and number of tracks which depends on the length. Pulse packing densities range up to at least 600 per inch, and the number of tracks may be as large as several hundred. Thus the total number of bits that can be stored is in the range of 100,000 to a million or two. Since a 10½-in. reel of ½-in.-wide tape can accommodate a few hundred million bits, the relatively low capacity of drums is apparent, and the short access time is clearly the major reason for their use. Storage cost per bit is considerably higher for drums than it is for tape but is appreciably lower than the cost per bit of higher-speed systems such as magnetic-core storage. As compared with other memory systems suitable for computer use, magnetic drums have the advantage that readout is nondestructive and stored information is not lost as a result of power failure, regardless of its duration.

Certain applications of computing equipment require very large storage capacity together with frequent and random modification of portions of the stored information. Normally, magnetic tape could provide the necessary capacity but, since access is required at random rather than in any ordered fashion, the time required to search the file for a specific piece of information would become excessive, the average access time for a reel of tape being in the order of minutes. On the other hand, the required capacity is so large that magnetic drum or other short-access-time systems are uneconomical. To fill this gap, storage systems with high capacity but access time of a few seconds have been devised. Two of them utilize magnetic tape, and one uses disks.

The disk system comprises 50 rotating disks mounted on one vertical shaft [2, 8]. Magnetic recording and reproducing heads can be positioned to any of 100 concentric tracks on each side of each disk. Each track can carry 500 alphanumeric characters, making a total storage capacity of 5,000,000 characters, corresponding roughly to 35,000,000 bits. One or more (up to a theoretical maximum of 20) head assemblies can be used, each of which is servo positioned to record or reproduce data from a specific track on a specific disk. Thus any part of the total store of information may be read out within a reasonably short time, in the region of a second or less. The spacing of the heads from the disk is maintained by air jets associated with the heads at a value of 1 mil so that the disks do not have to be perfectly flat. Disks are made of aluminum with magnetic oxide coating and are 24 in. in diameter.

The two magnetic tape systems use a number of strips of tape rather than reels. One [9] carries 50 pieces of tape, each 250 ft long and 3/4 in. wide, making a total of 12,500 ft of tape. This is equivalent to five reels of regular-thickness tape. The lengths of tape are passed over the top of the machine with the ends hanging in bins on the sides. Two counterrotating rollers running the length of the machine serve as capstans, and a head carriage is servo positioned to the desired strip of tape for recording or reproduction. Pressure rollers associated with the head carriage serve to press the tape against the continuously rotating capstan, the selection of pressure roller and capstan determining the drive direction for the tape strip. Drive speed is 60 ips.

Two separate six-track heads are mounted in the head carriage with tracks interleaved so that two separate "lanes" of six tracks each are available on each tape strip. Tape is lifted from the head not being used. There are 1000 blocks in each lane, making 2000 blocks per tape strip and 100,000 blocks total capacity. Each block comprises 20 eleven-digit computer words so that the total capacity is 22,000,000 characters. Maximum traverse time for the head assembly is 1.8 sec, and average access time for the equipment is about 14 sec.

The other magnetic tape random-access memory [10] employs 10 "bins" each fitted with a fast start-stop drive mechanism and a head. Each bin accommodates 500 ft of tape, of width up to 1 in. Total capacity depends on tape width and number of tracks but can easily be in the region of 150 to 200 million bits. Average access time is around 20 sec, although this can be reduced by certain duplicate recording techniques, with corresponding sacrifice in capacity.

Still another device, described by Begun [11] and Hollander [16], is a sort of hybrid tape-and-drum combination. A number of heads are mounted in a drum, and a sheet of tape, of width equal to the length of the drum, is partially wrapped around the circumference of the drum. The tape sheet can be much longer than the circumference of the drum, and it is formed into a continuous loop. When the drum is rotated, the heads scan that portion of the length of the tape sheet which is in contact with the periphery of the drum, and information may be written on and read from this portion of the tape. Moving the large tape loop lengthwise by an amount equal to the length in contact with the drum circumference exposes a fresh portion of the tape to the rotating heads, thus providing additional storage space. While the amount of data that can be stored and read without moving the tape sheet is appreciably less than could be handled by a conventional drum of the same size, the ability to move the tape sheet with respect to the drum makes the total area of the tape sheet available for storage and represents a capacity which can be considerably in excess of that available on a standard-type drum of the same size as the head mounting cylinder. If the tape wrap is half the drum circumference, two sets of heads diametrically opposed on the drum can be used to furnish repetitive sweeps of the tape without any dead time between sweeps. Under such circumstances the average access time would be one-quarter of the drum rotational period.

This combination of tape sheet and drum-mounted heads can provide a relatively high storage capacity with access time of not more than a few seconds to any part of the information. The rotation of the drum carries a film of air between it and the tape sheet, reducing wear. A 12-in.-diameter drum slightly over 12 in. long accommodates 128 tracks. Rotating at 1200 rpm, it provides 25-msec mean access time to one "page" of data, with about 200,000 bits capacity. The total loop of tape can be 400 pages long, giving 8×10^7 bits capacity. The tape advance speed is five pages per second, plus $\frac{1}{4}$ sec. Access time then depends on the total length of tape in the machine. Pulse packing used is 100 per inch.

Problems in which these large medium-access-time storage systems are useful include inventory control, certain phases of railroad accounting, bank-account information, and other similar situations. The multiple tape strip machines can also be usefully employed in certain sorting and collating operations to increase speed.

11.3 Delay Devices

A time delay is useful in many applications [12–14]. In analog computing, time delays are frequently needed to represent so-called "transit delays" in systems being simulated and for the computation of autocorrelation and crosscorrelation functions. In certain test work and in connection with "off-normal" operation of industrial processes or systems, it is frequently advantageous to utilize a delay device. As long as the test, process, or system is proceeding normally, no special data are necessary. However, if any phase of the operation departs from its normal functioning range, a delay device can permit reading or recording the system variables beginning at a time preceding the inception of off-normal conditions.

These time-delay applications may be digital, but most often they are likely to call for analog recording, and any of the techniques discussed in Chap. 3 can be used. For transit-delay simulation in analog computation, a PDM carrier technique is useful, particularly when the speed of the medium is changed during recording and reproduction. This particular application is mentioned in Chap. 3. Delay may be changed by moving the playback head as well as by changing the medium speed. The two methods are not exactly equivalent in a simulation problem. For example, if a delay is necessary to simulate the flow of fluid in a pipe, varying the speed of the medium would simulate exactly a varying rate of flow of the fluid, but changing the delay by moving the playback head requires relating the motion of the playback head to the average velocity of the fluid rather than the actual instantaneous velocity.

In the computation of autocorrelation and crosscorrelation functions, it is necessary to reproduce the function and a delayed representation of the same or another function. This process must be repeated a number of times with varying amounts of delay. Here the tape loop or drum serves as a temporary storage medium to permit the function to be repeated at will, in addition to introducing the necessary variable delays. In this situation, delay must be varied by motion of the reproducing head.

The functioning of an off-normal delay device can be best discussed in terms of a specific example. One such illustration is the recording of power-line transients that result from a fault in the system. When a fault occurs, it is desirable to obtain complete information on the resulting system voltage and current transients from the instant the fault occurs until normal operation is restored. However, since faults are quite infrequent, it is not feasible to record voltages and currents continuously to catch the transients at the time of a fault. Hence, without a delay device, the best that can be done is to start a recording device when the fault is first detected, which results in the loss of a portion of the information while the recording device is reaching its stable normal operating condition.

A tape loop or drum can be set up to record continuously the desired voltage and current information from the line, reproduce this information at a later time, and erase the recorded information just before the medium again returns to the record head for new data. The reproduced data from the playback head are ignored as long as all system conditions are normal. As soon as a fault occurs, however, an auxiliary recording device such as an oscillograph or a conventional tape recorder can be started, and the delayed information from the loop or drum reproducing head transferred for permanent reference. So long as the delay is somewhat greater than the starting time of the permanent recording device, the final record will contain information immediately preceding the fault and show everything that happened as the fault occurred, with no loss of information. Rerecording of the delayed information can continue as long as is desirable. It is to be particularly noted that the delay device need not have much information capacity; it need only carry information for a time equal to the required delay. Once rerecording is initiated, it may be continued as long as desired, without any relation to the amount of information stored in the delay device itself.

Either analog or digital recording can be used in such an off-normal delay system. For the case of power system fault transient recording, wherein an oscillographic or equivalent analog representation is desired as the final output, direct or FM carrier recording is applicable, depending on the accuracy desired. In this particular application, long-period unattended operation is desirable in some instances, so that noncontact drum recording is preferable to a tape loop. Tests have shown that loop operation, at speeds suitable for FM carrier recording with the proper intelligence bandwidth of about 600 cps, is feasible for periods up to about one week without changing loops, although for maximum reliability loops should be changed more frequently than this. With a noncontact drum, considerably higher peripheral velocities are required because of the impairment of resolution resulting from head spacing, but unattended operation for indefinite periods is possible. A drum 10 in. to 1 ft in diameter, rotating at 60 rpm, gives ample peripheral velocity for FM carrier recording and provides a time delay of almost 1 sec, sufficiently long to provide for the starting time of many applicable permanent recording devices.

Such off-normal delay devices are useful in many areas other than power line fault transient problems. The device has been applied to obtain information prior to and during a "scram" in nuclear reactors. In this case something approximating 50 channels of analog data were desired, delay times of the order of 10 sec were needed, and operating, personnel were always available so that long periods of unattended operation were unnecessary. These factors dictated a tape loop rather than a drum, with analog recording. Numerous other situations exist in which delays can be employed to reduce the amount of data that need be permanently recorded when system conditions are normal and still prevent any loss of information which is desirable in relation to an off-normal situation.

Another application for delay devices is in the area of short-term memory, frequently desirable in association with industrial operations and processes. For example, a tape loop can be slaved to the motion of a conveyor belt used to transport items to be discharged at various points. As an item is put on to the conveyor, data regarding its proper discharge point are recorded on the tape loop. When the item reaches the discharge point, a playback head on a corresponding point on the tape loop detects the discharge information and actuates necessary apparatus to remove the item from the conveyor. A similar short-term memory device can be applied in many areas wherein information regarding the materials undergoing processing is carried along synchronously with the motion of the materials through the processing operations and utilized to adjust these operations for optimum results.

11.4 Transient Repetition

For detailed study of nonrepetitive phenomena, and particularly such phenomena as are of short duration, an electrical memory device which makes it possible to repeat the phenomena as often as desired is extremely useful. Magnetic drums and tape loops are particularly efficacious in such applications. Additionally, the capability for time contraction or expansion is very helpful in bringing the time scales of the phenomena within the range of available measuring and analysis instruments.

One typical example is the frequency analysis of transients. For very short-duration transients, the frequencies involved may be beyond the range of conventional analysis equipment. Recording of the transient on a high-speed drum permits subsequent slowdown and corresponding lowering of the frequency content to facilitate analysis. In such work, the duty cycle of the repetitive train of transients should be fairly large, so that the energy in each of the frequency components is reasonably above the noise level in the measurement bandwidth. Hence it is desirable to adjust the drum speed for recording so that the transient duration is a large fraction of the period of drum rotation. A variable-speed drive for a drum makes such adjustment fairly easy over the range of control of the variable-speed drive. Thus, in such applications, the drum recording speeds are dictated by the duration of the transients to be recorded, and the reproducing speeds are governed by the characteristics of the analyzing equipment. Drum diameter must be chosen in accordance with the rate of change to be expected in the transients, and the resolution necessary to handle this rate of change with the recording technique chosen. Generally wideband FM carrier recording is most applicable for this purpose.

At the other end of the time scale, extremely low-frequency phenomena may be recorded at very low tape speeds with conventional reel-type recording systems. Extreme speedup in playback can reduce the signal-sample duration sufficiently to permit recording it on a tape loop or drum for subsequent repetition and analysis. This technique has been used with moderate speedup for studies of ocean waves and the motions of large ships. It is possible, by means of successive rerecordings and speedups, to compress the original-data time scale by factors of 10,000 or more. This would permit the study of phenomena having periods up to a year or so by the use of conventional electronic equipment operating in the low audio-frequency region. Phenomena occurring in chemical and other continuous processing operations can be studied in this way.

An example of how extreme time compression can be achieved may be useful. Let us suppose that FM carrier recording is used with final playback at 60-ips tape speed, carrier at 54 kc, and an intelligence bandwidth from direct current to 10 kc. If this tape were recorded at 0.3 ips, the carrier frequency would be 270 cps, and the intelligence bandwidth direct current to 50 cps. Now suppose that an original data signal modulates an FM oscillator with a center frequency of 1.35 cps, and this is recorded at a tape speed of 0.3 ips. Playback of this tape at 60 ips will result in a carrier frequency of 270 cps, which can be transferred to tape on another machine operating at 0.3 ips. This second tape, then, played back at 60 ips, gives the figures initially mentioned, 54-kc carrier and d-c to 10-kc bandwidth. The total frequency multiplication and corresponding time compression is 40,000:1. The *maximum* data frequency that could be handled in the original recording would be 0.25 cps, or one cycle in 4 sec. The *minimum* frequency will depend on the duration of the final-analysis sample. If we assume this to be 5 sec, for the sake of argument, then the minimum frequency at the final-analysis time scale is 0.2 cps, or 5 sec per cycle. Then at the time and frequency scale of the original recording, the minimum significant data frequency would have a period of five times 40,000 sec, or almost 60 hr. Thus, phenomena having periods ranging from 4 sec to over 2 days would be translated to a frequency range which can be studied in detail by means of conventional electronic laboratory equipment.

The speedup by a factor of 40,000 could be achieved by making the original recording at a speed of 0.0015 ips, as there is no basic limit on minimum recording speeds. Subsequent playback of this record at 60 ips would produce the results outlined above. However, a recorder operating at a speed as low as 0.0015 ips would require special and somewhat unconventional drive mechanisms, while the 0.3- and 60-ips speeds previously mentioned are achievable with essentially standard conventional tape transports. Sampling and digitization of initial data, with a comparable range of tape speeds, will permit increased frequency response in the direction of still longer periods, the maximum frequency in such a case being determined by the sampling interval. By this technique the maximum period which could be handled may be extended to weeks, months, or even years. Since, in the final reproduction at 60 ips, the ratio of maximum to minimum frequency that can be handled is of the order of 50,000:1, it is at least theoretically possible to analyze data accumulated over a period of more than 100 years and still have sufficient fineness of detail to retain daily fluctuations.

An ingenious method of time compression has been devised by Anderson [15]. Equipment utilizing the technique was described by Chynoweth and Page [1]. This uses a magnetic drum and is a sampling system. In the equipment described in the reference, pulse amplitude recording was used, although there seems to be no reason why digital recording would not be equally feasible to give higher accuracy. The system has the advantage of not requiring any change in drum speed and has the capability to record a low-frequency signal for a short period of time, with immediately following high-frequency reproduction. The basic principle involves recording one sample of the data signal for each revolution of the drum, except that successive data samples are advanced on the drum circumference by the pulse spacing allocated for the recording process. Thus, if the pulse spacing were 1 mil, 1000 data samples would be spaced 1 mil apart along 1 in. of the drum circumference.

The time required to record these samples would be 1000 times the rotational period of the drum; the time required to reproduce them, for a 10-in. drum circumference as an example, would be one-tenth the rotational period of the drum, and the resultant time compression and frequency multiplication would be 10,000:1. Furthermore, the data can be reproduced each revolution of the drum, and recording can be made continuous over a predetermined fraction of the drum circumference. This is accomplished by a progressive erase of the recorded data, beginning with the data first recorded, as the current data being recorded approaches the end of its preassigned sector. When the end of this sector is reached, recording reverts to the beginning of the sector and is separated from the previously recorded data by a narrow erase band.

Time compression is accomplished in "real time," and the frequency-multiplied data signal can be examined while it is actually occurring.

Since one data channel occupies only a fraction of the drum circumference, other data channels can be multiplexed in time and around the circumference of the drum, providing multichannel time-compression facilities in real time and without change of drum speed. The equipment described by Chynoweth and Page provided for 23 input signals, each having a data frequency range of 1 to 90 cps. The time-compression and frequency-expansion ratio was 82,800:1. Thus the output frequency range was 83 kc to 7.5 Mc.

REFERENCES

1. Chynoweth, W. R., and R. M. Page: Magnetic Drum Time Compression Recorder, *IRE Natl. Conv. Record,* vol. 7, part 4, p. 242, 1959.
2. Noyes, T., and W. E. Dickinson: Engineering Design of a Magnetic-disk Random-access Memory, *Proc. Western Joint Computer Conf.,* 1956.
3. Hagen, G. E.: Air Floating, A New Principle in Magnetic Recording of Information, *Computers and Automation,* vol. 2, no. 8, p. 23, November, 1953.
4. Malthaner, W. A., and H. E. Vaughan: An Automatic Telephone System Employing Magnetic Drum Memory, *Proc. IRE,* vol. 41, no. 10, p. 1341, October, 1953.
5. McGuigan, J. H.: Combined Reading and Writing on a Magnetic Drum, *Proc. IRE,* vol. 41, no. 10, p. 1438, October, 1953.
6. Buhrendorf, F. J., H. A. Henning, and O. J. Murphy: A Laboratory Model Magnetic Drum Translator for Toll Switching Offices, *Bell System Tech. J.,* vol. 35, p. 707, May, 1956.
7. Mulligan, J. H., Jr.: A Figure of Merit for Single-pass Data Recording Systems, *IRE Trans. on Electronic Computers,* vol. EC-8, no. 1, p. 48, March, 1959.
8. Lesser, M. L., and J. W. Haanstra: The RAMAC Data Processing Machine, *Proc. Eastern Joint Computer Conf.,* 1956.
9. MacDonald, D. N.: Datafile—A New Tool for Extensive File Storage, *Proc. Eastern Joint Computer Conf.,* p. 124, 1956.
10. Comstock, G. E., III: Multiple-address Magnetic Tape Transport, *Instruments and Automation,* vol. 30, no. 9, September, 1957.
11. Begun, S. J.: Magnetic Memory Device for Business Machines, *Elec. Eng.,* vol. 74, p. 466, June, 1955.
12. Daniels, H. L., and D. K. Sampson: Magnetic Drum Provides Analog Time Delay, *Electronics,* vol. 32, no. 6, p. 44, Feb. 6, 1959.
13. Douce, J. L., and J. C. West: The Application of Analog Techniques to a Continuously Rotating Magnetic Drum, *IRE Trans. on Instrumentation,* vol. I-5, June, 1956.
14. Goff, Kenneth W.: The Development of a Variable Time Delay, *Proc. IRE,* vol. 41, no. 11, p. 1578, November, 1953.
15. Anderson, Victor C.: The Deltic Correlator, Harvard University, Acoustics Research Laboratory, *Tech. Mem.* 37, Jan. 5, 1956.
16. Hollander, G. L.: Data Processing with Quasi-random-access Memory, *Instruments and Automation,* vol. 29, p. 690, April, 1956.

APPENDIX I

EFFECT OF TAPE-TRANSPORT FLUTTER IN RECORDING AND REPRODUCING A FREQUENCY-MODULATED CARRIER

Consider an input voltage of carrier frequency f_0, frequency-modulated at a single frequency f_1, with maximum carrier deviation Δf and modulation factor m. This input signal may be written

$$e = E_0 \cos \left(\omega_0 t + \frac{m\Delta f}{f_1} \cos \omega_1 t \right) \tag{I-1}$$

We may assume the recording current to be proportional to the input voltage.

The tape in the recording transport moves with a speed v which is not constant but fluctuates in time about an average value v_0. We assume that the flutter consists of a single sinusoidal component of peak amplitude a, frequency f_2, and phase angle ϕ_2, so that v may be written

$$v = v_0[1 + a \cos (\omega_2 t + \phi_2)]$$

Distance s along the tape may be obtained by integrating the speed with respect to time. Thus,

$$s = v_0 t + \frac{a v_0}{\omega_2} \sin (\omega_2 t + \phi_2) + v_0 C \tag{I-2}$$

where $v_0 C$ is the constant of integration.

Now, it can be shown that ϕ_2 and $v_0 C$ appear in the final result only as phase angles, and the algebra can therefore be simplified by assuming them to be zero. This gives

$$s = v_0 t + \frac{a v_0}{\omega_2} \sin \omega_2 t \tag{I-3}$$

It may be worth noting here that (I-2) rather than (I-3) must be used if one desires to determine time displacement error by computing the length of one unmodulated carrier cycle on the tape and then computing the period of the reproduced signal. The results of Appendix II can be obtained from (I-2), but the method used in Appendix II is simpler and more direct. For the purposes of this analysis, Eq. (I-3) is adequate.

The remanent flux in the tape is not necessarily proportional to the recording current when saturation recording without bias is used, but for wideband FM recording the over-all system does not pass harmonics of the carrier. Therefore we may neglect carrier harmonics produced by the nonlinear relation between recording current and remanent tape flux and consider only the fundamental carrier component of the flux. This is proportional to the recording current and hence to the input voltage defined by (I-1). Therefore, the flux distribution on the tape may be obtained by applying a proportionality constant to (I-1) and substituting for t its value in terms of s from (I-3). This also applies for subcarrier recording with bias.

Since (I-3) cannot be solved explicitly for t, approximation is necessary. The mean value of t is s/v_0, and this may be substituted for t in the argument of the sine function with negligible error, since a is very small. This gives

$$t = \frac{s}{v_0} - \frac{a}{\omega_2} \sin \frac{\omega_2 s}{v_0} \tag{I-4}$$

Letting $F(s)$ represent the flux pattern on the tape, we then obtain from (I-1) and (I-4)

$$F(s) = kE_0 \cos\left[\frac{\omega_0 s}{v_0} - \frac{a\omega_0}{\omega_2}\sin\frac{\omega_2 s}{v_0} + \frac{m\Delta f}{f_1}\cos\left(\frac{\omega_1 s}{v_0} - \frac{a\omega_1}{\omega_2}\sin\frac{\omega_2 s}{v_0}\right)\right] \tag{I-5}$$

If this tape is reproduced at speed v', where

$$v' = v_0'(1 + b\cos\omega_3 t)$$

we may again deduce the relation between s and t by integration. This gives

$$s = v_0' t + \frac{bv_0'}{\omega_3}\sin\omega_3 t \tag{I-6}$$

neglecting phase angle and integration constant. Substitution of (I-6) in (I-5) gives the flux in the playback head, $F(t)$, as a function of playback time, with another proportionality constant.

$$F(t) = k'E_0 \cos\left\{\frac{\omega_0 v_0' t}{v_0} + \frac{b\omega_0 v_0'}{v_0\omega_3}\sin\omega_3 t - \frac{a\omega_0}{\omega_2}\sin\left(\frac{\omega_2 v_0' t}{v_0} + \frac{b\omega_2 v_0'}{v_0\omega_3}\sin\omega_3 t\right)\right.$$

$$\left. + \frac{m\Delta f}{f_1}\cos\left[\frac{\omega_1 v_0' t}{v_0} + \frac{b\omega_1 v_0'}{v_0\omega_3}\sin\omega_3 t - \frac{a\omega_1}{\omega_2}\sin\left(\frac{\omega_2 v_0' t}{v_0} + \frac{b\omega_2 v_0'}{v_0\omega_3}\sin\omega_3 t\right)\right]\right\} \tag{I-7}$$

The voltage induced in the playback head winding will be proportional to the derivative of $F(t)$ and will be slightly amplitude-modulated by virtue of the terms arising from the differentiation of the argument of the cosine function. Also, the cosine function will be changed to a sine. However, we are not interested in the amplitude of the carrier, as the limiting amplifier will remove any amplitude modulation. The frequency, which is the derivative of the argument of the cosine in (I-7), is the quantity that determines the discriminator output. Thus the latter may be obtained, within a constant of proportionality, by taking the time derivative of the quantity inside the braces in (I-7). Denoting the output voltage by e_0, and letting $r = v_0'/v_0$, we get

$$
\begin{aligned}
e_0 = r\omega_0 \Bigg\{ &1 + b\cos\omega_3 t - a(1 + b\cos\omega_3 t)\cos\left(r\omega_2 t + br\frac{\omega_2}{\omega_3}\sin\omega_3 t\right) \\
&- \frac{m\Delta f}{f_0}\left[1 + b\cos\omega_3 t - a(1 + b\cos\omega_3 t)\cos\left(r\omega_2 t + br\frac{\omega_2}{\omega_3}\sin\omega_3 t\right)\right] \\
&\cdot \sin\left[r\omega_1 t + br\frac{\omega_1}{\omega_3}\sin\omega_3 t - a\frac{\omega_1}{\omega_2}\sin\left(r\omega_2 t + br\frac{\omega_2}{\omega_3}\sin\omega_3 t\right)\right]\Bigg\}
\end{aligned}
\tag{I-8}
$$

The first term in the brace represents a d-c voltage proportional to the carrier frequency, which is normally balanced out of the discriminator output so that an unmodulated carrier at center frequency produces zero discriminator output. This term can be dropped, then, and the signal plus noise output, without the constant $r\omega_0$, can be written

$$
\begin{aligned}
e_0 = \ &b\cos\omega_3 t - a\cos\left(r\omega_2 t + br\frac{\omega_2}{\omega_3}\sin\omega_3 t\right) \\
&- ab\cos\omega_3 t\cos\left(r\omega_2 t + br\frac{\omega_2}{\omega_3}\sin\omega_3 t\right) \\
&- \frac{m\Delta f}{f_0}\left[1 + b\cos\omega_3 t - a\cos\left(r\omega_2 t + br\frac{\omega_2}{\omega_3}\sin\omega_3 t\right)\right. \\
&\left. - ab\cos\omega_3 t\cos\left(r\omega_2 t + br\frac{\omega_2}{\omega_3}\sin\omega_3 t\right)\right] \\
&\cdot \sin\left[r\omega_1 t + br\frac{\omega_1}{\omega_3}\sin\omega_3 t - a\frac{\omega_1}{\omega_2}\sin\left(r\omega_2 t + br\frac{\omega_2}{\omega_3}\sin\omega_3 t\right)\right]
\end{aligned}
\tag{I-9}
$$

Terms with ab as coefficient are negligible, since both a and b are small, in the 0.01 vicinity. Then (I-9) reduces to the form given as (5-1) in Chap. 5:

$$e = b \cos \omega_3 t - a \cos \left(r\omega_2 t + br \frac{\omega_2}{\omega_3} \sin \omega_3 t \right)$$

$$- \frac{m\Delta f}{f_0} \left[1 + b \cos \omega_3 t - a \cos \left(r\omega_2 t + br \frac{\omega_2}{\omega_3} \sin \omega_3 t \right) \right]$$

$$\cdot \sin \left[r\omega_1 t + br \frac{\omega_1}{\omega_3} \sin \omega_3 t - a \frac{\omega_1}{\omega_2} \sin \left(r\omega_2 t + br \frac{\omega_2}{\omega_3} \sin \omega_3 t \right) \right] \quad \text{(I-10)}$$

The first term represents noise due to playback flutter. Its amplitude is $bf_0/\Delta f$ times the full-scale data signal, and, as would be expected, it is unaffected, in either amplitude or frequency, by the playback-record speed ratio. The second term is noise due to recording flutter; its amplitude is $af_0/\Delta f$ times the full-scale data signal. Its original frequency is multiplied by the speed ratio r and is frequency-modulated at the playback flutter frequency with a phase deviation of $br\omega_2/\omega_3 = brf_2/f_3$. This phase deviation can become rather large for $f_2/f_3 \gg 1$, and particularly when $r > 1$, corresponding to playback at a speed higher than the recording speed. Thus the higher-frequency recording flutter components have added to them many sidebands due to the lower-frequency playback flutter components, tending to produce a more or less uniform flutter spectral density at the higher frequencies. This effect is enhanced when playback occurs at speeds higher than the recording speed.

The second term also points up the rather obvious fact that speedup in playback may bring very low-frequency speed fluctuations, such as those produced by power-line frequency variations, up into the flutter frequency range, too high to be corrected by a speed control servo. Flutter compensation is the only method of eliminating this noise, when precise speed control during recording is impractical or inconvenient.

The data signal level is $m\Delta f/f_0$, and it is amplitude-modulated by the second and third terms in the following bracket. These are identical with the two preceding noise terms and are subject to the same comments. It is to be especially noted that the amplitude error produced by these cross-modulation terms is proportional to the level of the data signal and does not represent an error expressible as a fraction of full scale. It is properly denoted as a second-order effect and is of relatively little importance if a and b are reasonably small.

The argument of the sine function represents by its first term the original data frequency multiplied by the playback-record speed ratio. This is, in turn, frequency-modulated by the playback and recording flutter components, as indicated by the second and third terms. The recording flutter is again frequency-modulated by the playback flutter. The phase deviation of the data signal due to the playback flutter is proportional to the ratio of the *reproduced* frequency to the playback flutter frequency ($r\omega_1/\omega_3$), while the phase deviation due to recording flutter is dependent on the ratio of the *recorded* frequency to the recording flutter frequency (ω_1/ω_2).

APPENDIX II

TIME DISPLACEMENT ERROR DUE TO TAPE-SPEED VARIATIONS

Consider two events, separated by time T, recorded on a storage medium moving at nonuniform speed v. The "events" may be any recordable phenomena; two typical examples are pulses and the positive-going zero crossings of a sine wave.

The speed v can be represented by the equation

$$v = v_0[1 + af(t)] \tag{II-1}$$

where v_0 = uniform component of speed
a = peak deviation of instantaneous speed from v_0
$f(t)$ = time function defining speed variations

The time function $f(t)$ may be made up of one or more sinusoidal components, it may be random, or it may be a combination of both. The effect of sinusoidal components is discussed in the first part of this analysis, while random functions are covered in the second part.

II.1 Sinusoidal Speed Variations

Let $\qquad f(t) = \cos(\omega_1 t + \theta_1)$

where $\omega_1 = 2\pi f_1$ = angular frequency of flutter component
θ_1 = arbitrary phase angle

We choose $t = 0$ at the middle of the time interval between the two recorded events. Then the distance s on the tape between the two recorded events is given by

$$s = \int_{-T/2}^{+T/2} v \, dt = v_0 T + \frac{av_0}{\omega_1}\left[\sin\left(\frac{\omega_1 T}{2} + \theta_1\right) - \sin\left(-\frac{\omega_1 T}{2} + \theta_1\right)\right]$$

$$= v_0 T\left(1 + \frac{2a}{\omega_1 T}\sin\frac{\omega_1 T}{2}\cos\theta_1\right) \tag{II-2}$$

Letting $x = \omega_1 T/2$,

$$s = v_0 T \left(1 + a \cos \theta_1 \frac{\sin x}{x}\right) \tag{II-3}$$

Now let the recording be reproduced at speed

$$v' = v_0'[1 + bf(t)] = v_0'[1 + b \cos (\omega_2 t + \theta_2)]$$

The elapsed time T' between the two events separated by distance s on the medium will be given by

$$T' = \int_{-s/2}^{s/2} \frac{dx}{v'} = \frac{1}{v_0'} \int_{-s/2}^{s/2} \frac{dx}{1 + b \cos (\omega_2 t + \theta_2)} \tag{II-4}$$

This can be most easily handled by approximation. In the argument of the cosine function, $t = x/v'$, but this can be approximated by $t = x/v_0'$ with negligible error. Also,

$$\frac{1}{1 + b \cos (\omega_2 t + \theta_2)} \approx 1 - b \cos (\omega_2 t + \theta_2) \tag{II-5}$$

both approximations being valid because b is small (in the order of 0.01).

Then,

$$T' = \frac{1}{v_0'} \int_{-s/2}^{s/2} \left[1 - b \cos \left(\frac{\omega_2 x}{v_0'} + \theta_2\right)\right] dx$$

$$= \frac{s}{v_0'} - \frac{b}{v_0'} \left[\frac{v_0'}{\omega_2} \sin \left(\frac{\omega_2 x}{v_0'} + \theta_2\right)\right]_{-s/2}^{+s/2}$$

$$= \frac{s}{v_0'} - \frac{2b}{\omega_2} \sin \frac{\omega_2 s}{2v_0'} \cos \theta_2$$

$$= \frac{s}{v_0'} \left(1 - \frac{2bv_0'}{\omega_2 s} \cos \theta_2 \sin \frac{\omega_2 s}{2v_0'}\right) \tag{II-6}$$

If $y = \omega_2 s/2v_0'$,

$$T' = \frac{s}{v_0'} \left(1 - b \cos \theta_2 \frac{\sin y}{y}\right) \tag{II-7}$$

To determine T' in terms of the original interval T, we substitute in (II-7) the value of s from (II-3). However, if we use $s = v_0 T$ in the $(\sin y)/y$ function, we neglect only terms involving the product ab; these are negligible in comparison with the terms involving a or b alone. Thus, we obtain

$$T' = \frac{v_0 T}{v_0'} \left(1 + a \cos \theta_1 \frac{\sin x}{x}\right) \left(1 - b \cos \theta_2 \frac{\sin y}{y}\right) \tag{II-8}$$

We can assume $v_0 = v_0'$ without any loss of generality, and by again neglecting second-order terms involving the product ab, we finally obtain

$$T' = T \left(1 + a \cos \theta_1 \frac{\sin x}{x} - b \cos \theta_2 \frac{\sin y}{y}\right) \qquad \text{(II-9)}$$

where $x = \omega_1 T/2$ and $y = \omega_2 T/2$.

The time displacement error, as a fraction of T, is

$$\frac{\Delta T}{T} = a \cos \theta_1 \frac{\sin x}{x} - b \cos \theta_2 \frac{\sin y}{y} \qquad \text{(II-10)}$$

For two isolated events, the time displacement error is a random function of the phase angle of the flutter component with respect to the center of the time interval between the events, and the errors occurring during recording and playback are simply additive algebraically.

The maximum possible time displacement error is

$$\frac{\Delta T}{T} = a \frac{\sin x}{x} + b \frac{\sin y}{y} \qquad \text{(II-11)}$$

and this can be equal to $a + b$ only if x and y are negligibly small, i.e., the time between events is a negligible fraction of the period of the flutter. If the time between recorded events becomes equal to the flutter period or a multiple thereof ($x = y = n\pi$), then the time displacement error is zero.

If a continuing sequence of events is recorded, with equal times between each two events, then the phase angles θ_1 and θ_2 will be functions of time, and the time displacement error in successive intervals will likewise be a function of time. For a single flutter component, the time displacement error will be a sinusoidal function. Its peak value will occur when θ is near $n\pi$ and will be equal to the peak value of the flutter component times $\sin x/x$.

The maximum slope of a time plot of the time displacement error (as obtained, for example, by the method of Dingley and Sweeney) will occur when θ is equal to $n\pi/2$ and also will be equal to the peak value of the flutter component multiplied by the value of $\sin x/x$. Since $\sin x/x$ is approximately unity only for very small values of x, it can be said in general that the peak values and maximum slopes of the time-displacement-error plot are somewhat less than the peak value of the flutter component.

If there are a number of flutter components, as is usually the case in practice, the time displacement error can be expressed as

$$\frac{\Delta T}{T} = \sum a_n \cos \theta_n \frac{\sin x_n}{x_n} \qquad \text{(II-12)}$$

while the maximum slopes of the time-displacement-error plot would
be given by

$$\frac{d}{dt}\left(\frac{\Delta T}{T}\right) = \sum a_n \sin \theta_n \frac{\sin x_n}{x_n} \qquad \text{(II-13)}$$

The probability that all components would be in the proper phase at
the same instant to produce a maximum slope of $\Sigma\, a_n$ (sin x_n/x_n) seems
rather remote, and even in such an event the slope would be less than
$\Sigma\, |a_n|$ by virtue of the sin x/x factors.

Thus, the time displacement error and the slope of its time plot
can give a direct measure of flutter only if the time between recorded
events is very small in comparison with the period of the highest-
frequency flutter component and only when proper phasing exists
simultaneously between the recorded train of events and all flutter
components.

II.2   Random Speed Variations

If the flutter is purely random with negligible periodic components,
we cannot compute directly the time displacement error, as it also is
a random function. By making certain reasonable assumptions, we
can arrive at an expression for the root-mean-square error (or standard
deviation) of the timing error and thus obtain valuable statistical information regarding it.

To obtain a direct relation between rms flutter and rms timing
error, it is necessary to assume that the flutter is Gaussian and has a
uniform power spectral density over the flutter measurement bandwidth. This assumption seems reasonable in the light of available
data and in view of the probable effects and nature of the basic
causes of such flutter. If the power spectral density is not uniform,
it can be determined experimentally and the computations carried out
on the basis of the measured plot.

The rms value (standard deviation) of the flutter might be measured
by means of a true rms instrument, but certain experimental difficulties
are involved. We may deduce the probable rms value from conventional peak-to-peak measurements by assuming that such a measurement gives a peak-to-peak value equal to four times the rms value.
Peaks greater than twice the rms value occur about 5 per cent of the
time, and with oscilloscope measurements (either visual observation or
photography) it seems quite likely that about 5 per cent of the extreme
peaks are missed.

Now, if two events separated by time T are recorded, the distance
between them on the medium will be obtained by integrating the

velocity over the time T. This integral has a random variation, and its mean-square deviation may be found by using the results of Sec. II.1. The random flutter function can be expressed in the form [1]

$$F(t) = \sum_{1}^{N} (a_n \cos \omega_n t + b_n \sin \omega_n t) \qquad \text{(II-14)}$$

where a_n and b_n are random and normally distributed. The mean-square value of $F(t)$ is

$$\overline{F^2(t)} = \Sigma \; \overline{(a_n^2} \cos^2 \omega_n t + \overline{b_n^2} \sin^2 \omega_n t) \qquad \text{(II-15)}$$

and in the limit this becomes

$$\overline{F^2(t)} = \int_0^\infty W(f) \, df \qquad \text{(II-16)}$$

where $W(f)$ is the power spectral density of the flutter.

In Sec. II.1 we have seen that the effect of each sinusoidal component on the spacing error between two recorded events is dependent on $\sin x/x$, were $x = \pi f T$. The $\cos \theta$ term of Eq. (II-12) can be omitted as Eqs. (II-14) and (II-15) imply components of random phase by virtue of the sine and cosine terms with independent random coefficients. Thus, we can obtain the mean-squared-error of the integral of $F(t)$ over the time T by multiplying the power spectral density $W(f)$ by $(\sin x/x)^2$ and integrating over all frequencies. If σ_1 is the rms error in the integral, we then have [following Eq. (II-12)]

$$\sigma_1^2 = T^2 \int_0^\infty \frac{W(f) \sin^2 (\pi f T)}{(\pi f T)^2} \, df \qquad \text{(II-17)}$$

If $W(f)$ is uniform with respect to frequency and equal to W_0, then

$$\sigma_1^2 = W_0 T^2 \int_0^\infty \frac{\sin^2 (\pi f T)}{(\pi f T)^2} \, df = \frac{W_0 T}{2} \qquad \text{(II-18)}$$

The same result, using a different derivation, has been obtained by Bennett and Fulton [2].

Now, if $W(f)$* is uniform and equal to W_0, Eq. (II-16) gives

$$\overline{F^2(t)} = W_0 \int_0^\infty df = W_0 B \qquad \text{(II-19)}$$

where B is the flutter measurement bandwidth. $\overline{F^2(t)}$ is the mean-squared speed error (squared standard deviation) measured over the bandwidth B and will henceforth be denoted by σ_0^2. Then

$$W_0 = \frac{\sigma_0^2}{B} \qquad \text{(II-20)}$$

and
$$\sigma_1{}^2 = \frac{\sigma_0{}^2 T}{2B} \tag{II-21}$$

Equation (II-21) gives the square of the standard deviation in the distance along the medium between two recorded events separated by time T. It is to be noted that σ_1 is a distance, measured along the recording medium, while σ_0 is a speed. The mean distance between recorded events, s_0, is equal to the mean speed v_0 multiplied by T. Thus, if we divide the left side of (II-21) by $s_0{}^2$ and the right side by $(v_0 T)^2$, we obtain the normalized or fractional values for the standard deviations. Hence, we may rewrite (II-21) in the form

$$\sigma_1{}^2 = \frac{\sigma_0{}^2}{2BT} \tag{II-22}$$

where σ_1 and σ_0 are now to be interpreted as the *normalized* standard deviations in spacing and speed, respectively.

In playback at mean speed v_0, an additional error having normalized standard deviation σ_2 will be introduced. An attempt to derive this rigorously becomes rather involved, but by analogy with Sec. I.1, and noting that the square of the standard deviation of the time displacement error is the sum of the squares of the recording and reproducing errors, we deduce that the normalized standard deviation of the time displacement error is given by

$$\sigma^2 = \sigma_1{}^2 + \sigma_2{}^2 = \frac{\sigma_0{}^2}{2BT} + \frac{\sigma_0{}^2}{2BT} = \frac{\sigma_0{}^2}{BT} \tag{II-23}$$

or
$$\sigma = \frac{\sigma_0}{\sqrt{BT}} \tag{II-24}$$

Thus, the normalized (or percentage) rms time displacement error is proportional to the observed normalized (or percentage) rms speed error, and inversely proportional to the square root of the flutter measurement bandwidth and the square root of the time between recorded events. It should be noted that $\sigma_0/\sqrt{B}$ is a constant under the assumed condition of uniform flutter power spectral density, as under this condition the observed value of σ_0 will be proportional to the square root of the measuring bandwidth.

For a given per cent random flutter (per square root of bandwidth) the per cent time displacement error decreases as the time interval between recorded events increases. This is understandable, in view of the fact that the longer a random function is averaged, the closer the observed average approaches the true average value.

It is seen from (II-24) that the rms time displacement error is greater than the rms flutter for $BT < 1$, and less than the rms flutter for $BT > 1$. If $BT = 1$, the two errors are equal. If the flutter measurement bandwidth B were standardized at a value in kilocycles equal to one-sixth the tape speed in inches per second, then $BT = 1$ corresponds to a mean spacing of 6 mils (0.006 in.) between recorded events on the medium. The test frequency f required to give this spacing is equal to B and would thus be equal to the upper band limit used in flutter measurement.

The significance of (II-24) can be brought out by a simple example. Suppose that $BT = 1$ and the peak-to-peak flutter is measured as 1 per cent. The rms flutter is then 0.25 per cent, under the previously mentioned assumption that the peak-to-peak measurement is exceeded 5 per cent of the time. The expected time displacement error will be 0.25 per cent or less 68 per cent of the time, 0.5 per cent or less 95 per cent of the time, and will exceed 0.75 per cent only 0.27 per cent of the time.

REFERENCES

1. Rice, S. O.: Mathematical Analysis of Random Noise, *Bell System Tech. J.*, vol. 24, no. 1, pp. 46–156, January, 1945.
2. Bennett, R. R., and A. S. Fulton: The Generation and Measurement of Low Frequency Random Noise, *J. Appl. Phys.*, vol. 22, no. 9, pp. 1187–1191, September, 1951.

INDEX